Odin W. Anderson

$17

PATIENTS AND THEIR DOCTORS

A STUDY OF GENERAL PRACTICE

Reports of the Institute of Community Studies

PATIENTS AND
THEIR DOCTORS

A STUDY OF GENERAL PRACTICE

ANN CARTWRIGHT

LONDON
ROUTLEDGE & KEGAN PAUL

First published 1967
by Routledge & Kegan Paul Ltd.
Broadway House, 68–74 Carter Lane
London, E.C.4

Printed in Great Britain
by Cox & Wyman Ltd.
London, Fakenham and Reading

CONTENTS

v

Contents

ACKNOWLEDGEMENTS

This investigation was supported by U.S. Public Health Service Research Grant CH 00065 from the Division of Community Health Services. My colleagues and I are grateful to the members of this Division for their helpful interest in the study. Members of our advisory committee who gave encouragement and advice throughout are: E. M. Backett, John Fry, M. A. Heasman, John Horder, Margot Jefferys, Dick Joyce, Michael Warren, and John Wing. Wyn Tucker and Peter Willmott helped at all stages. The interviewing was done by Theresa Brown, Susan Chapman, Caryll Easthope, Joan Ellis, Janet Handel, Gwytha Peterson, Angela Skrimshire, Jill Stewart, Sheila Weston and Lesley Williamson under the supervision of Muriel Donald and Rosalind Marshall. Gwen Cartwright, May Clarke, Elizabeth Harnden and Hazel Houghton worked on the analysis of the data. Jacqueline White did most of the typing. Others who helped in various ways were: Ivan Clout, Eliot Freidson, E. M. Goldberg, Sheila Gray, Austin Heady, Albert Kushlick, John Last, Joyce Leeson, Peter Marris, David Mechanic, Peter Mond, John Pearson, Mary Stocks, J. E. Struthers, Mervyn Susser, Kerr L. White, Phyllis Willmott, Michael Young and other colleagues at the Institute of Community Studies. I am indebted to all these and to the patients and the general practitioners who made this survey possible.

October 1966

I

INTRODUCTION

In Britain general practice is the fulcrum of the National Health Service. In most other advanced countries it plays a less prominent role; in some it is defunct, in others declining, while here 'professional and lay opinion alike recognize that . . . general practice should continue to be the first-line of medical care'.[1] But is such reliance on this traditional form of medical care still appropriate? Critics hold that the increasing specialization of medical care makes the generalist redundant. One argument is that, as diagnosis has become more precise and treatment more effective and more dangerous, both depend on special techniques available only in hospital. So 'the centre of gravity is shifting from the doctor's surgery to the out-patient department'.[2] But Titmuss reasons that in this age of specialization the patient needs a family doctor to protect him from 'the excesses of specialized technocracy: to defend him against narrow-mindedness; and to help him humanely to find his way among the complex maze of scientific medicine'.[3]

The ideal way to resolve this issue would be to measure the extent to which general practice, as against alternative systems of medical care, meets patients' clinical, social and emotional needs. This is Utopian: our present techniques and resources are inadequate for such mensuration and such a study could not be made within one country where a single system of medical care predominates. But our inability to achieve the ideal should not discourage us from any assessment.

This book sets out to portray the relationship between patients and their general practitioners. To study this a random sample of nearly 1,400 people were interviewed in their homes and asked

[1] Review Body on Doctors' and Dentists' Remuneration. *Seventh Report*, p. 82. Full details of all references are in Appendix 9.
[2] Handfield-Jones, R. P. C., 'General Practice'.
[3] Titmuss, Richard M., 'Role of the Family Doctor Today in the Context of Britain's Social Services'.

about different aspects of their medical care. Their doctors were also asked for their opinions and about the way they ran their practices. So this is a study of both patients and doctors. It looks at general practice from the two points of view and relates the findings from the two sources. It considers the main features of general practice – family, personal, domiciliary, preventive and front-line care – describes the care given in each of these fields, the part general practitioners play in it, the attitudes of the patients to this care and the views of the doctors on the present organization. The relationship between front-line and specialist care, crucial in any medical care system, is also studied from the standpoint of both patients and doctors. So too are the ways in which doctors organize their work.

This book has two main purposes: first to describe the care given by the general practitioner service and secondly to discover the attitudes of both patients and doctors to this care. There are obvious limitations in the approach used. It is not easy to evaluate relationships which are so varied and which may be both complex and transitory. Contact between patients and their general practitioners is usually sporadic. Some people hardly know their doctor, others have such a close tie that they may be reluctant to discuss it with a stranger. The questions asked may sometimes be ambiguous or inappropriate. Patients' statements may be inaccurate because of misunderstanding or poor memory. They may be misleading, either deliberately or through vagueness. Their opinions may be based on wrong suppositions or inspired by prejudice. Doctors too may not always answer questions fully, frankly and accurately. These are the common hazards of questionnaire studies, to be constantly borne in mind. In addition to the difficulty of interpreting the data collected, there is the problem of incompleteness. Patients cannot assess the clinical acumen of their doctor: professional skills need professional evaluation. That would be another, different study.

This one gives a picture of the existing general practitioner service and its achievements and limitations as seen through the eyes of those giving care and those receiving it.

Methods

The study was carried out in twelve areas, parliamentary constituencies, in England and Wales during the summer of 1964. The areas were Newcastle-upon-Tyne North, Sheffield Hillsborough, Ashton-under-Lyne, Luton, Southampton Test, Bristol South-East, Wandsworth Streatham, Kingston-upon-Thames, Nantwich, Worcester, Conway and Cambridgeshire. Details of these areas and the way in which they were chosen are in Appendix 1. A hundred and forty-four people were selected at random from the electoral register in each of these twelve areas. This gave a sample of 1,728 'patients' and 1,397 were successfully interviewed in their homes.[4] Reasons for failure to interview all the people initially chosen are shown in Table 1. Four per cent had moved and just over 1 per cent had died. Of the rest – those who were available for interview – 86 per cent were successfully interviewed, 10 per cent refused, 2 per cent were temporarily away, 1 per cent were too ill or deaf, and 1 per cent were not contacted.

TABLE 1 *Response of patients*

	Number
Interviewed	1,397
Refused	166
Temporarily away	31
Too ill, deaf	16
Not contacted	23
Died	22
Moved	73
TOTAL	1,728

A copy of the patient's questionnaire is in Appendix 2. Mothers[5] of children under 15 were asked additional questions about their

[4] The great majority of people, 97 per cent, were interviewed personally. In the others factual information was obtained from a near relative as the subject was too ill, deaf or could not be interviewed for other reasons. Questions about attitudes were not asked when the subject was not interviewed.

[5] All members of the subject's household were listed and any children who were under 15 who did not have a mother living there were allocated a 'substitute mother' in the household.

children's contacts with health services and their own feelings about these. People aged 65 or more, those who had had any consultations at hospital out-patient departments in the last twelve months and those who had consulted a general practitioner in the two weeks before the interview were also asked additional questions.

People who were interviewed were asked for the name of their doctor[6] and all except 27, 2 per cent, gave us this information. Six did not wish to do so, seven could not remember or gave inadequate information and 14 were neither registered with a doctor under the National Health Service in the area in which they lived nor had a private doctor – one they had consulted before and whom they would go to again if they were ill.

The other 1,370 patients gave us the names of 552 doctors. A letter was sent to each doctor who was mentioned by a patient telling him about the study and asking him to complete a postal questionnaire. (A copy of the letter and questionnaire are in Appendix 3). After two reminders 422, 76 per cent, did so.

Details of this sample of doctors are given in Appendix 4. There are two sources of bias, the first because some doctors did not reply. Doctors who did not take part had qualified less recently, were less likely to be members of the College of General Practitioners, more frequently had licentiate qualifications only, and more often worked on their own or in a small partnership of two or three than those who filled in the questionnaire.

The other source of bias is that the chance of a doctor being asked to participate in the inquiry is related to his number of patients – that is to the people who regarded him as their doctor. For many purposes this built-in bias is a reasonable one. From the point of view of the service given to all patients, a doctor who has twice as many patients as another doctor is twice as important. Many of the analyses are therefore made on the sample of *patients' doctors*, with doctors reported by two patients included twice, by three patients three times, etc.

For analyses which involve doctors only–not patients–the unweighted sample of doctors is used although it is not a strictly

[6] This was either the doctor whose list they were on under the National Health Service, or a partner or assistant of the doctor whose list they were on, or, if they were not on a doctor's list under the N.H.S. it could be a private doctor – if they had consulted him before and would go again. A patient could have only one doctor.

4

random sample – the chance of being included at all is related in some way, but not directly, to a doctor's number of patients. But, as is shown in Appendix 4, the effect of this bias is relatively small even with things strongly related to list size.

In addition to filling in a postal questionnaire, 69 of the 422 doctors were interviewed personally. These were doctors who said at the end of the questionnaire that they would like to discuss conditions in general practice today. The data from these interviews are used only for illustration.

Patients' views of their doctors

To give some background to the detailed framework of general practice the book starts by looking at patients' general views and expectations of their doctors. Early in the interview patients were asked: 'What are the qualities, the things about your G.P., that you appreciate?' Eighty-eight per cent[7] mentioned something about his manner or personality, and 67 per cent made some comment on the way he looked after them; 4 per cent had only criticisms or could not recall anything particular that they appreciated.

One of the most frequent descriptions of their doctor, given by 18 per cent, was that he was approachable or homely:

'He's friendly, you can talk to him comfortably. He puts you at your ease.'[8]

Another 24 per cent described their doctor as 'thoughtful', 'considerate', 'sympathetic', 'understanding' or 'friendly':

'He does understand my point of view. He seems very reasonable about understanding that a man can't afford to have time off.'

And a further 15 per cent mentioned rather vaguer characteristics, describing him as 'pleasant' or 'a very good fellow'. Altogether 57 per cent made a comment of one of these three kinds.

[7] These percentages are based on the 1,248 patients who answered this question. The 3 per cent who were not interviewed personally, the 4 per cent who did not know their doctor well enough and a further 3 per cent who gave inadequate answers have all been excluded.
[8] Most of the quotations from patients are taken from a random twelfth of the interviews.

Rather more specific qualities were that he listened, had patience, took his time, and did not hurry them. Fourteen per cent said this.

'He always gives the impression of having plenty of time with you. Whether he has or not I don't know.'

Four per cent said he explained things:

'He explains things to you – almost like takes you into his confidence and you can understand what he says.'

Twelve per cent described him as frank, straight-forward or blunt:

'He won't stand any nonsense, but there's always that feeling that all the time he's very considerate and he understands. If he thought you were malingering or if there wasn't a great deal wrong with you, he'd soon tell you.'

Six per cent said he gave them confidence:

'Knowing he's interested in you gives you confidence.'

And 9 per cent found him good with children:

'He's got four children of his own and he understands children. We're all quite fond of him, it's a happy atmosphere. It's very good if children like a doctor.'

The most frequent comment about the way he looked after them, made by 19 per cent of patients, was that he visited promptly, when asked or without grumbling:

'I like the way he acts if you need him. If you sent for him in the middle of the night he'd be right there, even with the top of his pyjamas tucked in his trousers and his carpet slippers still on. He doesn't waste any time at all.'

Twelve per cent described their doctor as thorough or conscientious:

'I appreciate his attention. He's given me a thorough examination at the surgery – a really thorough overhauling.'

Five per cent said he referred people to hospital promptly or when necessary:

'If he thinks you want further advice he'll send you straight on.'

Twenty-two per cent made other appreciative references to their doctor's care or capabilities: 'He knows his stuff – pretty good at his job.' Eight per cent gave specific examples of what they felt had been good care, a number of them describing how he had looked after relatives.

'My mother died of cancer a year ago and he was very good then.'

'My daughter's been very ill most of her life and he's been right marvellous with her, especially when she was a kid.'

There were a number of other comments, from 14 per cent, which might have related to either the doctor's manner or his medical care, and of course it is in many ways inappropriate to separate these. 'Very attentive', 'a good doctor' are examples of such comments.

People were then asked if there were any other qualities they felt a general practitioner ought to have, but they thought theirs had not. Three-quarters could not think of anything – they were quite satisfied with their doctor. 'I wouldn't say he's lacking in anything.' 'I like her the way she is.' A fifth had some criticism. The remainder were doubtful or did not know. The most common criticism, made by 6 per cent, was that doctors were over-worked and had too many patients.

'Doctors today are overworked. If they had less patients they could give them more time. Being under N.H.S. they are just snowed under.'

Five per cent felt he did not always listen to what they had to say:

'Generally I think doctors haven't enough time to talk. They rush you in and out. You hardly have time to remember what you went for.'

Five per cent had other criticisms of his manner:

'The only thing I find he's a bit awkward to talk to. I think he's a very shy man.'

Three per cent gave specific examples of unsatisfactory care:

'We had one thing I thought a terrible let down at the time, but it was hardly his fault. He treated my husband for tonsillitis; he didn't get better, he got stiffer and stiffer. It went on for five weeks. I kept telling the doctor and he said, 'This happens with tonsillitis, I'll give him some penicillin if you like.' Then he got worse and it turned out to be rheumatic fever – he had to have the heart specialist it was so bad. The poor doctor was terribly apologetic.'

Two per cent felt he did not always go into things properly.

'Once or twice I've thought he could give you an examination instead of just relying on what you say. You might say "I've got a pain here". He says, "I think I can find something to help that". He might be barking up the wrong tree.'

'In my opinion sometimes he's a bit puzzled. He's so over-worked and tiredness may mean 101 things, but if I was knowing about these things I'd want to know more and have an examination done.'

A few people gave more detailed descriptions of their doctor and their relationship with him.

'I'll take his failings first. When you're ill he'll come to see you and do his best for you. He'll promise to call again – but God knows when. He's very remiss in following visits up unless there's real urgency. If you're ill you're lying in bed fidgeting for him to come. He says, "I'll call tomorrow or the next day". It'll probably be three or four days before he does. Whether it's deliberate policy to keep you in bed longer I don't know. Everybody wants to get out of bed as soon as possible. But if there's urgency then he'll come any number of times a day. Then they're damn bad time keepers. The surgery never opens at the time it's supposed to. Say I go down for 9.30 a.m. There's a few in – it might be quarter to eleven when he opens shop. Now what I like about him. Say I'm feeling ill and he prescribes something for me, I can go the next week and say, "Look your treatment hasn't done me a damn bit of good". He won't take offence, he'll try something else. You can talk to him. He will accept what you say, listen and take notice of it. Some doctors would put it down to a little bit of fads and fancies. But an understanding has grown up between us over the years. He doesn't seem to have any system at all of cards or records, but by God, he can always remember what has happened in the past. He has a very good knowledge of his patients. If I went down to-morrow, when he'd sorted me out, he'd remember what my wife went for last time – and "how was she now?" He's generally like this. He's always been very good to me. Some-times of course you come out saying "He's out of fettle today. He's taking no notice of me".'

The general picture that emerges from the response to these questions is of satisfied and appreciative patients. Many seem to feel a definite sense of identification with their doctor. If he appears hurried or even impatient, they tend to explain this in terms of overwork and conditions under the National Health Service. There are a few indications that their expectations about examinations and explanations are low, but their demands for home visiting might seem high.

II

STRUCTURE OF THE SERVICE

One of the basic principles of the National Health Service is that each patient has his own general practitioner. People choose their own doctor and can change to another when they want. How they do this will be discussed later in this chapter which starts by seeing what proportion of patients are registered with a doctor under the National Health Service.

Private and National Health Service practice

All except 24, 2 per cent, of the people interviewed said they were on the list of a doctor in their area under the National Health Service and that they would go to him if they needed a doctor.[1] Ten of the 24, 1 per cent, had private doctors they had consulted in the past and would go to again. Fourteen had neither a National Health Service nor a private doctor in the area in which they now lived. All these 14 had at some time been registered with a National Health Service doctor, but nine of them had since moved, the doctors of three had died or retired and the other two had just stopped going to their doctors. Eleven of the 14 intended to register with a National Health Service doctor again. Of the remaining three one said:

'I suppose if anything did happen I'd go privately but I don't really believe in these G.P.s. When anyone in our family breaks a bone we don't go to a doctor, we go to a bone setter.'

The second, himself a hospital registrar, said he would consult whichever specialist he needed, under the National Health Service. The third was an elderly patient who had been in hospital for

---

[1] Three said they were on the list of a doctor under the National Health Service in another area but that they would still go to him if they needed a doctor. They have been counted as having a N.H.S. doctor.

20 years. When she first went in her doctor had visited her once or twice a year but he had since retired and then died. She was given all her medical care at the hospital.

These data suggest that all except eleven, 1 per cent, of the patients interviewed were likely to get some or all of their front-line medical care through the National Health Service. There are a number of reasons, discussed in Appendix 5, why this may be an under-estimate, but it seems unlikely that the proportion of people who use only private practice exceeds 3 per cent.

through g.p.'s

There are also people who use both National Health Service and private doctors. Of the 1,373 people with a National Health Service doctor 22, 2 per cent, said they had consulted a private doctor in the last twelve months – this does not include consultations with specialists at hospital. There is little information from other sources about this. A study in 1952 of a sample of 7,027 randomly selected adults found that 97·7 per cent were on a doctor's list under the health service; 95·7 per cent relied solely on the service, but 2·0 per cent also used private practice. Of the remaining 2·3 per cent, 1·7 per cent were using or would use private practice and 0·6 per cent would probably use the National Health Service if they became ill.[2] More recently Townsend and Wedderburn[3] found 98·0 per cent of old persons had a National Health Service doctor, 1·9 per cent a private doctor and 0·2 per cent had no doctor.

Table 2 looks at private practice from the doctor's viewpoint. It shows the proportions with different numbers of private patients. The proportion with 100 or more is less than that found on an interview study of 157 doctors in 1963.[4] The discrepancy probably arises because only 12 or 13 areas were covered in each study and the proportion of doctors with large private practices varies greatly between one area and another in both studies. It is also difficult for doctors to estimate the number of private patients as they do not have to register and doctors may therefore be unaware of potential patients until they fall ill. But the information from the doctors supports the conclusion from the sample of patients that private practice is numerically a very small

[2] Gray, P. G., and Cartwright, Ann, 'Choosing and Changing Doctors'.
[3] Townsend, Peter, and Wedderburn, Dorothy, *The Aged in the Welfare State*, p. 61.
[4] Cartwright, Ann, and Marshall, Rosalind, 'General Practice in 1963'.

part of general practice. Only one of the doctors in the sample had private patients only.

TABLE 2   *Private patients*

Number of private patients	%
None	31
1–19	46
20–49	14
50–99	5
100 or more	4
NUMBER OF DOCTORS (= 100%)	418*

* The number of doctors here is less than the 422 in the sample because four did not reply to this question. On other occasions too, small numbers of doctors or patients are excluded for the same reason.

Why does private practice continue at all? Some private patients just kept on with the same arrangement as they had before the National Health Service.

'I had him before the N.H.S. and I never wanted anything else. I've had two emergency operations – a perforated appendix and a perforated ulcer four years later – and I think having a private doctor saved my life. I think time was everything.'

Loyalty to a particular doctor – even apparently under circumstances when some people might feel critical of his medical care – seems to play an important part in deciding to continue the relationship on the same basis. All but one of the ten people with a private doctor only had had him for 10 or more years and seven had had him for at least 15 years. This compares with a half and a third of all patients who had had the same doctor for at least ten and 15 years respectively. Another reason was that they felt they would get better or more 'personal' attention:

'I thought I'd get better attention and he was going to come so frequently I thought I ought to pay him – I was too ill to go up to the surgery.'

A frequent reason for people going to a private doctor when they also went to one under the National Health Service was to avoid delays in getting into hospital.[5]

'I went privately to save time. The N.H.S. hospital told me I'd have to wait 18 months for an operation.'

'My doctor wanted me to go to ———— hospital and I don't like that hospital so I asked for a second opinion. I said I'd prefer it to be a private specialist because I didn't want to wait.'

And there were a few, more general, criticisms of the National Health Service:

'I did it because I felt he had the extra sympathy. I always feel with N.H.S. you're more likely to be experimented on. If you pay privately you have faith that he would give you proper treatment. You get more consideration.'

'You get better treatment, less waiting. I don't like the N.H.S. but you have to follow it perforce because the other is too expensive. I think one is just a number – they think women are hypochondriacs and neurotic. All they do is seek a remedy – usually a patent one.'

An earlier study[6] showed that, among 157 doctors interviewed, about half themselves discouraged private patients or preferred not to have them. Reasons given suggest they found private patients snobbish, inconsiderate and 'unable to accept a reasonable doctor-patient relationship'. A third liked having some private patients and a fifth had mixed feelings. For some doctors, although private patients are few in numbers they can make up a substantial part of their income. One of those interviewed on the present study who estimated that he had less than 1,500 N.H.S. patients and between 50 and 100 private patients said:

'Private practice accounts for half my income. I send out 60 accounts and there are not many private *families* – just individuals. I never charge less than a guinea for a consultation and one and a half guineas for a visit. My income is made up of £1,000 industrial, £2,500 private practice and £2,500 panel.

[5] See also Cartwright, Ann, *Human Relations and Hospital Care*, pp. 27–9.
[6] Cartwright, Ann, and Marshall, Rosalind, op. cit.

The total is £6,000 gross and drugs and expenses attached to that are £400.'[7]

Another doctor made these comments about his mixed private and National Health Service practice:

'Some people call me privately for anything they're worried about and go to the Health Service for minor things. A family called me in when a child had spots and a temperature. I explained it was chickenpox and nothing to worry about. When other children came out in a rash they called the Health Service doctor. Then other N.H.S. patients come to me and say, "I've seen Sir ———, he gave me this prescription, would you copy it out?", or "I'm having a threatened miscarriage. I've seen ———. Please will you come and give the injections?"'

Such manipulations are probably an inevitable result of the co-existence of private and National Health Service practice.

What do most National Health Service patients feel about private practice? Three-fifths did not know whether or not their doctor had private patients, a quarter thought he did and the remaining seventh that he did not. When asked for their views about this, most people, 71 per cent, did not mind or felt it made no difference:

'If people have got money to spend – good luck to them.'

'I don't mind at all if he likes to make a little more money. He's young and has a family to bring up.'

Six per cent expressed approval or envy of private patients:

'If I had more money I'd do the same myself. It seems to me he takes more interest and knows the family. An ordinary doctor loses track of people.'

Fifteen per cent did not approve:

'I don't think they should have them – they would pay more attention to them than the N.H.S. patients.'

'I don't feel it's right. Why should money have an influence on health?'

[7] This means his private patients pay an average of just over £40 a year.

And another 8 per cent had some doubts or qualifications:

> 'I don't see any reason why a doctor shouldn't take private patients assuming it doesn't interfere with his work on the N.H.S. The only danger I can see is that it may detract from his service to the National Health patient.'

One who had no objection went on to say:

> 'I think you are treated better under the panel than as a private patient. Some drugs cost oodles of money and no ordinary patient would be given them unless he had oodles of money. Sometimes their treatment may be unnecessary.'

That only a small minority feel envious of an even smaller minority of private patients suggests that most people do not feel standards of care in private practice are greatly superior to those within the Health Service. But, as has already been shown, some people were concerned about the number of patients their doctor had to look after.

The doctors and their practices

Although patients are on the lists of individual doctors, when general practitioners work together they do not always organize their work so that they see only their own patients at their surgeries. This makes it difficult for some doctors to estimate the number of patients they look after, and the actual numbers on their list may be an unreliable index of this, particularly in partnerships with a relative newcomer or wide differences in seniority.

The doctors' estimates of the number of patients they look after are shown in Table 3 which also gives the number of patients they felt it would be *ideal* for them to look after under their present practice arrangements. A third of the doctors who took part in the study said they looked after 3,000 or more patients, but only 3 per cent thought that number ideal. Nearly half the doctors thought that between 2,000 and 2,500 would be ideal, but in practice three-fifths of them looked after more patients than that. Altogether two-thirds looked after more than they personally felt was ideal. The implications of present list sizes are discussed more fully later.

TABLE 3   *Actual and ideal numbers of patients*

	Estimated number doctors look after	Number regarded as ideal under present practice arrangements
Number of patients	%	%
Under 1,500	6	8
1,500–1,999	9	29
2,000–2,499	27	46
2,500–2,999	26	14
3,000 or more	32	3
NUMBER OF DOCTORS (= 100%)	420	413

The doctors in this study fall into four roughly equal groups – those working on their own,[8] those with one partner, those with two others and those with three or more other doctors.[9] Eighty-four per cent of the doctors said they had some ancillary help in the practice and this proportion rose from 72 per cent of the single-handed doctors to 98 per cent of those in groups of four or more. One in ten of the doctors ran an appointment system for all their surgeries. How much leisure did these sort of arrangements and patient loads leave them? A fifth said they were on call for more than one week-end in two, a quarter for one in two and just over half for less than one in two. For night calls a fifth said that in general they were on call every night, another fifth for five or six nights a week on average, two-fifths for three or four and a fifth for two or less. No questions about holidays were asked on this study but another inquiry,[10] with rather similar findings about week-ends and nights on call, found that 8 per cent of the general practitioners interviewed had had less than two weeks holiday in the previous year, 35 per cent had had between two and four weeks, and 57 per cent four weeks or more.

The amount of time they had free from practice responsibilities was related to the time they spent keeping up-to-date. Over half, 57 per cent, of the general practitioners had been on some course

[8] Includes 3 per cent working with an assistant only.
[9] For exact figures see Appendix 4 with discussion.
[10] Cartwright, Ann, and Marshall, Rosalind, op. cit.

during the previous five years and this proportion rose from 43 per cent of those on call every night to 62 per cent of those on call for two nights a week or less on the average. Nine per cent of all the doctors had been on five or more courses in the five years.[11]

General practitioners often had some direct links with local hospitals. Thirty-nine per cent of them had direct access to National Health Service beds where they retained full responsibility for the treatment of their patients while in hospital, and 23 per cent held an appointment on the staff of a National Health Service hospital.[12] Half the doctors had one or the other (or both) of these two types of hospital connection, but many did not have as much contact as they would like. Nearly half of those without a hospital appointment said they would like one, two-thirds of those without access to any hospital beds regretted this and an even higher proportion, four-fifths, of those with some access wanted more beds, or beds of a different type.

Access to various diagnostic facilities can obviously affect the efficiency and scope of the general practitioner's service. When asked whether they had direct access (i.e. not through casualty or a consultant) to full size chest X-rays, bone and joint X-rays, bacteriological examination of urine and glucose tolerance tests, just over half, 54 per cent, said they had direct access to all four. Sixteen per cent had access to three, 12 per cent to two, 9 per cent one and 9 per cent none. A third felt they did not have access to enough facilities, and this proportion rose from 16 per cent of those with access to all four of the specified facilities to 60 per cent of those with access to two or less.

To give some indication of the scope of work in general practice, doctors were asked whether they undertook various procedures in their practice when they arose – more often than not, occasionally or never. Replies are shown in Table 4. The question

---

[11] Courses can vary greatly in their duration, quality and content. No information about them was obtained on this study. Doctors were just asked to indicate how many they had been on in the previous five years.

[12] The Central Health Services Council in its report on *The Field Work of the Family Doctor*, p. 63, showed 3,408 general practitioners – about 16 per cent – working in paid appointments in hospitals – excluding those attending patients in G.P. hospital units. Sir George Godber is reported as saying that in 1961 one in four general practitioners carried out some kind of hospital appointment – See *British Medical Journal*, 'G.P's Role in Hospital of Future'. Cartwright and Marshall found that a fifth of the doctors on their study in 1963 had hospital appointments and two-fifths had access to N.H.S. hospital beds. Op. cit. and additional unpublished data.

was not precise but it seems unlikely that doctors would under-estimate the procedures they carry out. A fifth did not reckon to strap sprains 'more often than not', two-fifths to stitch cuts or do vaginal examinations with a speculum, half to open abscesses. Those who excised simple cysts 'more often than not' or estimated haemoglobin with a haemoglobinometer were in minorities of 29 per cent and 12 per cent respectively.

As for the doctors themselves, 5 per cent were women; 13 per cent qualified during or after 1955, 33 per cent between 1945 and 1954, 29 per cent between 1935–1944, 18 per cent during 1925–1934 and 7 per cent before 1925. Most of the doctors, 59 per cent, had a university degree and no further qualifications, 20 per cent had licentiate qualifications only. The remaining 21 per cent had some further qualification – 12 per cent a diploma in obstetrics, 4 per cent an M.D., 3 per cent a specialist qualification (2 per cent an F.R.C.S., 1 per cent an M.R.C.P.) and 4 per cent a diploma in something other than obstetrics.

Twenty-one per cent qualified in Scotland, 9 per cent in Ireland, 3 per cent abroad, 9 per cent had been to Oxbridge, 28 per cent to London and 30 per cent to other English or Welsh universities. These last three proportions varied in the different areas. Over half the doctors in Kingston-on-Thames, Luton and Cambridge-shire had been to London, a similar proportion of the Newcastle doctors had been to Durham or Newcastle, over two-fifths of those in Bristol to Bristol and two-fifths of the Sheffield ones to Sheffield or Leeds. Altogether over a quarter of the doctors were practising within forty miles of their medical school.

Information about the doctor's medical school and qualifica-tions are in the Medical directory, and lists in Post Offices, freely available to the public, give the address, names of any partners and the consulting hours of the doctors practising in the area. When people want a doctor what things do they take into account?

Choosing and changing doctors

When asked how they chose or got their present doctor the most frequent answer was that they 'inherited' him when he took over from another doctor who had the practice before him. Forty per cent of the patients said they had got their present doctor in this way, 24 per cent chose him because he was accessible, 22 per cent

TABLE 4 *Action on certain procedures*

Undertakes procedure in their practice :	Strap sprains	Excise simple cysts	Open abscesses	Stitch cuts	Do vaginal examination with speculum	Estimate haemoglobin with a haemoglobino-meter	Use of laryngoscope
	%	%	%	%	%	%	%
More often than not	80	29	52	60	60	12	9
Occasionally	18	33	42	34	28	15	26
Never	2	38	6	6	12	73	65

NUMBER OF DOCTORS
= 100%)   421

19

said he was recommended to them, or that other members of the family had him previously. Nine per cent had had him since childhood so their parents had chosen him for them, and 6 per cent went to their husband's or wife's doctor when they married. Other ways were mentioned by less than 5 per cent of people – they had met or known him before, 4 per cent; they wanted a woman doctor, 1 per cent; and they consulted him first in an emergency, 1 per cent.

Comments illustrate the casual way in which many people apparently select their doctor:

> 'He was the nearest. We went to the surgery and it was just a random choice out of the partners – the one with the shortest list at the time.'

> 'I just happened to pick on that one, one day when I was passing and thinking about getting a doctor.'

'Recommendations' were usually in very general terms:[13]

> 'He's got a reputation as a good doctor. It's just a matter of common gossip.'

Other descriptions of recommended doctors were 'straight-forward', 'dependable', 'go-ahead', 'efficient', 'patient with children', 'always comes when you call and modern and up-to-date with his methods' and 'a lovely person, very kind and pleasant in her manner and very attentive'.

One person who had made his choice on rather different criteria said: 'We had a choice but knew one of the doctors was very inclined to give you a prescription and that's all – before he knew what was wrong with you, and these doctors were the only others.'

Middle-class patients[14] chose their doctor by recommendation rather more often than working-class ones, 28 per cent compared with 20 per cent, but they 'inherited' their doctor and mentioned his accessibility as a reason for choosing him just as often. Recommendations were most frequently made by friends or

---

[13] Parsons, writing about medical practice in America says: 'A very large proportion of people choose their physicians on the basis of recommendations of friends or neighbours who "like Dr. X so much", without any sort of inquiry beyond that. . . .' *The Social System*, pp. 441–2.
[14] For a description of the classification of social class see Appendix 8.

neighbours, 59 per cent; then by the patient's own relatives, 17 per cent; people at work, 12 per cent; their husband's or wife's relatives, 8 per cent; other doctors, 5 per cent; and other sources, 2 per cent. (A few people gave more than one answer.)

Few, if any, people appear to consider the doctor's qualifications, and they probably realize that they cannot assess his professional competence. More surprisingly perhaps they do not mention such things as whether he practises on his own or in a partnership, or whether or not he runs an appointment system. Most people either go to the nearest one or accept the doctor who moves into a practice when their doctor retires or dies. In spite of this somewhat arbitrary method of selection, people do not change their doctor frequently. Table 5 shows the length of time they had had their present doctor.

TABLE 5   *Time with present doctor*

Length of time patients had had their doctor	%
Less than a year	9
One year but less than two years	6
Two years but less than five years	17
Five years but less than ten years	17
Ten years but less than fifteen years	15
Fifteen years or more	36
NUMBER OF PATIENTS (= 100%)	1,381

The third who had had their doctor for less than five years were asked how many times they had changed their doctor in the last five years, and the reason for the most recent change. Most of them, 84 per cent, had only changed once, 11 per cent twice and 5 per more often. Reasons for the change were that they had moved, 47 per cent; the doctor had retired, moved or died, 42 per cent; they were dissatisfied with their previous doctor, 8 per cent; and for other reasons, 3 per cent. Putting it in relation to all patients, less than 3 per cent had changed their doctor in the last five years because they were dissatisfied. The great majority of changes, nearly nine-tenths, occur either because the patient moves or because the doctor retires or dies.

21

Probably dissatisfied patients do not change their doctor often enough. The mechanism is simple when people move but on other occasions there is a delay of about two weeks or people have to tell their doctor that they want to leave him. People may not know how to set about it. One who was dissatisfied with her present doctor and had thought of changing said: 'I'm not quite sure if I can change doctors without moving'. And the way it has to be done may well inhibit people. Patients are likely to want to change when they feel the care they are getting from their doctor is unsatisfactory. This is most likely to happen when they are ill so delays will be unacceptable and they will not want to risk antagonizing their doctor by telling him they wish to change. Even when they decide to change they may encounter other difficulties as doctors in some areas adopt a 'closed shop' policy and are unwilling to accept patients who wish to change from a doctor in the same area.

'It can be difficult for patients to transfer. There's eight of us in a rota. We say "If you don't like him you won't like me".'

When patients were asked if they had ever thought of changing their present doctor 10 per cent said they had, 3 per cent because he was inaccessible, 7 per cent for other reasons – mainly dissatisfaction. A tenth of those who had thought about it said they did not know how to do it and a fifth that there was no other doctor they could go to.

Conclusions

This chapter reinforces the impressions built up from patients' general comments about their doctors – most people are apparently happy with their National Health Service general practitioner. Very few go outside the service for their care, and few change their doctor because they are dissatisfied with his care. But there is evidence of a passive acceptance and uncritical approach which may discourage and even inhibit improvements in the Service. Most people go to the doctor who is nearest to their home or who takes over from their previous doctor. They do not choose a doctor because he runs an appointment system, or employs a nurse, or has a diploma in obstetrics or is newly qualified.

In this uncritical atmosphere there may be a tendency for general practice to stagnate. Only about a quarter of the doctors worked in partnerships of four or more and over a fifth were single-handed.[15] Some had no ancillary help, appointment systems for all surgery sessions were rare and more than two-fifths had not been on any courses in the previous five years.

Working in small groups among admiring patients doctors may feel little incentive to modernize and adapt to developments in medical techniques and to changes in society. Many of them appear to look to the hospital for professional stimulation. Three-quarters wanted a part-time hospital appointment or access to (more) beds in hospital. These ambitions seem appropriate to a hospital-oriented medical care system but inconsistent with one which puts its main emphasis on community care.

[15] There is a continuing trend away from single-handed practice. In 1952 the proportion of single-handed practitioners was 43 per cent, in 1962 it was 27 per cent and in 1965 24 per cent. See Annual Reports of the Ministry of Health.

III

CONTACTS BETWEEN PATIENTS
AND DOCTORS

General practitioners' desires for more hospital contacts may stem, in part, from dissatisfaction with their own work. This chapter looks at consultations in general practice – their frequency, what happens at them, and variations in consultation rates.

How often?

A third of the people interviewed said they had not consulted their doctor (or his partner, assistant or locum) at all in the previous twelve months. Two-fifths had had between one and four consultations and a quarter five or more. The distribution is shown in Table 6. Obviously such estimates are liable to error, but people were only asked to give an estimate within fairly broad groups and it seems unlikely that many would be more than one group out.

It would be dangerous to try to estimate an average rate of annual consultation from such data.[1] A more reliable estimate from this study can be obtained from the number of consultations in the two weeks before interview. This gives an average annual rate for adults of 4·5 consultations. Memory errors are likely to reduce the number of consultations reported,[2] and the last estimate is based on patients' experience in April, May, June and July, when people consult rather less than at other times, so the average is likely to be reduced by a further 5 per cent.[3]

A joint study by the College of General Practitioners and the General Register Office of 106 general practices in England and

---

[1] If mid-points are taken for the 2–4 and 5–9 groups and 15 for the last, the estimated average annual consultation rate is 3·8.

[2] Cartwright, Ann, 'Memory Errors in a Morbidity Survey'.

[3] Logan, W. P. D., and Brooke, Eileen, *Survey of Sickness 1943–1952*, p. 44.

Wales in 1955–1956 found average consultation rates in different areas varying from 2·7 to 9·2 with an overall average of 3·8,[4] and other studies have shown rates from 3·0 to 5·1.[5] All these inevitably relate to volunteer practices. Figures obtained by Regional Medical Officers visiting over 3,000 doctors in the winter and spring of 1964–5 'show an annual equivalent of 5·6 contacts'.[6] It seems probable from all the various studies that the average consultation rate in England and Wales is about five a year.

TABLE 6   *General practitioner consultations in previous 12 months*

Patients' estimates of their number of general practitioner consultations in the previous 12 months	%
None	34
Once	15
Two–four times	26
Five–nine times	11
Ten times or more	14
NUMBER OF PATIENTS (= 100%)	1,394

In a country with completely free access to the general practitioner this does not seem unduly high. The National Health Survey in the U.S.A. shows an average of 4·5 physician visits per person per year.[7] Data relating to insured populations in seven European countries[8] show one, Sweden, with a very much lower general practitioner consultation rate of 2·2; two, Italy and Switzerland, with slightly higher rates of 5·5 and 5·4; and four, Spain, Yugoslavia, the Federal Republic of Germany and Czechoslovakia, with substantially higher rates of 7·8, 9·1, 10·2 and 10·7. Obviously many factors are likely to contribute to the rates in different areas and studies; the age, sex and occupations

[4] Logan, W. P. D. and Cushion, A. A. *Morbidity Statistics from General Practice.* Vol. 1, p. 55.
[5] For a comparison of different studies see College of General Practitioners. *Present State and Future Needs of General Practice,* p. 18.
[6] Review Body on Doctors' and Dentists' Remuneration, *Seventh Report,* p. 26.
[7] National Center for Health Statistics, 'Volumn of Physician Visits by Place of Visit and Type of Service'.
[8] Weber, A, 'Some Characteristics of Mortality and Morbidity in Europe'.

of the populations covered, the supply and accessibility of physicians, morbidity and peoples' perceptions of it, expectations about the outcome of medical care, housing and other social and economic variables and availability of alternative sources of care.

On the present study, consultations with people's own general practitioner, or his representatives, accounted for nearly all medical consultations outside the hospital. When asked about consultations with private doctors, consultations at work or for insurance or anything like that, only 8 per cent said they had had any such consultation in the last twelve months – 3 per cent with a works doctor, 2 per cent with a private doctor, and 1 per cent with their previous general practitioner. Just under 1 per cent had consulted other general practitioners for insurance or because they were away, and 2 per cent had had various other types of consultations at ante-natal clinics and elsewhere.

But the implications of an average consultation rate in itself are limited. Doctors' work loads also depend on the distribution of consultations and on their duration, while the quality of medical care is related more to what happens at consultations than to their frequency.

The consultations

A fifth of the 230 consultations reported as taking place in the two weeks before interview were in the patients' homes.[9] Four-fifths were at the doctor's surgery, only one was over the telephone.

The patients' descriptions of the conditions for which they saw the doctor are shown in Table 7. Bronchitis and other respiratory conditions accounted for nearly a fifth of the consultations. This may be compared with the 23 per cent found in the joint study by the General Register Office and the College of General Practitioners carried out in 1955–6,[10] but of course the present study refers only to summer months. The proportion of consultations for mental, psychoneurotic and personality disorders and symptoms was 6 per cent on the present study and 5 per cent on the G.R.O. and College one.

[9] This, and other data in this section, are related to adult consultations only.
[10] Logan, W. P. D., and Cushion, A. A., op. cit.

TABLE 7 *Conditions for which general practitioner consulted*

Patients' descriptions of conditions for which general practitioner consulted in previous two weeks	%
Infective and parasitic diseases (001–138)*	2
Neoplasms (140–239)	1
Allergic, endocrine system, metabolic and nutritional disorders (240–289)	9
Diseases of the blood and blood forming organs (290–299)	3
Mental, psychoneurotic, personality disorders and nervousness (300–326, 790)	6
Diseases and symptoms of the nervous system and sense organs (330–398, 780, 781)	11
Diseases and symptoms of the circulatory system (400–468, 782)	9
Bronchitis (500–502)	4
Other diseases and symptoms of the respiratory system (470–481, 483–493, 510–527, 783)	14
Diseases and symptoms of the digestive system (482, 530–587, 784, 785)	8
Diseases and symptoms of the genito-urinary system (590–637, 786)	3
Deliveries and complications of pregnancy, childbirth and puerperium (640–689)	7
Diseases of the skin and cellular tissue (690–716)	2
Diseases and symptoms of the bones and organs of movement (720–749, 787)	9
Other general symptoms, senility and ill-defined conditions (788, 789, 791–795)	5
Accidents, poisonings and violence	4
Check-up, no symptoms	1
Social, preventive, regular visit to old people	2
NUMBER OF CONSULTATIONS (= 100%)	226

* Numbers in brackets refer to the International Statistical Classification of Diseases 1955 Code.

For nearly a third of the consultations it was, according to the patient, the first time he had consulted the doctor about that particular condition or episode of illness.[11] Respiratory conditions

[11] 'Was that the first time you had consulted a G.P. for that?' Clute, Kenneth F. in his study of *The General Practitioner* found 45 per cent of doctors' home and office visits were for new illnesses in Ontario, 57 per cent in Nova Scotia.

other than bronchitis accounted for 22 per cent of 'first' consultations against 9 per cent of 'follow-up' ones. Accidents were also
more prominent among the first consultations, 9 per cent against
3 per cent of repeat consultations whereas bronchitis, allergies and
mental conditions all figured more often in the follow-up ones.

People were asked what they thought or hoped the doctor
might do for them at that particular consultation, and then
whether he did a number of specific things. Replies are shown in
Table 8. In nearly all instances the doctor did rather more than
the person recalled they had expected, but this is almost certainly
partly because the various possibilities were read out just at the
second question. The biggest discrepancy between the two is for
advice and reassurance which patients felt they were given at
two-fifths of the consultations.

TABLE 8   *Expectations about consultations and what happened at them*

	Hoped or thought doctor might do	What did he do
	%	%
Medicine/prescription	52	71
Examination	23	44
Advice/reassurance	18	41
Certificate		
First	— ⎫	2 ⎫
Intermediate	5 ⎬ 9	9 ⎬ 14
Final	4 ⎭	3 ⎭
Referral	6	10
Specific treatment (e.g. ear syringed)	7	6
Not expecting him to call	1	—
'Cure it' uncertain	6	—
NUMBER OF CONSULTATIONS* (= 100%)	212	214

*The percentages add to more than 100 because several things could happen
at the same consultation.

People were given certificates at 14 per cent of the consultations,
but at only 2 per cent was this the sole action that was reported.
In a study in Edinburgh, in which doctors recorded their actions

at consultations, certificates were given at a similar proportion, 13 per cent.[12] Most people, 88 per cent, thought their general practitioner was reasonable about giving certificates to stop off work.[13] Two per cent thought he was too inclined to give them and 10 per cent that he was rather reluctant to do so. Few in this last group appeared to resent this.

'If I wanted one he'd ask the reason and if he thought I was capable of doing any work, he'd say so. He's very, very straight in that way. He doesn't pull any punches.'

When asked if they had suggested to him that he should give them a certificate in the last year, 7 per cent of those who worked and had seen a doctor in the previous year said they had asked for a certificate to go back to work and 5 per cent had asked for one to say they were not fit for work. Obviously these replies cannot be accepted entirely uncritically, but they do not suggest either that many consultations are simply to get a certificate or that many patients exert pressure on their doctor to sign them off work. People seem to be at least as likely to ask to go back to work.

'She doesn't like to give a certificate for return to work on your say so. She doesn't like you going back before you're fit. She's very fair on that. On occasions in the last few years I've decided it was stupid talk and I've gone back and come unstuck on each occasion. She doesn't do it haphazard.'

People were given medicines or prescriptions at seven-tenths of the consultations,[14] and at a quarter this was the only thing that was recalled. Only 3 per cent said they had asked the doctor for a prescription or medicine he had not given them before. Two per cent felt their doctor was too inclined to give prescriptions, 4 per

---

[12] Scott, Richard, Anderson, J. A. D., and Cartwright, Ann, 'Just What the Doctor Ordered'.

[13] 'In general would you say your G.P. was too inclined to give certificates to stop off work, rather reluctant to give them or reasonable about this?' Only people who were working were asked this.

[14] This was at a time when people were charged 2s. for each item prescribed, unless they were receiving National Assistance or were war pensioners. This charge was removed in February 1965. The proportion of consultations at which prescriptions or medicine were given on this study, 71 per cent, was nearly twice as high as on the study at Edinburgh University General Practice Teaching Unit where it was 38 per cent. See Scott, Richard, et al., op. cit. Forsyth, Gordon, in 'An Inquiry into the Drug Bill', a study of 19 doctors and 9,405 consultations in one area in 1960 and 1961, found a rate of 66 per cent.

cent that he was rather reluctant and 94 per cent that he was reasonable about it. Comments from this last group were:

'She studies you. She looks at you. She doesn't just give you a note. She listens to you.'

'I've never known him prescribe anything when it wasn't needed. He'll tell you to take soda bicarbonate for a stomach upset, rather than make out a prescription.'

And from someone who felt their doctor was rather reluctant:

'Not really reluctant, but obviously not very keen on drugs. Friends have had penicillin much more easily from their doctors. The cheapest things on the market are what this doctor goes for and I admire her for it.'

No examination was reported at just over half, 56 per cent, of all consultations and at nearly half, 45 per cent, of those for a first consultation about a particular condition or episode of illness. Another question asked all the people who had had any general practitioner consultations in the previous twelve months whether, at any of the consultations, they had had to undress at all – apart from outdoor clothing – so that he could examine them. Forty-two per cent said they had – or they had been in bed when the doctor saw them. The proportion undressing rose from a quarter of those with one consultation to two-thirds of those with ten or more during the year. But this rise is not as great as might be expected.[15] It seems that there are a number of regular, chronic or high attenders who are rarely or never asked to undress for an examination.

Eight per cent of the patients with any consultations felt the doctor might have examined them more thoroughly.[16]

'Well, with me going with the same complaint all the time. They look at your card to see what you had last time and they think "I'll give him the same again" like.'

'After I had quinsy I got cystitis, and had an awful lot of inflammation and irritation, and I feel he left it a bit too long

---

[15] If doctors asked a random quarter of their patients to undress for examination at consultations, 94 per cent of those with ten or more consultations in the year would have been examined.

[16] 'Was there any occasion when you think he might have examined you more fully?'

before he examined me. I feel that most doctors these days don't. They have so many patients that they haven't got time to give attention that's needed. You talk to them but they haven't time to sit and fathom problems out. They don't explain things to you fully.'

When they were asked specifically about particular consultations, 95 per cent said they felt the consultation was long enough for them to tell the doctor all he needed to know and for him to do all that was necessary. Some comments from the few who were dissatisfied about this were:

'I'd have liked an exam. You feel you're wasting your time talking to him. I've had it (phlegm, catarrh and breathlessness) three months and I feel he should have spent more time.'

'Before you've finished saying "I've got a sore throat" you've got a prescription and you're out.'

So far only the parents' views on consultations have been considered. Once again only a small minority are directly critical of their doctor even though examinations were reported at slightly less than half the consultations and the doctor carried out relatively few procedures himself.

Variations in consultation rates

Most doctors, 76 per cent, agreed that: 'A good general practitioner can train his patients not to make unnecessary or unreasonable demands on him.' Eighteen per cent disagreed and 6 per cent had no particular feeling either way. When patients were asked: 'Whose idea was it that you should consult the G.P. that particular time?' nearly half said it was their own idea, two-fifths that it was the doctor's. The others had gone at the suggestion of relatives or friends. Follow-up consultations and home visits were both made more frequently at the doctor's suggestion, 57 per cent and 64 per cent[17] respectively. These data suggest that doctors can exert a lot of influence on the number and nature of their patients' consultations.

[17] In a study of the Edinburgh University General Practice Teaching Unit the doctors recorded that 67 per cent of their home visits were initiated by them. Scott, Richard, personal communication.

But the consultation rate within a practice may also be affected by the age, sex and social class distribution of the patients. Groups of relatively high users are children under two, women of childbearing age (21–34), and older people. This can be seen from Table 9 which shows the variation by age and sex in the proportions reporting five or more consultations in the previous twelve months.

TABLE 9 *Consultations by age and sex: the proportion of patients reporting five or more consultations in year*

	Male	Female
Age in years		
Under 2	33% (58)	
2–4	21% (101)	
5–9	23% (130)	
10–14	15% (116)	
21–24	4% (41)	30% (30)
25–34	13% (131)	34% (133)
35–44	14% (145)	18% (130)
45–54	15% (136)	28% (138)
55–64	33% (117)	29% (143)
65–74	20% (69)	45% (95)
75 and over	30% (30)	42% (53)

The figures in brackets are the numbers on which the percentages are based.

A first analysis by social class showed a clear trend in the proportion who had consulted a general practitioner five or more times in the previous year. This rose from 16 per cent of the professional group to 33 per cent of the unskilled. Estimates of annual consultation rates – based on the number of consultations reported in the last two weeks – showed a similar trend from 3·5 for the professional and intermediate group to 6·0 for the unskilled. However, further exploration showed that variations in the age composition of the social class groups accounted for a large part of these differences. Two-thirds of professional people were under 45 compared with less than half, 43 per cent, of the others, and there was a relatively high proportion of old people aged 75 or more among the partly skilled and unskilled, 9 per cent, compared with 6 per cent of the skilled manual group and 4 per cent of the middle-class people. Looking at it the other way round, the under 45 age group contained a relatively high proportion of professional people, and those aged 75 or more a high proportion of partly skilled and unskilled workers. There was however no apparent variation in the social class grouping of those aged 45 to 74. Analysis of consultation rates within these three broad age groups reveals little difference between middle-class and working-class patients for those aged 45–74 or those 75 or more, but among those under 45 working-class people consulted their doctor more often than middle-class people. (See Table 10.)

Associated with these variations with social class are differences between the twelve study areas. In the purely urban areas consultation rates were lower in the middle-class areas than in the working-class ones. Estimated annual rates were 4·8 in the working-class areas, 4·0 in the in-between ones and 3·1 in the middle-class districts while the proportion reporting five or more consultations in the previous year were 30 per cent, 24 per cent and 20 per cent in the three groups respectively. The partly rural areas had a high annual average of 6·0 but this was because of the very high rate, 8·1, in one of the three constituencies in this group.

How far do variations in age and sex composition, in social class distributions and in type of area explain the wide differences in consultation rates between practices and areas? In the General Register Office and College of General Practitioners study of 106 practices, annual consultation rates in the 29 areas varied from 2·7 to 9·2. In three areas it was 3·0 or less, in four more than 4·5. If the expected rate is worked out for each area, taking the age and sex distribution into account,[18] the expected averages vary only from 3·5 to 4·0 in the 29 areas, and there is no correlation between these and the observed rates. Neither can the wide difference observed between the areas be explained by urban/rural differences or social class differences, since the observed rate for all the urban areas was 3·8, compared with 3·7 in the semi-urban and 3·6 in the rural. And, on that study they found no indication

[18] Only broad age groups – under 15, 15–44, 45–64, 65 and over – are given.

TABLE 10   *Age, social class and frequency of consultation*

Number of general practitioner consultations in last twelve months:	Under 45		Aged 45–74		Aged 75 or more	
	Middle-class	Working-class	Middle-class	Working-class	Middle-class	Working-class
	%	%	%	%	%	%
None	34	32	34	36	25	29
One	22	16	16	11	10	12
Two–four	30	29	23	25	15	28
Five or more	14	23	27	28	50	31
Estimated annual consultation rate*	3·0	4·6	4·1	4·9	10·4	6·4
NUMBER OF PATIENTS (= 100%)	212	378	246	425	20	58

* Based on consultations in previous two weeks.

of any systematic social class gradient when all reasons for consultation were taken together.[19]

It seems then that the explanation for the wide variations lies either in local habits, morbidity and attitudes, or in differences between the doctors and the way they run their practices. In Chapter IX it will be shown that consultation rates tend to decrease as the number of patients a doctor looks after increases, but this may be because doctors whose patients consult relatively infrequently can take on more patients.

Large differences between general practitioners in their prescribing habits, referral rates and use of the pathological laboratory and X-ray facilities – all of which may be influenced by their consultation rates – are well known and various attempts have been made to explain them.[20] Although a number of factors have been found to be related to these habits most of the variation remains unexplained.

In an attempt to see whether there were differences in patients' attitudes which might account for some of the variations between areas, patients were asked whether they would consult their general practitioner if they had certain things the matter with them. Obviously this is a difficult question to answer. The replies are shown in Table II together with the proportions of those who had had the condition in the last twelve months who had seen a doctor about them.

People seem rather less likely to consult the doctor in practice than they estimate – although of course those who had had the condition in the last twelve months are not likely to be a random sample of the people interviewed. The largest discrepancy between what they did and what they thought they would do was for a boil on the neck and a heavy cold, but possibly the most disturbing difference was in the proportion of women who thought they would and who actually did consult about unusual bleeding or discharge. With these exceptions their estimates seem fairly realistic.

[19] Logan, W. P. D., *Morbidity Statistics from General Practice*, Vol. II, p. 15.
[20] Lee, John A. H., Draper, Peter A., and Weatherall, Miles, 'Primary Medical Care: Prescribing in Three English Towns'. Forsyth, Gordon, and Logan, Robert F. L., *The Demand for Medical Care*, pp. 90–1. Morrison, S. L., and Riley, M. Mary, 'The Use of Hospital Diagnostic Facilities by General Practitioners'. Scott, Richard, and Gilmore, Margaret, 'The Edinburgh Hospitals.'

TABLE II   *Consultation about selected conditions*

	Proportion who thought they would consult their G.P. about condition	*Proportion of those who had condition in the last 12 months who had consulted their doctor about it**
A constant feeling of depression for about three weeks	54%	50% (137)
Difficulty in sleeping at nights for about a week	45%	41% (273)
Feeling tired for about four weeks for no particular reason	64%	Not asked
Dandruff	8%	6% (204)
Loss of voice for three or four days	48%	37% (91)
Boil on neck	41%	17% (29)
A heavy cold with a sore throat, temperature and running nose for two days	49%	31% (404)
Unusual bleeding or discharge (women only)	96%	85% (48)

* The figures in brackets are the numbers on which the percentages in the last column are based. Those in the first are based on 1,335 patients or more except for the 'Unusual bleeding or discharge' which relates to women only and is based on 701 patients.

Those who thought they would consult their doctor about one condition were more likely to say they would consult about another one. Nevertheless only 12 per cent would consult about five or six of the first six conditions listed in Table 11 and 10 per cent about none of them. The observed distribution and the theoretically expected one, if predicted consultation about the different conditions were independent, are given in Table 12. This shows more people at each end of the distribution – either not consulting about any conditions or consulting about five or six of them – than would be expected by chance. But the number of conditions they would consult about did not vary between the twelve study areas – although the estimated consultation rates varied from 3·0 to 8·1 a year, and whether a person had consulted a doctor or not in the previous year was related to the number of things he thought he would consult about. The proportion who had seen their doctor rose from 54 per cent of those who would not consult about any of them to 76 per cent of those who would consult about five or six.

TABLE 12   *Number of conditions, out of six, patients would consult doctor about. Observed and expected number of conditions for consultation*

Number of conditions	Observed distribution	Expected distribution
	%	%
0	9·5	2·6
1	14·8	14·1
2	23·6	32·7
3	23·1	30·4
4	16·7	15·7
5	10·0	4·2
6	2·3	0·3
NUMBER OF PATIENTS (= 100%)	1,329	

There were a number of differences between men and women, and between middle- and working-class people in the conditions they said they would consult a doctor about. These will be discussed later, in Chapter XI. But, once again an attempt to explain wide variations in consultation rates by differences in the characteristics or attitudes of the patients has been abortive. The next chapter looks at doctors' viewpoints and shows how variations in their attitudes are related to differences in consultation rates.

Summary

Two-thirds of the people interviewed said they had consulted their doctor in the previous twelve months. It is probable that the average annual consultation rate for adults is about five which does not seem unduly high in a country where everyone has free access to a general practitioner. However, the average rate conceals wide variations between areas.

37

A fifth of the consultations are at the patient's home and a third are first consultations for a particular episode of illness. The doctor prescribes some medicine at 71 per cent of consultations, gives a certificate at 14 per cent, refers the patient elsewhere at 10 per cent, gives some specific treatment at 6 per cent, advice or reassurance at 41 per cent and examines the patient at 44 per cent. Just over two-fifths of the people who had consulted their doctor in the previous twelve months had had to undress so that the doctor could examine them. Eight per cent felt the doctor might have examined them more fully, so once again only a small minority of patients were directly critical of their doctor.

Most doctors agreed that a good general practitioner could train his patients not to make unnecessary or unreasonable demands on him and two-fifths of all consultations, 57 per cent of 'follow-ups' and 64 per cent of home visits were felt, by the patient, to have been initiated by the doctor. It seems therefore that doctors can exert a lot of influence on the number and nature of their patients' consultations. Attempts to relate the wide differences in consultation rates between areas observed on both this and other studies to characteristics or attitudes of the patients were unsuccessful.

IV

THE DOCTORS' VIEWPOINTS

So far the structure of the service and the contacts between patients and doctors have been considered mainly from the patient's point of view. But the quality of a relationship depends on both participants, and the views of doctors clearly affect their relationship with their patients and the efficiency, indeed the existence, of the service. It is therefore pertinent to look more directly at the doctors' satisfactions and discontents.

Enjoyment and frustration[1]

When doctors were asked what they enjoyed about their work as a general practitioner the most frequent answer, given by 46 per cent of them, was their personal contact with their patients – 'The friendship of my patients and their respect.' Other aspects of their work which they stressed were the variety, 18 per cent, and their freedom, 10 per cent:

'Not knowing what will turn up next and the freedom to do what I like within the limits of good clinical practice.'

'The variety and opportunity to take a case as far as one's wits permit.'

'Being my own boss – able to take pride in my own achievements and blame for my own failures.'

Seventeen per cent mentioned the feeling that they were being a help to people:

'The sense of doing a useful job for one's fellows.'

The fieldwork on this study was done in the summer of 1964, just before the doctors' unrest fermented to crisis level. The conditions which produced the crisis existed but frustration and irritation had not reached their peak.

'The satisfaction of giving a personal service of a fairly high standard of medical care to all the families on my list.'

Nine per cent maintained that they enjoyed 'all of it' and 4 per cent 'nothing'. Seven per cent recorded their interest in diagnosis and 'the detective work' involved, 4 per cent 'the gratitude of patients' or 'being "someone" in the community', 4 per cent their enjoyment of visiting people in their own homes, and 4 per cent their pleasure in treating 'the genuine cases of real illness' or 'professionally dealing with medical emergencies first hand'. A fifth commented appreciatively on various other aspects of their work:

'I prefer the National Health to the previous private system in view of there being no fees. I can treat the ill patients and not the ones who can pay well.'

'The combination in the job of mental effort and practical application.'

Included in this last group were some who mentioned a specialized interest in such things as obstetrics or paediatrics. Of course some doctors recorded several different things that they enjoyed about their work:

'The interest of the work. Meeting different kinds of people. Its use in character training (mine) especially humility. Enjoyment of the countryside.'

'I still believe that friendship and kindness are worthwhile and as a G.P. there is scope enough for that. A lot of people sometimes really need a doctor and to be able to help them is satisfying. I like to be able to take a pride in personal services.'

Doctors were then asked what they found frustrating about their work as a general practitioner. Unnecessary consultations about trivial conditions was the most common complaint – made by a third. A quarter were critical of some or all of their patients, and a tenth specifically mentioned late calls or calls at the wrong time. These three complaints were often associated:

'The numerous visits at quite a distance for very minor ailments. The multiple consultations when they have got you into the house.'

'Unnecessary late calls and unnecessary night visits and the hundreds of neurotics who take advantage of free treatment.'

Several stressed that it was only a small proportion of their patients who were responsible. 'Unnecessary calls which are usually confined to the same families but are a very small proportion of patients.' 'The 5 per cent of humanity who make 80 per cent of the demands.'

A fifth felt they had too many patients or inadequate time to do their work properly and nearly as many complained about clerical work, certification or repeat prescriptions. One in 10 mentioned inadequate leisure and one in 20 the feeling of being tied and always on call:

'Never being left in peace at home even when off duty.'

'Not enough time – *ever* – to do one's work adequately and still have time to live a normal family life. "Time off" has to be eaten into to catch up with work, reading and postgraduate study.'

One in 8 complained about the amount or method of payment and a third about a variety of other things:

'The Ministry's attitude to the drug bill and the lengthy wait for hospital consultation and often unsatisfactory standard thereof. It is utterly ridiculous for a patient to wait six to eight weeks to see a consultant who then orders treatment which the G.P. knew was required in the first place but had not access to facilities, e.g. physiotherapy. Or, as often happens, when a consultant's *opinion* is required the patient sees an exceedingly junior doctor whose opinion is often quite valueless.'

'The other frustrating aspect of general practice is the scheme dividing the G.P. from the hospital. The only solution here is to allow G.P.s to look after their own patients in hospital and to enter hospital as a right and not simply a privilege. From then on the G.P. can exert his influence directly on the house staff, consultants and ultimately on the teaching hospitals in order that the training of medical students should be more oriented towards general practice. At the moment the general practitioner is more of the waste product of the medical schools than an end product. As a G.P. one cannot help but feel that the N.H.S. is a Consultant's Charter and there is no incentive for the G.P. to practise good medicine.'

'I hate the fact that patients can make "complaints" to the local Executive Council. In fact I have never had a complaint against me (touch wood!) but I know that I sometimes respond to *unreasonable* demands *only for fear of an official complaint.*'

Once again some doctors recorded several different things:

'(i) The unfair terms of service. (ii) Far too much work. (iii) The unsatisfactory financial reward. (iv) Loss of freedom to move.'

'Form filling. Lack of intelligent use of the G.P. service by patients. Interference by Ministry officials, especially in prescribing costs. Lack of full co-operation with Local Authorities. Too much political control.'

'(i) Much unnecessary certification. (ii) Time wasted just issuing prescriptions. (iii) Irresponsible late calls. The ubiquitous "blanket welfare" of the state and of industry with the G.P. as dogsbody and wet nurse produces many unnecessary calls and consultations which THE PATIENT CANNOT HELP. This needs legislation and changes in social attitudes.'

Doctors were also asked whether they had any special interests in medicine and if so what they were. Eighty-four per cent said they had. The ones most frequently mentioned were obstetrics and midwifery by 31 per cent, paediatrics by 18 per cent, general medicine by 13 per cent, psychiatry by 11 per cent, social medicine by 7 per cent, geriatrics by 4 per cent, then a variety of other interests and specialities.

In an attempt to discover how important these various interests, frustrations and pleasures were, they were analysed by the extent to which the doctors said that on the whole they enjoyed general practice. Just over half, 52 per cent, said they enjoyed it 'very much', 37 per cent 'moderately', 9 per cent 'not very much' and 2 per cent 'not at all.'[2]

Naturally those who enjoyed their work very much were less likely to mention any frustrations, but the only complaint that varied consistently with their enjoyment was about their pay – either the actual amount or the method of payment. It is probable that general dissatisfaction with a job makes people feel that rewards are inadequate.

Of the things they enjoyed, the variety of their work and their personal contact with their patients were more frequently stressed by those who enjoyed general practice. These differences are shown in Table 13. But those who mentioned being appreciated, doing good or being a help to others, and diagnosis as things they liked about their work did not enjoy their work more than others who did not mention such things. Neither did a special interest in medicine seem to increase doctors' enjoyment of general practice.

TABLE 13   *Variations in* type *of frustration and pleasure with* amount *of enjoyment*

| | Enjoys general practice | | |
	Very much	Moderately	Not very much or not at all
Mentioned as frustrating:			
Pay	9%	14%	20%
Mentioned as something they enjoy:			
Everything	15%	3%	—
Nothing	—	3%	18%
Patients	50%	45%	27%
Variety	23%	15%	5%
Doing good	15%	19%	20%
Diagnosis	6%	6%	11%
Appreciation	2%	3%	11%
NUMBER OF DOCTORS (= 100%)	203	145	44

[2] In the absence of comparative data about other professions it is difficult to interpret these proportions on their own.

Although those who mentioned inadequate leisure as one of the frustrating things about their job did not apparently enjoy their work less than the others, the actual amount of free time was related to their general satisfaction. The proportion who enjoyed their work 'not very much' or 'not at all' was 7 per cent of those on call for four nights or less each week, 14 per cent of those on five or six nights, and 18 per cent of those on every night.[3] It also rose from 9 per cent of those on call for less than half their week-ends to 16 per cent of those on more than one week-end in two but this last difference might have occurred by chance.

Expressed enjoyment was unrelated to statements about trivial conditions made in response to the open question about frustrations, but at a later question doctors were asked to estimate what proportion of surgery consultations were for reasons they felt to be trivial, unnecessary or inappropriate. Replies are shown in Table 14.

TABLE 14 *Trivial consultations*

Proportion of surgery consultations doctors feel are for trivial, unnecessary or inappropriate reasons	%
90% or more	2
75% but less than 90%	5
50% but less than 75%	19
25% but less than 50%	30
10% but less than 25%	29
Less than 10%	15
NUMBER OF DOCTORS (= 100%)	420

As some of them pointed out: 'What may appear trivial to me is presumably worrying to the patient', or: 'There is often some emotional background to a trivial complaint.' Both these doctors felt the proportion was less than a quarter. Others sounded more cynical:

[3] The Review Body on Doctors' and Dentists' Remuneration in its *Seventh Report* proposed an additional payment for doctors undertaking services at night and weekends, p. 52.

'Since I want to maintain my family without undue financial hardship, I have to waste a lot of time on these people with a resultant loss of time for real patients and energy for study.' (Thought that between 75 and 90 per cent consultations trivial, unnecessary or inappropriate.)

The proportion who said they enjoyed general practice 'very much' fell from 71 per cent of those who regarded less than 10 per cent of consultations as trivial to 18 per cent of those who thought at least three-quarters of them fell into this category. Feelings about the importance of much of their work naturally affects their general pleasure and pride in their job. And when over half the doctors apparently regard at least a quarter of their surgery consultations as trivial, inappropriate or unnecessary it seems worth looking at this in some detail.

Trivialities

In the last chapter it was shown that patients regarded two-fifths of the consultations as initiated by the doctor. This might suggest that the quarter of the general practitioners who regarded half or more of their surgery consultations as trivial were exaggerating their irritation or being illogical. But doctors may advise people to come again for certificates – or they may call at a person's house to give a certificate – thus initiating a consultation they feel to be trivial or inappropriate. Certification was certainly felt to be one of the reasons for trivial consultation. Here are comments from two doctors who recorded as one of their frustrations:

'Trivial visits to patients' homes to issue a certificate for three days' incapacity for a cold.'

'Certification – both private and National Insurance. In other words, dealing with large numbers of people with minor illness or injury who would not attend me if a certificate was not required. I feel strongly that the Ministry of Pensions and National Insurance and employers should evolve some means, other than the present types of certification, to determine whether an employee's short absence from work for some minor illness or injury not requiring medical attention is justifiable or not. With the increasing population a general practitioner has not the time to do justice to his ill patients and take on this type of "clerking" as well.'

Since this study was done, the regulations about National Insurance certificates have been radically changed. This should reduce irritation but will not eliminate complaints about private certification.

'There's an increasing tendency for private certificates, even if they're off for one shift. They often want it in retrospect. It degrades general practice more than any other single thing.'

'The other week a patient came for a sick note because he had an appointment at the hospital. He'd shown the appointment letter to the foreman who said he must get a note from his doctor otherwise he'd lose his pay.'

As one put it: 'More employers should have more trust. Only one in a thousand is skrim-shanking.' Another suggested 'They could put National Insurance certificates in the Post Office so that people could help themselves. Instead of looking after themselves when they've got a cold they've to come to surgery – or to send for a visit.' One or two felt they were under pressure from some patients to give certificates:

'I wonder how many G.P.s are really honest? If you have a person you really know is swinging the lead, but if you sign him off you know all the family will leave and there's so many other doctors they can go to.'

Obviously if doctors succumb to such pressure from their patients one of the main points of the exercise is lost. It might be argued that employers' needs would be more appropriately met by their own medical or personnel officers.[4] If National Insurance certificates did not require a general practitioner's signature presumably some other type of check would be needed. This might be done on a sample basis and/or by non-medical people in the first instance. It would be interesting to try such a scheme on an experimental basis to see how far doctors' consultations were reduced and whether, and to what extent, sickness absence was affected. But the legitimation of patient's exemption from normal

[4] But in Holland, where this is undertaken by different doctors and many patients have to see two doctors, other problems arise. (Warren, Michael, Personal Communication.)

social responsibilities is traditionally one of the accepted functions of the patient's doctor.[5] If he no longer did this it is difficult to see that the number of consultations would be drastically reduced. As shown in the last chapter, people reported that they were given a National Insurance certificate at 14 per cent of the consultations but at only 2 per cent of the consultations was the giving of a certificate the only action recalled by the patient.

would help anyway

At 9 per cent of consultations the doctor gave both a certificate and a prescription. Some doctors resented consultations for repeat prescriptions and the occasional one mentioned a 'shopping list' approach:

'Half who come now would have gone to the chemist before – they previously had the guts to look after themselves. Now they come for the odd diarrhoea, coughs and simple tummy upsets. Having come they ask for several things' (at interview).

Another doctor, in the same area as the one just quoted, felt it was 'up to doctors to educate patients'. He described how one patient, who had been put off another doctor's list, came in and said his doctor gave him two pints of olive oil and two pints of liquid paraffin each month. 'I told him "If you come on my list I do the prescribing. Get undressed, and let me examine you." I found he was three stone overweight. I gave him a diet and he's lost one stone already.'

A random two-fifths of the doctors studied were asked, two years later, to complete a record of one day's surgery consultations, indicating for each consultation whether or not they felt it was trivial, unnecessary or inappropriate, and if so the reason. They were reminded of their previous estimate about this. Sixty-five, 46 per cent, co-operated.[6] They recorded about 2,500 consultations, an average of 38 each, and of these one fifth were felt to be trivial.[7] The proportions for the doctors ranged

---

[5] Parsons, Talcott, *The Social System*, p. 436.

[6] Ten questionnaires were returned because the doctor was no longer in practice in that area. These have been excluded when the response rate was calculated. No reminder letters were sent on this part of the study. Among those who replied the distribution of their estimates of the proportion of trivial, inappropriate or unnecessary consultations was almost identical with that for the total sample who responded initially.

[7] Trivial is used here, and later, as an abbreviation for trivial, inappropriate or unnecessary.

from none to 72 per cent 'and they tended to record as trivial a smaller proportion than they estimated in the earlier postal questionnaire. Four per cent recorded a higher proportion, 40 per cent a proportion in the same range as their earlier estimate[8] and 56 per cent a lower proportion. Four who recorded a lower proportion explained that they had introduced an appointment system and felt this had cut down the proportion of trivial consultations.

Fifty-three per cent of the 'trivial' consultations were attributed to minor illnesses which the doctors did not feel needed medical care. Conditions recorded included colds, coughs, catarrh, headaches, morning sickness, small boils, hair falling out, minimal wax in ears, obesity, dandruff, constipation, dysmenorrhea, indigestion, teething, cuts, bruises and 'a girl with pains in her limbs after keep fit classes'. There were also a number who had been ill but were now better: 'Felt terrible four days ago. O.K. now'.

Eighteen per cent were for certificates or other forms to be signed. 'He didn't need me, only my signature on a form' was one comment. Some of these certificates were for National Insurance, others for glasses, elastic stockings, a friendly society, and one was 'a certificate to enable patient to drive into a cemetery to visit her husband's grave'.

Eleven per cent were for repeat prescriptions, some of which had been recommended by the hospital, and 4 per cent were occasions on which the patient asked for a certificate or prescription when the doctor felt he was not ill and did not need one. 'Feeling need for a tonic – looking fit'. 'Travelling shortly, wants something to prevent getting "chesty" as was troubled last winter. Chest quite clear'.

In 2 per cent of the 'trivial' consultations, patients asked for certificates or medicine for other members of their family and in another 2 per cent the doctor just recorded such phrases as 'malingerer', 'constant attender', 'time waster'. For 6 per cent some sort of emotional trouble, domestic anxiety or personality inadequacy was given as the reason. 'Settle family quarrel'.

---

[8] On the postal inquiry they were asked whether the proportion was 90 per cent or more, 75 per cent but less than 90 per cent, 50 per cent but less than 75 per cent, 25 per cent but less than 50 per cent, 10 per cent but less than 25 per cent, or less than 10 per cent.

'Husband worried about wife being unfaithful'. 'Continually attending surgery for one reason or another – not organic. Due to not being legally married'. 'Came to discuss her love life'. And there were 4 per cent of other reasons including one patient who wanted to be transferred to the doctor's list from another local doctor and was refused and one who 'brought flowers and tomatoes from her garden'.

Doctors who felt a relatively small proportion of their consultations, less than a quarter, were trivial recorded – proportionally as well as absolutely – few consultations in the first category of minor illnesses – 35 per cent compared with 56 per cent. Possibly these doctors found another condition besides the one first presented or offered by the patient.[9]

Further indication of what affects doctors' views on the proportion of trivial conditions is given by analysis for all the study doctors of various aspects of their practices and attitudes and some of the characteristics of their patients. Believing a high proportion of consultations to be trivial seemed to be partly a function of professional isolation since doctors who felt a high proportion of consultations fell into that category were less likely to have attended any courses in the last five years, and less likely to have direct access to hospital beds. (See Table 15.)[10] However it did not appear to be related to size of partnership or having a hospital appointment.

Doctors' views on the triviality of their consultations also appeared to be related to the work they undertook in their practices. If they did various procedures themselves when they arose they were less likely to regard a high proportion of consultations as trivial; similarly if they had access to a relatively high number of diagnostic facilities. In addition doctors who had expressed a special interest in psychiatry thought relatively few

[9] See Balint, Michael, *The Doctor, his Patient and the Illness*, p. 18.
[10] Cynics might argue that the associations in Table 15 with attendance at courses and access to beds arise because doctors who have more contact with professional colleagues know the 'right' answers and are therefore unlikely to say they have a high proportion of consultations for trivial reasons. However if that is a 'right' answer it is not correlated with another question which might also be regarded as having a more professionally acceptable response – whether they think middle-aged women should have regular cervical smear tests. Eighty per cent of those who felt half or more of the consultations were trivial thought they should, compared with 70 per cent of those who thought less than a quarter were, and 78 per cent of the intermediate group.

consultations were trivial. These differences are also shown in Table 15.

TABLE 15   *Trivial consultations and aspects of the doctor's work*

	Proportion of consultations estimated by the doctor to be for reasons he felt trivial, unnecessary or inappropriate				
	Less than 10%	*10% < 25%*	*25% < 50%*	*50% < 75%*	*75% or more*
Proportion who had attended any courses in the last five years	67%	58%	58%	54%	34%
Proportion with direct access to N.H.S. hospital beds	48%	45%	38%	29%	21%
Proportion with a special interest in psychiatry	20%	13%	8%	5%	7%
Average score on procedures carried out themselves*	4·0	3·9	4·1	3·3	2·1
Average number of diagnostic facilities available (Out of 4)†	3·3	3·1	2·9	2·8	2·7
NUMBER OF DOCTORS (= 100%)	65	121	126	79	29

* A description of this score is given in Appendix VI.
† These four were: full size chest X-rays, bone and joint X-rays, bacteriological examination of urine and glucose tolerance tests.

Table 16 shows the relationship between doctors' estimates of the proportion of trivial consultations and various characteristics of their *patients*. The proportion of patients who had consulted their doctor *at all* in the previous twelve months did not seem to vary, and this ties up with the fact that the number of selected marginal conditions their patients thought they would consult their doctor about was also unrelated to the doctors' estimates of the proportion of trivial consultations. But the proportion of patients who had seen the doctor *five or more times* fell from 31 per cent of those whose doctor regarded less than 10 per cent of the consultations as trivial to 19 per cent of those whose doctor felt 75 per cent or more were. This suggests that when a doctor regards a consultation as trivial, some patients are somehow discouraged from coming to see him again. Attendance at hospital out-patient departments was also comparatively infrequent among patients whose doctors felt a high proportion of consultations were trivial – although these doctors carried out fewer procedures themselves. The most plausible explanation for these differences is that doctors' perceptions of people's need for care differ and are associated with their estimated 'triviality level'.

TABLE 16 *Trivial consultations and characteristics of patients*

	Proportion of surgery consultations estimated by the doctor to be for reasons he felt trivial, unnecessary or inappropriate				
	Less than 10%	10% < 25%	25% < 50%	50% < 75%	75% or more
Number of consultations in previous 12 months	%	%	%	%	%
None	35	32	32	31	36
One to four	34	40	44	46	45
Five or more	31	28	24	23	19
Estimated annual consultation rate*	5·1	4·3	4·2	4·6	3·8
Proportion attending hospital out-patients in last 12 months	25%	30%	23%	21%	13%
Proportion middle-class	32%	35%	35%	37%	48%
Proportion thinking prestige of general practitioners had gone down in last 10 years	19%	22%	23%	25%	35%
NUMBER OF PATIENTS (= 100%)	152	312	295	225	62

* Based on consultations in previous two weeks.

There was some indication that doctors with high estimates of trivialities had a relatively high proportion of middle-class patients. It may be easier to understand and tolerate consultation for a condition that the doctor sees as medically trivial, when the social distance between patient and doctor is greater. The doctor may accept that working-class people feel unable to cope with certain 'minor' conditions, but resent it more when middle-class people react in the same way. It will be shown in Chapter 11 that middle-class patients were rather more critical of their doctors than working-class patients, and a critical reaction in a patient may incline doctors to regard consultations as trivial. The proportion of patients mentioning some quality a general practitioner ought to have that theirs lacked was 41 per cent of the patients whose doctor felt three-quarters or more of the consultations were trivial compared with 25 per cent of those whose doctors put fewer consultations in that category.

There was some suggestion too that the doctor's standing in the community is related to his evaluation of the importance or triviality of his work. The doctors who thought a higher proportion of consultations were for trivial, unnecessary or inappropriate reasons had patients who were more likely to think the prestige of doctors had gone down in the last ten years. But, as will be shown in the next pages this difference is also associated with social class variations.

Prestige

Patients in the survey were asked to rank six occupations according to their prestige or social standing.[11] The results are shown in Table 17. A low figure indicates a high prestige rating.

TABLE 17   *Prestige rating of six occupations*

	Average rank
A hospital specialist (consultant)	1·6
A general practitioner	2·4
A headmaster of a grammar school	3·6
A university professor of history	3·8
A solicitor who is a senior partner in a small firm	4·0
A manager of a branch of Marks & Spencer	5·7
NUMBER OF PATIENTS MAKING ASSESSMENTS	1,301

[11] If they did not understand these expressions it was explained by the phrase 'who people thought most of.'

The general practitioner was generally ranked second. Another doctor, the hospital specialist, was the only one to take precedence. The general practitioner's prestige is greater than would be expected if it was related simply to earnings since a university professor earns more than the average general practitioner. A further question asked whether people thought the prestige of general practitioners had been going up or down in the last ten years – or whether they thought it had stayed about the same. Half thought it had changed and they were equally divided between those thinking it had gone up and those thinking it had gone down. The proportions in these last two groups varied markedly between people in different social classes as can be seen from Table 18.

The proportion who thought it had gone down fell consistently from 54 per cent in the professional group to 12 per cent among those in the unskilled one. This may be a reflection of the different experience of private and panel practice among people in different classes. Comments from some working-class people who felt the general practitioner's prestige had gone up were:

'I can remember as a little boy going to the surgery. It was cold and damp and you waited a hell of a long time. It used to be a miserable ordeal. Most of them are in groups now.'

'I think they take more interest in people now. There's a great difference. In years gone by we couldn't afford to go to the doctor. We had to dose ourselves first.'

Advancements in medical knowledge were often quoted as a reason for greater prestige:

'Medical research and all that has improved. People look up to a doctor now. I do for one, I really admire him.'

'The achievements of the past ten years have been staggering. The old fears of T.B. have disappeared and I'm sure in some few years they'll find the answer to cancer. Then there are some really miraculous things done in surgery these days and the public knows more about illnesses nowadays.'

More education and greater equality was felt to work both ways as the next three comments illustrate. The first is from someone who felt the general practitioner's prestige had gone up:

TABLE 18 *Social class and beliefs about general practitioner's prestige*

| Believes that in the last ten years G.P.'s prestige has: | Social class | | | | | | All patients |
	I Professional	II Intermediate	III Skilled non-manual	III Skilled manual	IV Partly skilled	V Unskilled	
	%	%	%	%	%	%	%
Gone down	54	37	29	15	15	12	23
Gone up	7	17	14	31	29	31	24
Stayed the same	34	42	53	48	52	52	48
Other comments	5	4	4	6	4	5	5
NUMBER OF PATIENTS (= 100%)	58	245	163	509	231	78	1,333

'We're more intelligent now and realise how clever they are. We respect their opinions more.'

The next two are from people who thought it had gone down:

'It's an outcome of improved general education in a way. The mystic figure of a doctor who was almighty 20 years ago is disappearing.'

'Because a lot of other people are coming up – not necessarily rightly – he's not treated with quite the respect he used to be. People used to equate him with the local squire and vicar. Nowadays very few people live in villages. And it might be because people know more doctors now. Since I've got older I've found them more human than I used to think as a young lad.'[12]

Looking after a lot of patients was also given as a reason why their prestige had gone both up and down:

Up. 'You hear so much talk about the number of patients they have to cope with and people discuss this and feel sympathetic.'

Down. 'Most of them seem to get an overloaded practice so people feel they're being treated like a herd of sheep. Too many go with trivial things – serious ones don't get enough time and attention.'

There was some suggestion that disputes over pay had adversely affected people's view of doctors:

'Under the present doctoring system they haven't got that interest. They used to make the medicine up at one time. They don't do it now. They're all in it for what they can get out of it.'

'Everything is changing. I don't think doctors were exceptionally clever in my young days, but now it's a case of money. They're always grumbling about not getting enough. I think people lose all confidence in their doctors. I liked the old style who'd talk to you. It's all rush these days'.

[12] The proportion who felt the general practitioner's prestige had gone down was slightly higher in urban than in rural areas – 24 per cent compared with 17 per cent.

From the general practitioner's standpoint it seems probable that it is the apparent fall in status in the eyes of professional people – and more particularly of medical colleagues in hospital – that rankles. 'In old days the consultant depended on general practitioners'. 'Now the hospitals have no respect for G.P.s'. Most of them, 79 per cent, agreed with the statement: 'A doctor should not expect patients to respect him just because he is a doctor. He has to earn their respect.' But some expressed regret at what they saw as a fall in status in the eyes of their patients:

'The big thing is that respect for the doctor has gone completely in this area. You're just a stooge. My father was looked up to' (at interview).

'The G.P. has not got the standing in the eyes of the patient that he used to have before the N.H.S. Although he still has a certain amount of respect, at the same time one feels one doesn't get the respect one ought to' (at interview).

TABLE 19 *Doctors' views on demanding patients*

Doctors' views on statement that patients nowadays tend to demand their rights rather than ask for help and advice		%
Strongly agree	2	22
	1	34
	0	14
	1	20
Strongly disagree	2	10
NUMBER OF DOCTORS (= 100%)		413

Some had other explanations:

'I'll tell you the main cause of doctors' discontent – it's finance and the fact that our incomes are relatively lower in relation to other people's than they used to be. And this means a loss in prestige' (at interview).

'If you rent a goggle-box you pay £2 for servicing – they come two days after you ring up and bring it back ten days after that. The Ministry expects me to service a patient for

£1. I feel if the retainer to mend TV is more than to look after a patient something is wrong.'

Doctors were asked to indicate their agreement or disagreement with the statement: 'Patients nowadays tend to demand their rights rather than to ask for help and advice.' Replies are shown in Table 19.

It seems possible that some general practitioners – and some patients – feel the formal definition of patients' rights under the National Health Service has detracted from their prestige in the community. The impression that patients 'demand their rights' was strongly associated with the idea that a high proportion of consultations were trivial.[13] (See Table 20.)

TABLE 20   *Views on demanding patients and trivial conditions*

Proportion of surgery consultations estimated to be trivial; inappropriate or unnecessary	*Attitude to statement: 'patients nowadays tend to demand their rights rather than ask for help and advice'*				
	Strongly agree				*Strongly disagree*
	2	1	0	1	2
	%	%	%	%	%
90% or more	7	1	—	—	—
75% but less than 90%	12	3	2	4	2
50% but less than 75%	26	19	31	10	3
25% but less than 50%	31	38	31	24	10
10% but less than 25%	20	29	24	42	30
Less than 10%	4	10	12	20	55
NUMBER OF DOCTORS (= 100%)	91	143	58	81	40

One woman who felt the prestige of general practitioners had gone down put it this way:

'They're not made as much of as when I was a child. Their social standing is high but people – the general public – treat them as a servant of theirs. He's there for their convenience.'

[13] In a multi-variate analysis of 13 things related to the proportion of consultations the doctors felt to be trivial, this accounted for the largest proportion of the variation between doctors. The number of X-rays they had access to and their enjoyment of their work were also important.

And another who held the same view said:

'You've got an awful lot of people who want something for nothing. They consider their doctor not as a family friend and expect him to their bidding. They make no bones about demanding their rights.'

Doctors who made this point when they were interviewed usually qualified it by saying only a few patients were like that:

'We're swamped with trivialities. This isn't the sort of work one spent years at university preparing oneself for. There's the utter futility and humiliation of a professional man who feels his training is wasted. The G.P. has no status because he doesn't do medicine. Ninety per cent of our work is with 10 per cent of our patients. The vast majority are very reasonable' (at interview).

Several criticized what they felt was the one-sided nature of the doctor-patient responsibility.

'People have an increasing belief that they have a right to a doctor's services for anything at any time of day or night and can have him over a barrel if he doesn't do what they want. But if they abuse the service there is no redress except to get rid of the patient and that's slitting your own throat' (at interview).

'There's no come-back to the patient. They can phone you up and you go and find the child running in the garden. They say: "She did have a temperature – can you give the immunization now?" But if the doctor avoids visiting once, immediately there's a come-back' (at interview).

'If a patient says "jump" we must jump. Not everyone is prepared to be a door mat. It should be acknowledged that G.P's are highly trained specialists' (at interview).

The patients who abuse the scheme may be few and far between but if the general practitioner has no redress or organizational support he may feel caught between the demanding patient and a remote bureaucracy.

Bureaucratic interference

General practitioners have great freedom in their work under the National Health Service. Their grumbles about the few existing controls seem to stem from four causes. First the feeling that any control is irksome and inappropriate for their profession, secondly doubt about the relevance of particular controls, thirdly a spill-over of discontent about other aspects of their work and work situation, and finally – if their statements are accepted – the ineptitude with which the controls are occasionally administered.

Several general practitioners complained about restrictions on their prescribing:

'I prescribed some barrier cream for a patient. I wrote a long letter explaining why. They still said they were unable to accept it, but I could appeal if I wanted. Who's going to waste time appealing for the sake of 4/6 or 6/6 or whatever it was? And how much would it cost them if I appealed? I just paid the money' (at interview).

'You should be free to prescribe for one's patients whatever one thinks necessary. If you exceed the national average by a certain amount you get a statistical analysis which is fantastic. It must cost the statisticians a fortune to produce. I was investigated. One item they were critical of was a life saving antibiotic which had obviated the need for hospital treatment – and the cost that that would have entailed. Another item they criticized was a proprietary drug containing three items. They told me I should have used National Formulary equiv-alents of the three items. I costed this in front of them and it came to 50 per cent more.'

One said he had taken logical but somewhat inhuman steps to reduce his costs:

'Two or three years ago I had trouble over my prescribing costs. I was told "If you don't improve we might take it further." I analysed my patients' age groups and found I'd collected a lot of chronics. Instead of sending them to hospital I had treated them. The Ministry said "What steps have you taken to reduce your prescribing costs?" So I asked all the chronics who lived a mile or so away to leave my list. It was a terrible thing to have to do really' (at interview).

Another illustration, this time of the pettiness of the Executive Council, was given by one who said they threatened to deduct 6s. 2d. from his salary because he prescribed an ointment to a patient with a colostomy. The ointment had previously been prescribed by the consultant for skin irritation resulting from the colostomy and the patient had found it helpful. The Executive Council maintained it was a toilet preparation and should not be prescribed (at interview).

Disciplinary committees were also criticized. 'Patients can take us up for very trivial complaints. I do not think the committees should necessarily be completely abolished but it would be better if doctors could also complain about patients.' An example he gave of the unsatisfactoriness of the disciplinary committee was of one doctor fined 50 guineas for charging a patient two shillings for a bandage:

> 'What he should have done, according to the committee, was give the patient a prescription which he would take to the chemist, pay two shillings and get a bandage and then bring it back to the doctor for him to bandage it up' (at interview).

This same doctor's partner felt that if patients were making a serious complaint they should do it through the General Medical Council or the courts. There was no need for this additional machinery.

Pernickety applications of rules, and sometimes the existence of rules, are seen as a slight to their professional status. At the same time the appropriateness of the rules is also questioned. 'They don't investigate the cheap prescribers'. Certainly the few controls that exist are nearly all negative, preventing certain abuses but neither stimulating good medical care nor even ensuring minimum standards. Investigation of prescribing costs, if combined with studies of hospital referrals and use of other services, could encourage higher standards and the more efficient use of different types of service. The officers involved attempt to take into account other aspects of the general practitioners' work and their local reputation with hospitals and other medical colleagues. They may not always be successful but of course general practitioners, in making suggestions about changes, are unlikely to have told us about occasions when their prescribing was reasonably criticized and constructive suggestions made by the investigating officers.

It also seems that some of the general practitioners' criticisms of bureaucratic controls arise from a feeling that they are 'carrying the can' in a way which the government and the Ministry do not appreciate.

'The government is running this health service on the cheap. I think the N.H.S. is an excellent concept but I do not see why I need to have hypertension at 50 and a coronary at 55' (at interview).

'The N.H.S. is a wonderful idea but they're doing it on a shoestring at the expense of the labour – the doctors and the nurses' (at interview).

Conclusions

Most general practitioners say they enjoy their work but there are various aspects of it which many of them resent. Consultations for trivialities are the most frequent object of their expressed irritation and such feelings are probably linked with their own evaluation of their job and their related concern about prestige.

To some extent doctors' feelings about the 'triviality' of their consultations seem to be of their own making: doctors who feel a high proportion of their consultations are trivial carry out few procedures themselves. In addition these doctors tend not to go on courses for general practitioners so they are more likely to retain the outlook of their hospital-based training and to value their work in clinical rather than social terms. Using this yardstick they may underestimate their potential worth, and feeling somewhat insecure as a result look for support in respect from their patients and prestige in the community. If they do not always receive the respect they expect they may regard their patients as demanding. They may also feel, particularly if they come from a medical family, that they are not so well-off in relation to people in other jobs and professions as they expected or as their parents were, and this feeling of 'relative deprivation' may aggravate their sense of frustration.

Conversely, the general practitioner who regards few of his consultations as trivial is likely to have more self-respect for his job. His views about this may have been influenced by his attendance at courses and his opinion about the general practitioner's role in relation to social and psychological difficulties probably differs from that of his less happy colleague.

These descriptions are over-simplifications, but in a National Health Service with free access to general practitioners, it is important to inculcate the outlook of those doctors who do not feel their work is trivial among those who at present do. An initial training, or a post-graduate training, more oriented towards general practice[14] should help future doctors; attendance at appropriate courses may help those at present in practice, but there is a danger that a spiral of cynicism, job-depreciation and anti-patient feeling has built up among some general practitioners and will be difficult to break down. Some action which the doctor can take if he feels a patient is making inappropriate demands might help to convince these doctors that the National Service is not the anti-doctor charter which they sometimes claim. The availability of some machinery for dealing with this type of grievance would probably assure them of this. In practice it would probably rarely be used.

[14] Such as that outlined by the College of General Practitioners in their report on *Special Vocational Training for General Practice.*

V

FAMILY AND DOMICILIARY CARE

In Britain the terms 'general practitioner' and family doctor are sometimes regarded as synonymous. For example, the sub-committee set up in 1961 by the Standing Medical Advisory Committee to study the future scope of general practice called its report 'The Field of Work of the Family Doctor'.[1] In it they comment: 'The general practitioner's field of work has no formal limit. It is his contribution as the medical adviser who knows his patient as a person and as a member of the extended family as it evolves and develops that is specially important.' Perhaps it was because they took this aspect of his care for granted that they did not discuss it in detail or at all critically. Yet this concept of the general practitioner's role is not without its critics. McKeown[2] puts forward the view that family care stands in the way of clinical competence and believes that a more satisfactory basis for the future of medical practice would be provided by basing domiciliary care on four types of doctors – obstetrician, paediatrician, adult physician and geriatric physician – each functioning as a personal doctor.

Part of the difficulty of evaluating the importance of family care arises from its elusive character. When members of a family have the same doctor it is hard for both patients and doctor to assess what difference this makes, and even the definition of a family doctor can vary. In the sample, 72 per cent of the people who lived in households with relatives had the same doctor as all their relatives in the household, 5 per cent had different doctors within the same partnership and 23 per cent had entirely different doctors. The proportion with different doctors was smaller for people living just with a husband or wife and children than for people living in more complicated households, 25 per cent

[1] Central Health Services Council, *The Field of Work of the Family Doctor.*
[2] McKeown, Thomas, *Medicine in Modern Society*, p. 178.

compared with 39 per cent. When households consisting of just a married couple and their children had different doctors in three-quarters of them it was the husband who had a different doctor from the wife and children. The longer people had been married the more likely they were to have the same doctor. For people living with just their husband or wife, the proportion with the same doctor rose from 49 per cent of those under 35 to 83 per cent of those aged 55 or more.

When asked the reason why people in their household had different doctors the most frequent reply, given by 45 per cent, was that husband and wife had kept their old doctor after marriage. When this happens the advantage of continuity of care conflicts with the ideal of family care. Apart from this, 8 per cent wanted a doctor of a particular sex, 4 per cent said the doctor's list was too full for him to accept any more patients, in 1 per cent some members of the family had private doctors and others were under National Health Service and another 1 per cent did it as a deliberate policy, feeling it was better to have different doctors. Many people gave vague reasons which again reflect the casual way doctors are often chosen.

TABLE 21   *Relatives not in household who have the same doctor*

	%
None	61
Relationship to subject	
Siblings (and their families)	15
Child(ren) or children-in-law (and their families)	10
Parent(s)	10
Parent(s)-in-law	6
Spouse's siblings (with/without children)	6
Other	4
NUMBER OF PATIENTS (= 100%)	1,366

Apart from relatives in their own household, two-fifths of the people had the same doctor as other relatives who did not live with them. The relatives involved are shown in Table 21. There was no difference between men and women in the proportion who had the same doctor as other relatives not in their household, and the ratio of parents to parents-in-law and siblings to siblings-in-law with the same doctor did not vary appreciably between the sexes. Similarly, when both the subject and spouse had lived in the same area before marriage and just one of them had changed their doctor so they could have the same one, the wife had changed in 51 cases and the husband in 44. So it does not seem that the tie between mothers and daughters, stressed by Young and Willmott,[3] influences married women to stay with the doctor of their family of origin any more than it does married men.

The proportion with the same doctors as relatives not in their household was greater among working-class patients than among middle-class ones, 43 per cent compared with 32 per cent. This difference probably arises because working-class people live in the same district as other relatives more often than middle-class people.[4] In contrast, middle-class patients more often had the same doctor for all the household – 76 per cent of them did so, and 69 per cent of the working-class patients.

The proportion of people with a family doctor obviously depends on definition. It might be thought of as all those people who have the same doctor as at least one other relative, whether or not the relative lives in the same household. Eighty-five per cent fulfilled this criterion. But in attempting to look at the difference between people with and those without a family doctor a more rigorous criterion has been adopted in the discussion that follows – whether people have the same doctor as all the relatives in their household. People who live alone or just with unrelated people are excluded from these comparisons.

People who had the same doctor as all the other members of their family were more likely to regard their relationship with their doctor as friendly rather than businesslike[5] – 48 per cent, compared with 35 per cent of those in households who had some members with doctors in quite different partnerships, while those in households having different doctors in the same partnership fell in between, 43 per cent. However, this may be simply that if a doctor inquires about other members of the family this is regarded as being friendly. People with family doctors were no more likely than others to feel the general practitioner a suitable person to

[3] Young, M., and Willmott, P., *Family and Kinship in East London*, pp. 156–62.
[4] See Willmott, P., and Young, M., *Family and Class in a London Suburb*, p. 78.
[5] 'Do you consider your doctor to be something of a personal friend or is your relationship pretty much a businesslike one?'

talk to about such problems as children getting into trouble or difficulties between husband and wife, nor were they any more likely to feel they would discuss a personal problem that was not strictly a medical one. Similarly there was no difference between those with family doctors and others in the proportion who felt their doctor was good at listening to what they had to say and explaining things to them fully. From the viewpoint of the patient then, having a family doctor as opposed to an individual one seems to make little difference to their relationship and feeling about him. However, it is possible that two things are being confounded. It could be that, given a particular doctor, the patient-doctor relationship is in general more satisfactory if the doctor is a family one but that, because people within a family are presumably more likely to retain different doctors if they feel their relationship with their doctor is a good one, there appears to be no difference.

In an attempt to discover some of the ways in which having a family doctor affected the doctor-patient relationship, mothers of children under 15 were asked if they could give any examples of ways in which they had found it helpful to have the same doctor as their children.[6] Several made comments agreeing that it was helpful: 'It's so much easier to have the same doctor for all the family. For a child the doctor knows the mother's and father's background and this can be helpful.' But few gave any definite examples except for the convenience of the doctor seeing two people on the same occasion: 'If anything is wrong with me he also asks about her and checks on us both.'

All the people who had consulted their doctor in the previous twelve months were asked whether their general practitioner had asked to see any other member of the family when they had consulted him themselves. Fourteen, 2 per cent, said he had. In one instance at any rate the doctor seemed to be checking for possible family-associated disease.

'The wife's got blood disease and he asked all the rest of us to come along for tests and when I went he told me to send the girls down.'

[6] 'It is often said that it is helpful for mothers to have the same doctor as their children. Can you give an example of any way in which you have found it helpful in the last two years?'

Sometimes he appeared to be using one member of the family as an interpreter for another, and on other occasions to be checking on people he felt ought to be coming to see him.

'When I went down he asked if my daughter-in-law would come up. She was expecting a baby and he said he'd like to see her.'

Two mothers mentioned that he had asked them to bring their children for immunization or vaccination.

There was another example of the general practitioner functioning as a family doctor from the consultations which took place in the fortnight before the interview. A woman, suffering from shock and worry because her husband was ill had been visited by her doctor.

'I did not expect him to call and see me and I was very pleased when he did.'

So there were a number of instances when having the same doctor as other members of the family made a difference. The surprise is that they apparently occur so infrequently. Of course people may be under-reporting, but other information suggests that having the same doctor as other people in the family does not influence the relationship greatly. Although some mothers recalled the doctor asking them to take their children for immunization or vaccination when they were consulting him about other things, children with a family doctor were no more likely to be immunized against diphtheria or vaccinated against smallpox than those without one, nor was the general practitioner more likely to do the immunization or vaccination himself when all the members of the household were his patients.

When the doctors themselves were asked what they enjoyed about their work as a general practitioner the most frequent answer, given by nearly half, was their personal contact with patients, and several of them stressed their pleasure at knowing their families: 'I enjoy the personal contact with patients within their own family and domestic background'. But the data from this study certainly do not suggest that the advantages of a family doctor are so great that they should necessarily outweigh other considerations of efficiency and specialization, though there is little information about the clinical importance of family doctoring, or about the family doctor's awareness of possible hereditary conditions in his patients.[7]

Domiciliary care

In Britain, unlike Sweden and America, there is a strong tradition of home visiting by doctors. It has already been shown that about a fifth of general practitioner consultations take place in the patients' homes.[8] Nearly a quarter of the adults interviewed said they had a home visit from their doctor in the previous twelve months, and the proportion was much higher, a half, for children under 15. The distributions are shown in Table 22. This amount of home visiting is a formidable work load. In a pilot study into work-load, carried out by the College of General Practitioners, 27 per cent of the consultations were home visits and took up 50 per cent of the doctors' time spent with patients.[9]

TABLE 22 *Home visits*

Proportion of patients with different numbers of home visits during previous 12 months	Children	Adults
	%	%
None	51	77
One	16	8
Two to four	26	8
Five to nine	4	3
Ten or more	3	4
NUMBER OF PATIENTS (= 100%)	403	1,394

Older people and young babies had both more home visits and *proportionally* more home visits as against surgery consultations

[7] Stevenson, Alan C. and Davison, B. C. Clare in a study of 'Families Referred for Genetic Advice' recorded that 9% were referred by general practitioners.
[8] Data from the U.S.A. National Health Survey show 5 per cent of physician consultations taking place in the home. In Sweden, for the insured population, the proportion is also about one in 20. See National Center for Health Statistics, 'Volume of Physician Visits by Place of Visit and Type of Service', and Weber, A., 'Some Characteristics of Mortality and Morbidity in Europe'.
[9] College of General Practitioners, *Present State and Future Needs of General Practice*, p. 23.

than other people. The proportion with five or more home visits
in the year was 28 per cent of the people aged 75 or more, 13 per
cent of those aged 65–74, 4 per cent of other adults, 2 per cent of
children aged 10–14, 6 per cent of those aged 5–9, 10 per cent of
those aged 1–4 and 18 per cent of babies under one. But whereas
much home visiting to young children is for acute conditions and
involves just a single visit, older people are usually visited several
times for the same condition (see Table 23).

TABLE 23   *Home visits for episodes of illness involving at least one visit**

	Children			Adults	
Number of visits	Under 2	2–4	5–14	21–64	65 or more
	%	%	%	%	%
One	61	54	46	51	28
Two	4	24	25	20	15
Three or four	22	15	23	18	21
Five or more	13	7	6	11	36
NUMBER OF EPISODES (= 100%)	23	46	65	231	85

* Adults who had had a visit in the last 12 months were asked about the
most recent occasion a doctor visited them, and the number of times
he came – for that episode – altogether. Mothers were asked about the
most recent occasion a doctor visited any of her children, if any of
them had had a visit in the previous year. This procedure does not give a
random sample of home visits, or of episodes of illness having a home visit.

This means that the doctor himself has more control over his
home visiting for older people and least control over the visiting to
young children. When the doctor came more than once it was his
decision[9] in all but 6 per cent of visits for both adults and children,
whereas the initial visit was generally at the request of the patient
or his relatives. Of the 47 home visits reported by adults in the
two weeks before interview only eight, less than a fifth, were first
visits, the others follow-ups.

If doctors in this country did not do so much home visiting,
how would people manage? What proportion of visits are to

[9] 'After the first time, did he call on his own accord or did you – or your family –
ask him to come again?'

people who would otherwise need to be admitted to hospital? How far is the problem one of transport? If people had their own cars, or a car service was available could more of them get to their doctor's surgery? Does the possibility of a longish wait at the surgery deter people from going there when they are feeling unwell and sometimes tip the balance in favour of asking the doctor to call? If more people had telephones of their own and the idea of sometimes getting advice and reassurance over the phone was more generally accepted by both doctors and patients, would this reduce the number of home visits? To answer these questions conclusively would entail carefully designed studies but some clues are given by this study.

First, on the conditions for which people were visited, Table 24 compares peoples' descriptions of the most recent condition for which adults were visited, with all the conditions for which they consulted a doctor in the previous two weeks. Respiratory conditions were responsible for an even larger proportion of home visit episodes than surgery consultations – nearly one third. When conditions involving a home visit were divided into those with only one visit for the episode and those with two or more, bronchitis accounted for 14 per cent of the second group compared with only 3 per cent of the first, whereas other respiratory conditions accounted for 26 per cent of single-visit episodes against 19 per cent of those with more than one. All the adults who had had a consultation at home during the previous twelve months were asked: 'Just supposing doctors did not visit people in their own homes what do you think you would have done during that episode (i.e. the last one for which they were visited)? – How would you have felt about that?' Many of them found this hard to envisage:

'We'd have to get someone else – or get his advice on the phone. I don't really know – he'd always come, he always does.'

Some reckoned they would have had to go straight to hospital:

'I'd have got my wife to get an ambulance and take me to hospital. Dr ——— sent me to hospital then and there as it was, but it was better he should know about it all' (heart attack).

TABLE 24   *Conditions for all consultations and home visits*

	All consultations in last two weeks	*Most recent episode in last 12 months involving home visit*
	%	%
Infective and parasitic diseases	2	3
Neoplasms	1	—
Allergic endocrine system, metabolic and nutritional disorders	9	3
Diseases of the blood and blood forming organs	3	1
Mental, psychoneurotic, personality disorders and nervousness	6	2
Diseases and symptoms of the nervous system and sense organs	11	6
Diseases and symptoms of the circulatory system	9	10
Bronchitis	4	9
Other diseases and symptoms of the respiratory system	14	22
Diseases and symptoms of the digestive system	8	12
Diseases and symptoms of the genito-urinary system	3	5
Deliveries and complications of pregnancy, childbirth and the puerperium	7	4
Diseases of the skin and cellular tissue	2	1
Diseases and symptoms of the bones and organs of movement	9	10
Other general symptoms, senility and ill-defined conditions	5	1
Accidents, poisonings and violence	4	7
Check-up, no symptoms	1	—
Social, preventive, regular visit to old people	2	4
NUMBER (= 100%)	226	316

In this instance hospitalization was not averted and of course it is not possible to tell from these data how often people might have needed to go there. Some would have relied on medicines from the chemist:

'I wouldn't have phoned the ambulance. I would have tried to work it off with aspirin and the usual remedies from the chemist' (gastric influenza).

Others would have got to the doctor's surgery themselves somehow:

'The doctor calls every week to see if everything is all right. He has been doing that for two to three years. If he didn't, we'd have to make some arrangements to get there. My son would have to take me.'

Several expressed concern at this possibility, describing it as 'a regression of 100 years' and 'a poor state of affairs' while others 'hoped they'd never be in that predicament' or would have been 'not very happy as I felt terrible', although some 'would not have minded'.

'It would not have mattered. It was just that I'd been discharged from hospital and he came to satisfy himself. I would have got on a bus and gone down.'

'On that particular occasion I wouldn't have bothered. If it hadn't been for my mother I wouldn't have seen him anyway. It was my mother who sent for him'.

A few reacted aggressively:

'I couldn't have done anything. They're forced to come. I should have stopped in bed. I should have been ready to report him. It'd be his place to come.'

'I don't know. They're for us aren't they? They're to come when we phone.'

For some the difficulty of getting to the surgery may have been the reason for home visiting. Certainly patients who said it took them half an hour or more to get to their doctor's surgery were more likely to have had a visit in the last twelve months than those who lived nearer – 35 per cent compared with 23 per cent. But data from this study do not suggest that increasing private transport will cut down the demand for home visits. Those who usually went to their doctor's surgery by private transport were no less likely to have had a home visit in the previous twelve months than those who normally used public transport to get there.[10] Indeed among older people of 65 or more, those who travelled by private transport were if anything more likely to have had a home visit in the last twelve months than those who went by public transport (41 per cent compared with 26 per cent), probably because relatives and friends of older people may be more inclined to take them to the surgery by car if they are rather frail.

The length of time people had to wait in the doctor's surgery was not related to the proportion who had home visits so it does not seem that people ask their doctor to call if they expect a long wait.

Access to a telephone did not appear to reduce the demand for home visits, but this is hardly surprising since so few people consulted the doctor over a telephone anyway. Only 3 per cent of adults said they had had any advice over the telephone from their doctor in the previous twelve months, and this proportion was 7 per cent of those with a telephone in their dwelling. Advice was rather more frequently sought over the phone for children; 16 per cent of mothers of children under 15 had had some advice over the phone about their children in the previous twelve months, and this proportion was 28 per cent of mothers with a telephone in their dwelling. But their children had just as many home visits as children in homes without a telephone.

Home visits for children were for a relatively homogeneous group of conditions (see Table 25). Respiratory conditions accounted for 37 per cent of the episodes and common infectious diseases for 22 per cent.

When asked what they would have done then 'just supposing doctors did not visit people in their own homes', a third of the mothers said they would have taken the child to the surgery:

'I'd have just had to wrap him up well and take a chance and take him down in a taxi, I expect. I'd have been very annoyed. I wouldn't really have liked to take him out. He was very poorly.'

A fifth would have got his advice on the telephone, but several

10 This analysis was done by patient's age, since people under 45 more often travelled by private transport than others and those aged 65 or more were least likely to go by private transport.

TABLE 25 *Conditions for which children were visited at home*

	%
Common infectious diseases – mumps, measles, chickenpox, german measles, whooping cough, scarlet fever	22
Hay fever, asthma	3
Diseases of the ear and mastoid process	7
Tonsillitis	9
Other acute upper respiratory infections and influenza and croup	14
Bronchitis	4
Other respiratory diseases and symptoms including 'chill', cough, 'chest trouble'	10
Sickness, diarrhoea, gastro enteritis, stomach trouble, gastric 'flu, colic	10
Skin diseases and symptoms	1
Rash N.O.S. and possible infectious diseases, swollen glands	7
Accidents	5
Other	8
NUMBER OF HOME VISITS (= 100%)	135

of them would have felt unhappy about doing so: 'I don't think you can talk over the phone the same as direct.'

'I'd have rung him and asked what I should do. I'd have managed all right because she's been bad with asthma before, so I know. But I wanted him to see her to check it wasn't anything worse.'

One in seven said they would have contacted the hospital or taken the child there. Some of the illnesses these children had and the mothers' comments were: 'An ear infection. He was in too much pain for me to have let him go on.' 'Bronchitis – she was terribly ill. I definitely think we'd have had to take her to the hospital. I think myself they could give the wrong advice over the telephone. A layman could miss something out.' 'Tonsillitis. I was very worried and frightened. I thought it was meningitis. His temperature was 103 and he was going frantic with his head.'

An eighth of the mothers would have got the doctor's advice by going to the surgery themselves without the child, a twelfth would have managed on their own:

'I'd have kept him warm and given him aspirin, but I'd have been a little bit worried.'

A few said they would have called in a doctor privately.

The conditions which would have caused least anxiety if the doctor had not been prepared to visit seemed to be the common childhood infectious diseases. A few, in retrospect, appeared to recognize that it had not been necessary to ask the doctor on that particular occasion:

'Well he was very miserable at the time but not infectious, so we could have gone up to the surgery' (bad ear-ache).

'As it turned out it would have been all right' (swollen glands, thought it might be mumps).

Obviously it is not possible to tell what proportion of home visits were unnecessary. A tenth of the general practitioners said late calls or calls at the wrong time were one of the frustrations of general practice and others who were interviewed complained about unnecessary calls.

'I'm continually getting calls from people who could damn well come to the surgery. They put in calls at all times. My partner puts up with it. I tell mine, but on my partner's side I feel a bit chary of telling them off.'

On the other hand, visiting patients in their own homes was mentioned by a few doctors, 4 per cent, as one of the things they enjoyed about their work. An American study[11] in which the site of care was varied experimentally showed that mothers of sick children expressed a striking preference for the 'house call' while the student doctors involved found the lighting and other facilities better in the office but more often thought there was something 'particularly satisfying' about home visits. On the present study there was no difference between home visits and surgery consultations in the proportion of patients who said the doctor examined them.

General practitioners in Britain do not seem to regard home visits as anachronistic, unlike some of their American colleagues. But some question the efficiency of making so many. Occasional doctors offer patients they would otherwise visit a car service

[11] Gibson, Count D., and Kramer, Bernard M., 'Site of Care in Medical Practice'.

to bring them to the surgery. One partnership offers this just to chronic patients whom they used to visit regularly. They reckon the cost of the service is repaid by the time saved.[12] Another group also offers it to all patients who request a visit before 10.30 a.m. They estimate that they have reduced their visiting by 40 per cent.[13]

It is sometimes argued that the patient's home and family may provide clues that may be left behind if he goes to the doctor's office[14] and this is doubtless true but is no justification for repeated home visits, and it is repeat visits which make up the large majority, four-fifths, of home visits to adults, although the proportion is less for children. The relief of anxiety is probably the main outcome of many home visits for children but this surely is an important part of a general practitioner's role.

Conclusions

Knowing that their doctor will come and visit them in their home when needed is one of the aspects of the general practitioner service that is much appreciated by patients, and seems to be particularly popular among mothers of young children. But it is probably inefficient for doctors to do as much home visiting as they do at the moment: a fifth of their consultations are in people's homes. One way to reduce the proportion of home visits is to bring some of the people who would otherwise need them into the surgery. A few schemes to do this have been introduced, and the doctors using them find their efficiency increased. More doctors may be encouraged to try arrangements of this kind when they can recover some of the expenses.[15] Another possible way to reduce home visiting by doctors would be for nurses to visit selected cases. The nurses would need to work in close collaboration with the doctors, some social work training would be helpful, and a car essential. Obviously the acceptance of such a scheme by patients would be all-important and it might be reasonable to offer them a choice when it was first introduced. If mothers were

[12] Seddon, T. M., and Smith, F., 'Car Service in General Practice'.
[13] Floyd, Clifford B., 'Car Service'.
[14] Lancet, 'House Calls and Home Visits'.
[15] The Review Body on Doctors' and Dentists' Remuneration recommended, in its *Seventh Report*, that up to 70 per cent of expenditure on ancillary help be directly reimbursed (p. 52).

offered a choice of a doctor or nurse to visit when they suspected their child had got chickenpox or measles they might well ask for the nurse spontaneously on other occasions. Total requests for visits might increase but at the same time there might be a reduction in late night and emergency calls – and in patients' anxiety.

It is less easy to reach any definite conclusions about the importance of family doctoring. In some ways it seems to be the 'sacred cow' of general practice which everyone, apart from a few critics such as McKeown, worships without question. Both patients and doctors accept it, patients find it convenient, some doctors enjoy it. Its demise would almost certainly cause consternation, but what other effects it would have only a direct comparison with other systems would reveal.

VI

PREVENTIVE CARE

It has been argued that the changing disease pattern, and the present dominance of chronic degenerative disease among the middle-aged and elderly, challenge the traditional role of the general practitioner as the person to whom his patients turn when they are ill. The reasoning is that many chronic conditions could be prevented, or cured if identified early enough, but the early discovery of these diseases involves screening people before they would normally seek medical care and their prevention depends not so much on environmental control but on changes in personal habits. Backett concludes: 'the future family doctor will be forced increasingly to switch his attention from sick people to the habits and behaviour of healthy people'.[1]

This chapter looks first at the preventive care adults receive at present and then at their expressed desires for regular check-ups. The needs of children are considered next and finally doctors' views and the implications are discussed.

Present preventive care for adults

People were asked whether they had had any sort of check-up such as a chest X-ray or general examination in the last two years. Just under half, 47 per cent, said they had. However half of these did so because of symptoms, pregnancy or an earlier illness so only a quarter had had what could be described as a preventive or screening check. How did they come to have such examinations? Over half of them, 56 per cent, were arranged through their work or done while a mobile X-ray unit was at their office or factory, 'They were visiting the offices and we were asked if we would like to have the X-ray and I volunteered'. Just over a quarter,

[1] Backett, E. M., 'Social Aspects of the New Patterns of Disease: The Role of the Family Doctor'.

28 per cent, were their own idea in the sense that they responded to a campaign or went to an M.M.R. clinic of their own accord.

'The X-ray clinic suggested everyone should have it done. It was in the papers and on Southern TV. You can just go and there's no need of appointments like at hospital. All my family was done. It was over in no time.'

'We just went. My husband said: "Let's see if our chests are all right".'

Five per cent were examinations for pension or insurance purposes or before they were accepted for a job, another 3 per cent were examinations for the Territorial Army or demobilization and 2 per cent for university or training college. Other reasons were contact with a relative who had tuberculosis, hospitals doing chest X-rays routinely when patients attended with other unrelated illnesses, and 3 per cent where the general practitioner had instigated the examination although the patients reported they had no symptoms.[2]

'Dr ——— gives a general examination to everybody when he takes them on his list.'

But in some of these instances there may have been indications to the doctor if not to the patient that something might be wrong.

'To my knowledge there was nothing wrong but he was obviously looking for something.'

Among the other check-ups where the patient was aware of symptoms or had had an earlier illness, the general practitioner figured more prominently. He initiated just over half of these, the hospital just over a fifth, an eighth were associated with ante-natal or post-natal care, and a seventh had asked for the examination themselves.

'I demanded it because I was feeling so down and under the weather at all times, so I thought it would be a sensible thing.'

What did the check-ups involve? Half of them were chest

[2] 'Did you have any symptoms or was there any other reason why you should have a check-up?'

X-rays only, so 23 per cent of all adults had had this, 15 per cent had had a chest X-ray with some other type of examination and 8 per cent some other examination but no chest X-ray. Ten per cent of the women said they had had an internal or vaginal examination during the two years. A minority of those who had a chest X-ray only had some symptoms or earlier illness, about one-quarter; whereas other types of examination were more often associated with some condition, about three-quarters. Just over a third of the internal examinations were done as part of ante-natal or post-natal care, and only about one in seven were not related to either symptoms, earlier illness or pregnancy.

It seems probable that fewer people had actually had chest X-rays in the two years than reported them. Data from the Ministry of Health show that 8·4 per cent of adults aged 20 and over had mass miniature radiography in 1963, and a similar proportion in 1962[3] whereas, to take the minimum corresponding figures from this study, 24 per cent said they had had a chest X-ray

TABLE 26   *Place of check-up*

	Chest X-ray only	Other examination with or without chest X-ray	All check-ups
	%	%	%
Chest clinic or mobile X-ray*	81	23	52
Hospital (not ante-natal clinic)	21	51	36
General practitioner	1	42	21
Works doctor*	—	9	6
Ante-natal clinic	—	4	2
Other	—	7	3
NUMBER OF PATIENTS† WHO HAD HAD CHECK-UP (= 100%)	320	313	638

* A mobile X-ray visiting a factory or office has been included under mobile X-ray.

† The percentages add to more than 100 as some patients had had a check-up at more than one place.

[3] Ministry of Health, *On the State of the Public Health.*

at a chest clinic or mobile X-ray in the previous two years. Two years is obviously too long a period to study such things with reasonable accuracy. The figures from the present study can therefore only be taken as indicating the proportion who feel they have had some sort of check-up fairly recently (the actual period is likely to vary for different people) but it is of some interest that people over- rather than under-estimate this. This does not suggest that such checks breed hypochondriacs. On the contrary it seems they may give more security than is realistic.

Table 26 shows where people had their check-ups separately for those with a chest X-ray only and those with some other type of examination. (The percentages add to more than 100 as some people reported a check-up at more than one place during the two years.) Most of the check-ups done by general practitioners were because of symptoms in earlier illness or pregnancy. More men than women had had a chest X-ray, and this difference, as Table 27 shows, is related to whether they were working or not. For those working full time there was no difference between men and women. Another difference was that more people in urban than in rural areas had chest X-rays, 40 per cent against 32 per cent, but there was no variation with people's education or social class.

Younger people were more likely to have had a chest X-ray than older people (Table 28) and this difference persisted within the three employment groups. Thus among those working full-time 61 per cent of those under 35 had had an X-ray, 44 per cent of those aged 35–64 and 25 per cent of those aged 65 or over. Among those not working at all these proportions were 40 per cent, 28 per cent and 19 per cent. On other kinds of examinations there was no clear trend with age. The drop with age in the proportion of people who get their chest X-rayed is unfortunate since the proportion of tuberculous cases revealed increases from 0·1 per cent for people aged 15–19 to 0·9 per cent for men of 65 or more and 0·5 per cent for older women.[4] The Ministry data also show that general practitioners refer a higher proportion of older people than of younger ones for chest X-ray and at all ages it is in the general practitioner referrals that the highest proportion of tuberculous cases are found – with the single exception of examinations of people in prisons or Borstals.

[4] Ministry of Health, op. cit.

TABLE 27 Sex, employment and check-ups

	Men				Women			
	Working full time	Working part time	Not working	All men	Working full time	Working part time	Not working	All women
	%	%	%	%	%	%	%	%
Had chest X-ray	48	48	33	46	50	34	25	32
Had other examination*	19	26	33	22	21	21	22	21
No check-up	47	48	59	48	43	57	66	59
NUMBER OF PATIENTS† (= 100%)	534	31	90	655	147	169	398	714

* Internal, vaginal examinations have not been included here.

† The percentages add to more than 100 because some patients had had a chest X-ray and another examination.

TABLE 28   *Age and check-ups*

	Age in years						
	21–24	25–34	35–44	45–54	55–64	65–74	75 and over
	%	%	%	%	%	%	%
Had chest X-ray	60	53	38	39	34	25	12
Had other examination*	31	26	21	19	20	15	25
No check-up	36	40	54	54	58	70	71
NUMBER OF PATIENTS (= 100%)†	70	262	271	272	256	160	76

* Internal, vaginal examinations have not been included here.
† The percentages add to more than 100 because some people had had a chest X-ray and another examination.

Check-ups and examinations are not of course the only form of preventive care and possibly many general practitioners in this country would put more emphasis on their role as health educators. People who had consulted their general practitioner during the previous twelve months were asked whether they had discussed their diet with him at all, 15 per cent said they had and the majority of these felt they had been given helpful advice which they had been able to carry out.

'He told me to cut down on starches and sugar. I had to lose weight for my varicose veins. I'm fond of anything with starch or sugar so I did find it helpful. I lost a stone.'

But a diabetic who had not discussed diet with her doctor said:

'The diabetic clinic does that for you. Doctors don't seem to have the time. This is the curse of the National Health Service. If you go to the hospitals for treatment they delve into everything but G.Ps appear to be rushed.'

Nineteen per cent of the people who smoked and had consulted their doctor in the last twelve months discussed smoking with him during this period, but few, 3 per cent, felt he had given them helpful advice which they had been able to carry out. Some comments here were:

'It was a bad habit – so he said. I should give up fags or I'd die. Slow down if possible, he said. But it won't do me any harm now. I've smoked all my life.'

'He said keep it down to five – I make it ten.'

The general practitioners' 'routine' visits to elderly patients may also be regarded as a form of preventive care as may much of the supportive help they give to people with emotional and social problems. These will be discussed in later chapters. Another aspect of check-ups is discussed next: people's desire for them.

Desire for check-ups

All those who said they had had some form of check-up in the last two years were asked whether they would have liked a more extensive or general check-up. Seventeen per cent said they would. The proportion was much higher, 26 per cent, for those who had only had a chest X-ray than for those with some other type of examination, 7 per cent.

Everyone was asked whether they would like a doctor to give them a regular check-up, say every two years. Nearly two-thirds, 64 per cent, said they would. A third said they would not want this, and a small proportion, 3 per cent, were uncertain. Half of those who would like one gave prevention or the early diagnosis or treatment of illness as the reason.

'Even if you're not ill, there can be things wrong you don't know about.'

'A medical exam can probably catch things at a start before it's well advanced. If I'd had a check-up before this diabetes affair they would have found out sooner and been able to treat it and prevent me from becoming a sick man.'

'If there was something amiss it would probably be found out in the early stages. A lot of people don't bother to go and see a doctor unless they really have to – and I'm one of them.'

A quarter felt it would give a sense of security and relieve anxiety – 'You'd know how you were going on. There'd be no cause to worry.' 'You'd find out then if anything were wrong with you and not worry so much.'

'Just to make sure you're fit. A lot of people worry about certain things – pains and aches. They think they've got things when they haven't got it at all. They dwell on it so much they make themselves ill.'

A tenth said it would mean the investigation of symptoms they would otherwise not consult about.

'As you get older you get different sorts of pains and you wonder what they are. A doctor checking up would tell you.'

'You get a nasty pain and it goes off so you put off going, but if you had a regular check-up you'd know.'

Two-thirds of those who said they would like a regular check-up would prefer their own doctor to do it himself.[5] A seventh would not mind who did it, and a fifth would rather some other doctor at a clinic or hospital – mainly because they felt they would be better equipped, or: 'They've got specialists in different things and the G.P. is too busy.'

The main reason for *not* wanting one was that it was unnecessary.

'If you're not right you know it without a check-up.'

'In older people it's necessary – but not for myself.'

'I'm all right. I'm 72 and I feel as fit now as when I was 40.'

Five per cent thought a check-up might reveal something they would rather not know about.

'Now that I'm older I don't want to get involved in something. I don't want him looking for things that might be wrong. I'm feeling all right and I don't dwell on illness.'

Four per cent had various other worries and anxieties and 7 per cent said they just did not like going to doctors. 'It might be *advisable* but I don't say I'd like it. I don't like going to the doctor's in any case.' Again there were a number of vague and other answers.

[5] 'Would you prefer your doctor to do this himself or would you rather some other doctor did it – at a clinic or hospital?'

Everyone, whether they wanted a check-up or not, was asked whether there was any particular illness or symptom they felt a regular check-up might set their mind at rest about. Just over a third, 36 per cent, said there was. The most frequently mentioned things were cancer, by 13 per cent of all people; tuberculosis or lung infections, by 8 per cent; and heart troubles or conditions, by 5 per cent. Ten per cent indicated that they had the symptom or condition they mentioned here.

Middle-class people were more likely to mention cancer than working-class, 17 per cent compared with 10 per cent, but working-class people were more likely to mention something they had already got, 12 per cent against 8 per cent. However the proportion who said they would like a regular check-up did not vary between the two groups – although of course the proportions who might take advantage of one if it were offered might not be the same.[6]

The proportion who wanted a check-up decreased for older people. It was 68 per cent of those under 65, 47 per cent of those aged 65–74 and 39 per cent of those aged 75 or more. Older people were also less likely to say there was a particular illness or symptom a check-up might set the mind at rest about, but if they did mention one it was more likely to be something they had.

More men said they would like a regular check-up than women, 69 per cent compared with 59 per cent. The difference was most marked between the sexes for those aged 25–34 and 55–74. It may be that it was their feeling of responsibility towards their families that made men more anxious to have a check-up, and rather more married than single men did say this: 71 per cent compared with 61 per cent. Married and single women also varied in the same way: 63 per cent compared with 43 per cent. The group least likely to want a check-up were elderly single women – only 20 per cent.

---

[6] A study on 'Community Aspects of a Mass Radiography Campaign' by Ann Cartwright, F. M. Martin and J. G. Thomson found that before the campaign a somewhat lower proportion of those in the professional and intermediate social classes than of those engaged in manual or clerical work said they were likely to attend for X-ray but that in the event the proportion X-rayed did not vary significantly between occupational classes. In Aberdeen a study by J. Elizabeth MacGregor and Sir Dugald Baird on 'Detection of Cervical Carcinoma in the General Population' obtained a higher response rate in one of the three general practices and concluded: 'the higher response rate in Practice A was thought to be due not only to the helpful attitude of the doctors but also to the fact that more of the women came from the upper social classes.'

In spite of there being more older people and more women among those who did not want a check-up, they were less likely to have consulted their doctor in the last twelve months: 59 per cent of those who did not want a check-up had done so compared with 71 per cent of those who would like one. In general this group seemed unlikely to seek medical help. Out of six particular conditions asked about[7] those who did not want a regular check-up said they would consult about an average of 2·3, those who wanted one about 2·8.

People who had had some sort of a check-up in the last two years more often said they would like a regular check-up than those who had not had one, 71 per cent compared with 58 per cent. When this is taken into account differences between men and women in the proportion who would like a check-up remain among those who had not had a check-up for both those under and those over 65. But among those who had had a check-up, the sex difference virtually disappeared for both those under and those over 65.[8]

It is not of course possible to say whether the association between wanting a regular check-up and having had some sort of check-up in the previous two years arises because people who want a check-up arrange it, or because having had a check-up they feel it an appropriate thing to do. It seems probable that both tendencies are at work.

Children and preventive care

For children, unlike the majority of adults, local authorities give a systematic personal preventive care service. Child welfare clinics, health visiting, and the school health service all developed before the National Health Service, when mothers and children did not have free access to a general practitioner. Mothers of children under five therefore have alternative sources of advice

---

[7] See Chapter III.

[8] For those who had not had a check-up the proportions who would like a regular one were:

men under 65	67%	women under 65	58%
men 65 and over	55%	women 65 and over	35%

For those who had had one the proportions were:

men under 65	76%	women under 65	71%
men 65 and over	44%	women 65 and over	54%

about child-rearing problems and most can choose whether to have their child vaccinated or immunized by their general practitioner, at the clinic – or not at all.

Mothers were asked whether each of their children under five had been vaccinated against smallpox and immunized against diphtheria. Of children aged between one and two years they said half had been vaccinated and three-quarters immunized. General practitioners and clinics had done about half of each. Mothers were less certain about their children aged two to four and could not recall whether a fifth of them had been either vaccinated or immunized, however they thought seven-tenths had been vaccinated and a similar proportion immunized, and again the general practitioner and the clinics had each done about half.[9]

These mothers with children under five were asked whether their doctor had any special sessions for children such as well-baby or immunization clinics. Forty-one per cent said he had, 50 per cent that he had not and 9 per cent were uncertain. There was some suggestion that when the general practitioner held special clinics a slightly higher proportion of the children under five had been vaccinated: 73 per cent compared with 58 per cent, but this difference might arise by chance in a sample of this size. Certainly when the general practitioner did have a special clinic he did a higher proportion of the vaccinations, 67 per cent compared with 42 per cent, and of the immunizations, 62 per cent compared with 39 per cent.

About half the mothers whose doctors did not have any special sessions for children said they would like him to. 'You don't want a lot of grown-ups coughing and spluttering over your child' was one of the comments here. But attendance at general practitioner clinics is low compared with attendance at those of the local authority ones even when it is remembered that only two-fifths of the doctors held one at all. This can be seen from Table 29 which also shows that attendance at a G.P. clinic is often regarded as an addition rather than as an alternative to local authority clinics. But the fall off in attendance as children get older so

---

[9] The Ministry of Health calculates that in 1964 the 'percentage of children under five that may be regarded as remaining protected against diphtheria' was 69 per cent and 'the vaccination rate for children under two years' was 32 per cent, but they believe that there are more vaccinations performed than recorded.

apparent for the local authority clinics does not occur for the special G.P. clinics.

TABLE 29   *Attendance at clinics*

	Children under 2	Children aged 2–4 years
	%	%
G.P. special clinic only	2	8
Local authority clinic only	74	31
Both G.P. and local authority	11	4
No clinic	13	57
NUMBER OF CHILDREN (= 100%)	55	95

Mothers of children under five were asked which they found most helpful when they wanted advice about feeding and problems like that – the general practitioner or the people at the clinic. Fifty-nine per cent said the people at the clinic, 27 per cent the general practitioner, 4 per cent said they were both good or the same, 1 per cent found neither very helpful and 9 per cent gave other answers. In reply to a further question 38 per cent thought it confusing to have two possible sources of information about this, 37 per cent thought it helpful and 25 per cent made other comments. The two main reasons for feeling it helpful were that the doctor was accessible when the clinics were shut and the availability of a second opinion.

'Being nurses you can talk to them better – being women. Clinics are only there on Mondays and Thursdays. Say you couldn't get to the clinic when you wanted to talk about feeding problems, you could get to the doctor.'

'They seem to take more interest at the clinic and they're more helpful because they work with babies all the time. If I didn't think the clinic's advice agreed with my own ideas I'd go to the doctor for a second opinion. I haven't yet had to go to the doctor for this.'

An illustration of the possible confusion was:

'The Welfare Clinic advises rubbing gums for teething, the doctor says don't put your finger near the child's mouth.'

One criticism was:

> 'I'm not a believer in the clinic: they tell you all you should do and shouldn't do and they've never had a baby all their lives. If it's not gaining weight they worry you to death. I think the mother's best judge of what's good for the baby.'

Some comments from the doctors about this will be discussed in the next section, but before that the school health service is considered.

Half of the school children aged 5–9 were reported as having had a school medical examination in the previous twelve months and a third of those aged 10–14. At a quarter of these examinations the mothers said they were given some advice. Half the advice was about something they had already discussed with their own doctor, while the other half related to things they had not discussed with him. Examples of conditions first 'discovered' by the school doctor, and not discussed subsequently with the general practitioner, were:

> 'He told me to cut her diet down as she was a bit on the bonny side.'

> 'He said she had bad flat feet but it was a problem she'd grow out of.'

> 'His eyes – told me he needed a change of glasses and got the clinic to change the lens of his glasses. We didn't know – he had never complained.'

> 'A couple of bad teeth – he needed them out. They weren't hurting him but they were bad. He went to the school dental clinic.'

Illustrations of the school doctor referring people to their general practitioner were:

> 'For bed wetting. He directed me to my own doctor. Actually there's nothing can be done about it.' (Had consulted own doctor after school medical examination).

> 'He said to have fourth polio shot. Our G.P. gave it. I'd forgotten about it.'

Occasionally people got contrary advice:

'The school doctor said he might need his tonsils out in summer. The G.P. had said he didn't need them out. I don't know who to believe.'

Sometimes parents looked to the school doctor when they felt dissatisfied with their general practitioner's advice.

One child aged five had frequent attacks of tonsillitis and the parents wanted his tonsils taken out. Their previous G.P. was against it and would not send them to a specialist. The mother asked the school doctor about it and he said he'd grow out of it. When their G.P. moved they tried their new one and were sent to a specialist at the hospital. He said 'the sooner they come out the better'.

When medical fashions change and opinion is divided, as it is on the criteria for advising tonsillectomy, it is not surprising that mothers sometimes get different advice nor that they can find some doctor to support their own views. Most mothers of school children thought that school medical exams were a good thing, 89 per cent. Only 7 per cent thought them unnecessary and 4 per cent were uncertain.[10] This seemed a reflection of the general approval of regular check-ups, but mothers who did not want a regular check-up for themselves seemed no less likely to think school medical examinations a good thing. Reasons for approval were phrased rather differently from the reasons for wanting a check-up for themselves. Probably because of their practical experience they used fewer theoretical terms such as 'prevention', 'early diagnosis' or 'reassurance'.

'Well you're liable, if your children are not complaining or not having any illness not to take them to the doctor so it's a good thing if they have a check-up at school.'

'Because they do rope in a lot of children who have careless mothers or mothers who go to work and don't cotton on as quickly as they might that their children are not A1 – and things often go undetected for a long time and this could be dangerous for the kiddy.'

[10] 'Do you think that school medical examinations are a good thing or unnecessary?'

'I think I'll take back what I said about them being unnecessary. It was through them that they found Lilian wasn't hearing properly. No, it's a good thing.'

More of the mothers felt it was appropriate for these exams to be done by a different doctor rather than their G.Ps. – 58 per cent compared with 22 per cent – with 14 per cent feeling it did not matter and 6 per cent making other comments.[11]

This of course is in contrast to their views about who they would like to give them a regular check-up, when two-thirds said they would prefer their own doctor to do it. But people tend to be conservative and to appreciate existing arrangements rather than to want changes. This will be demonstrated again when people's preferences for single-handed or partnership doctors and for appointment systems or waiting in turn are discussed.

Some reasons given for preferring a different doctor were convenience, specialization and a second opinion.

'It's helpful to see a different doctor – you get another opinion and different ideas on it.'

'A school doctor who is entirely taken up with children would know more what to look for – like verrucas.'

'It's done so much quicker at school. If you had to wait in the doctor's surgery it would be full up and his other patients would suffer. By the school system defects and ailments can show up there and then you have the opportunity to go to your own doctor. I don't think it matters a lot seeing a strange doctor. Some children don't like strange doctors especially when they're younger. The older ones don't mind.'

Children's adverse reactions to a strange doctor were the main reason for preferring the general practitioner to give them a regular check-up.

'Our Sally is ever so nervous of the school doctor and she isn't of our own.'

But Sally's mother is in a minority. Most mothers seem content

---

[11] 'Do you think it would be a good idea for your general practitioner to do a regular check-up instead of having a school medical examination – or do you think it is helpful for your child(ren) to see a different doctor for that?'

with the present arrangements for the preventive care of school children; in contrast about half the mothers of children under five would like their general practitioner to play a more active role in this and there appears to be a latent wish, but not an active demand, for him to give regular check-ups to many of his adult patients.

Doctors' views on preventive care

When general practitioners were asked whether they thought middle-aged women should have regular cervical smear tests three-quarters said yes.[12] Comments from the other quarter were:

'Too much fuss is made about this. It would be better to get every breast palpated every day of life.'

'I doubt whether the case for doing these tests and the accuracy of the results is fully made out yet.'

'If vaginal smears, why not sputum cytology? Carcinoma of the bronchus is commoner than that of the cervix – or white blood cells for leukaemia, etc., etc. There would be no limit to the number of tests and it would become an impossible burden on any doctor – in general practice or hospital – as well as being crippling to the country.'

It is not clear whether the doctor who made this last comment believes that the prognosis for leukaemia and lung cancer is improved as much by early diagnosis as is the prognosis for cancer of the cervix. But the majority of general practitioners appeared convinced of the desirability of regular cervical smear tests for middle-aged women and nearly half of them, 46 per cent, felt it would be appropriate for general practitioners to collect the smears if hospitals did the cytological examination. Some added a qualification to this: 'but we must somehow be remunerated for the extra work' or 'but I'm afraid, being single-handed, I couldn't cope at the moment'. Rather similar comments were made by some of the quarter who thought middle-aged women should

---

[12] Wolfendale and Handfield-Jones, in a study of the 166 general practitioners in their area found that 98 per cent of them approved in principle of cervical screening and 77 per cent said they would be prepared to take smears from their patients given the necessary facilities. 'The prevention of cervical cancer. Who takes the smears?'

have regular cervical smear tests but that it would not be appropriate for general practitioners to collect the smears if hospitals did the cytological examination.

'Not at present. This would be ideal, but because of the large numbers of patients for which doctors are responsible time is not available to collect smears.'

Others had different doubts: 'We must guard against a nation of hypochondriacs'. And some were concerned about the organization: 'It would be over-complicating what essentially is a simple thing to set up' or 'Delay in transport frequently ruins a pathological specimen'.

A further question asked whether they thought that *ideally* general practitioners should carry out any (other) regular checkups on middle-aged people. Just over half, 54 per cent, thought this desirable but comments suggest the ideal is seldom attained.

'Yes, given time. I feel a doctor should spend part of his time on routine examinations. By this method he could discover disease earlier but he *cannot* do this in addition to his work as he sees it now. There are not enough doctors to cope efficiently with what I believe to be adequate medical attention for the population.'

'Once again I'm forced to say yes but how the hell can I find the time?'

But nearly half were unconvinced that it was ideal.

'No, you can't anticipate much that goes wrong. Most patients attend more than once a year and especially in middle-age their symptomatology is a more delicate indication than a general examination. Nature's built-in warning mechanisms are way ahead of us – except in a few instances, such as a chance finding of glycosuria.'

'Time is not available and in any case searching out those who rarely see the doctor would not be appreciated.'

No questions on preventive care for children were asked in the postal survey. An earlier study[13] found that 73 per cent of 157

[13] Cartwright, Ann, and Marshall, Rosalind, 'General Practice in 1963'.

general practitioners who were interviewed felt that immunization clinics 'should be in the field of general practice', 22 per cent were uncertain or gave qualified responses and only 5 per cent felt it should not be. Some of those who were interviewed on the present study discussed this.

> 'Everyone talks about us doing well-baby clinics and school exams, but we haven't really got time to look after our patients – although we only have what some people think of as an ideal number.'

Some were critical of the local authority services.

> 'It's often said that the G.P. doesn't get on very well with welfare clinics where mothers with babies are asked to report on advice on feeding, etc. The reason is that advice is given without consultation with the G.P. but any harmful results of such advice falls on the G.P. to sort out – usually in the early hours of the morning. I take a dim view of stepping up the strength of food for infants so they're all having the same strength at a certain age – they treat them as units not individuals. It creates emergency work. If possible, even at the risk of filling up forms we should be able to claim a fee for emergency services in such cases from the Local Authority. Perhaps that would make them revise their practices – they would see the bad results. The same applies to hospital. They never see their mistakes because they're cushioned by G.Ps.'

> 'If they (School Health Service) find a congenital heart that we know about and are treating they set things in motion without consulting us. I had a mother a bit ago, in a case I was aware of, came in a great flap because the school doctor had said the girl had a weak heart. I'd like to see the School Health Service taken over by the G.Ps. They have a better understanding.'

A few thought them obsolete.

> 'The Local Authorities should opt out of clinical medicine. They developed a clinical service between the wars for people who could not afford it, but there is no need for that now.

But they still have their statutory duties to perform. The G.Ps should take over – I have a child welfare clinic.'

Others thought them a waste of scarce and valuable manpower or 'A sheer duplication of effort'. One doctor even made the suggestion that health visitors ought to have some nursing training.[14] A number felt that both health visitors and district nurses could work more profitably with the general practitioners than under the Medical Officer of Health. A few who had some attachment scheme expressed appreciation:

'We are particularly fortunate. I have the ideal arrangement as I'm practically within one parish. There is one nurse/midwife combined and we work together. I have an ante-natal clinic and she comes and we take it together. I think it would be perfectly sensible to abolish infant welfare clinics – they could well be run by G.Ps.'

The issue raised by these general practitioners is whether the personal preventive care at present given by local authorities should be separated from curative services given by general practitioners.

Conclusions

The aims of preventive care are to discover conditions which can be cured or alleviated, to protect (by immunization, etc.), to inculcate habits which promote health and the effective treatment of early disease, to discourage those associated with the development of disease and, more controversially, to relieve misplaced anxiety and stimulate confidence and security. There are essentially two approaches to the first aim: to use a procedure which will detect just one or two diseases. This is the approach of the mass X-ray and the community diabetic surveys. The second approach is to examine certain groups of the population for a wide variety of conditions, signs and symptoms. This is the approach of the school medical examination, and, to a lesser extent, of the child welfare services.

The first approach is more sharply focused and more limited, the second more likely to achieve some of the other aims of

---

[14] All health visitors are of course trained nurses.

preventive care besides the detection of disease. Either approach will discover a higher proportion of disease if it covers only the more vulnerable groups in the population. Yet older people of 65 or more who not only have more morbidity but probably more undetected morbidity[15] than younger people are the ones least likely to have any form of check-up, although much of their undetected morbidity could be cured or alleviated. Mass X-ray campaigns need to make even greater efforts to include the old, but is there not also a good case for giving older people particularly a regular check-up? The examination should look particularly for the common chronic and degenerative conditions which can be arrested or alleviated. Who would be the most appropriate person to do such check-ups? One general practitioner who was interviewed described how the Medical Officer in a nearby area had started such a scheme:

'The M.O.H. gets in touch with every old pensioner and has them up for a medical. He writes to the G.P. for information. There must be a lot of undiscovered illness amongst old people. It's a good scheme but whether it's right that the M.O.H. should have to do this, I'm not so sure.'

Traditionally the local authority has entered the field of personal health because of the inadequacy of existing care. Other studies[15] have shown the shortcomings of present arrangements. But it might be more appropriate to encourage general practitioners to do regular specific checks on their elderly patients rather than to get them to see a strange doctor at a local authority clinic. Elderly people were more resistant than others to the idea of a regular check-up but, of those who said they would like one the proportion who would prefer it done by their own doctor increased from 63 per cent of those under 65 to 78 per cent of those aged 65–74 and 86 per cent of those aged 75 and over. This suggests that the general practitioner would be more successful in persuading his elderly patients to have a check-up. However he would need help in organizing this and the elderly people would need help in undressing and dressing. Health Visitors might help to organize this since a visit to the old person's home to persuade

[15] See Williamson, J., et al., 'Old people at home. Their unreported needs', and Maddison, John, *How to Keep the Old Folks Young.*

them to come and arrange a suitable time would enable her to assess home conditions, and particular need for care. She might also carry out some of the tests and collection of specimens. Where necessary transport could be arranged to take the patient to the doctor's surgery.

General practitioners could be paid a fee for these examinations[16] in the same way as they are for immunizations and vaccinations.[17] Carbon copies of the examination form could be signed by the patient and sent to the Executive Councils for payment. As an incentive to the doctors to encourage as many of their elderly patients as possible to attend for check-up payment might increase in relation to the proportion of elderly patients on their lists who had had a check-up in a two year period. For example, if the payment was 20s. per examination for the first 25 per cent of elderly patients it might be 25s. for the next 25 per cent, 30s. for the next and 35s. for each one over three-quarters. Once such a scheme was established it could be extended to other age groups, but it would probably be unwise to start with a general scheme for all adults even though many of them would apparently welcome such check-ups.

At present general practitioners play little part in either suggesting or carrying out check-ups for healthy adults, even though most of them recognize that this is desirable. If they are to take on this extra work many of them will need more time and help. When medical manpower is short how can this be done? One possibility is that more women doctors could be attracted back to work by suitable opportunities.[18] Another possibility is a redistribution of work and resources between the local authority and general practitioner services. At the moment there is duplication of several functions. Many general practitioners are critical of the present system of Local Authority child-welfare clinics and school medical examinations, believing them to be wasteful of medical and nursing manpower. Some also feel that they inhibit the development of a good patient-general practitioner relation-

[16] The Review Body on Doctors' and Dentists' Remuneration in its *Seventh Report* recommended that general practitioners be paid 'separate fees for services carried out in pursuance of public policy' (p. 52).
[17] In fact they are paid fees for the immunization or vaccination *record*.
[18] Jefferys and Elliott in *Women in Medicine* p. 37 (suggest) that about two-thirds of the unemployment among women doctors was involuntary and over a third of those working part-time felt they were under-employed and could do more.

ship and that it would be much more appropriate and effective for these functions to be carried out by the general practitioners – with clerical and nursing assistance. This view seems in many ways reasonable but it is clear that in such a reorganization care would need to be taken to ensure that mothers felt they were gaining a more helpful service and not just losing one they value. Most mothers with young children take them to local authority clinics and in general they feel these clinics are a more helpful source of advice about such problems as feeding than their general practitioners.

VII

PERSONAL CARE

Fox has described the personal doctor in this way: 'His essential characteristic is that he is looking after people as people and not as problems. . . . His function is to meet what is really the primary medical need. A person in difficulties wants in the first place the help of another person on whom he can rely as a friend – someone with knowledge of what is feasible but also with good judgement on what is desirable in the particular circumstances, and an understanding of what the circumstances are. The more complex medicine becomes, the stronger are the reasons why everyone should have a personal doctor who will take continuous responsibility for him, and, knowing how he lives, will keep things in proportion – protecting him, if need be, from the zealous specialist.'[1] By this definition the personal doctor gives continuous care, is accessible in times of need and has that quality which enables him to act as teacher and therapeutic listener – approachability. How far does the general practitioner fulfil these criteria?

Continuous care

Two-thirds of the adults interviewed had had the same doctor for at least five years. Half had had him for at least ten and just over a third for at least 15 years. (See Table 5 in Chapter II). Continuity of care, taken as having the same doctor over several years, is then very much a reality under the National Health Service. The chief limits on this continuity are the mobility of the population and the mortality of doctors. A few doctors questioned the desirability of their being so geographically static and tied to one place, and if there is to be a career structure in general practice, like that envisaged by Crombie,[2] this would probably involve

[1] Fox, T. F., 'The Personal Doctor and his Relation to the Hospital'.
[2] Crombie, D. L., 'A Career Structure for General Practitioners'.

rather more mobility among doctors with an inevitable loss of some continuity. How much would this matter?

The proportion of patients who felt their doctor would know their name if they met him in the street – which may suggest a feeling of personal relationship – rose steadily from 29 per cent of those who had had the same doctor for less than a year to 78 per cent of those who had been with him for 15 years or more. There was a rather similar trend – from 26 per cent to 52 per cent – in those who felt their relationship with their doctor was 'friendly' rather than 'business-like'.[3]

There was no variation with the length of time they had had their doctor in the proportion who felt a general practitioner was a suitable person to talk to about 'such problems as children getting into trouble or difficulties between husband and wife', but those who had been with their doctor five years or more were rather more likely to feel they might themselves discuss a personal problem not strictly medical with him, 31 per cent compared with 20 per cent.[4] The length of time people had their doctor did not appear to be related to whether or not they would consult him about any of the specific conditions asked about including depression and difficulty in sleeping. Nor did it seem to influence the patients' views on whether their doctor was good or not so good about taking his time and not hurrying them or listening to what they say, but the people who were *most* critical about him not explaining things were those with their doctor between ten and 15 years. The proportion who said he was 'not so good' about explaining things rose from 7 per cent of those who had had their doctor less than a year to 20 per cent between ten and 15 years, and then fell slightly to 15 per cent of those with the same doctor for 15 years or more. Possibly familiarity can lead to a lack of interest, patience and acuity on occasions, or people's expectations may be higher when they have had the same doctor for several years. Other possibilities are that doctors may underestimate people's needs for repeated explanations, or that the longer a person has a doctor the more likely he is to have the conditions about which he wants explanations.

[3] 'Do you consider your doctor to be something of a personal friend or is your relationship pretty much a business-like one?'
[4] The difference is accentuated by older people who are more likely to consult their doctor about such things and to have had their doctor longer. But if older people are excluded the difference still persists.

But continuity of care can mean more than just having the same doctor for several years. McKeown[5] argues that the need for a 'medical friend' is greatest when patients and relatives are under stress, at the time of serious illness, and suggests that personal care breaks down when it is most needed, when the patient enters hospital. A study of hospital patients and general practitioners[6] showed that only very rarely did the general practitioner bridge the often wide gap in communication between patients and hospital staff, but to imply that serious and stressful illness necessarily involves hospital care is surely unrealistic. After all, about two-fifths of people die at home and it is probable that nowadays chronic illness which is often treated at home causes more stress and anxiety than short-term hospital episodes. And emergencies – whether they lead to hospital care or not – usually start outside the hospital. The part played by general practitioners in times of crisis, or supposed crisis, is discussed next.

Accessibility

Eighty-four per cent of the patients thought they would be able to get hold of their general practitioner – or someone acting for him – if they needed him on a Sunday afternoon or in the middle of the night. Only 2 per cent did not think they would be able to and the rest were uncertain. These views seem reasonably realistic. Fourteen per cent said they had in fact tried to get hold of him in a hurry or in the evening or at night sometime during the previous twelve months for either themselves, their husband or wife or their children. In 57 per cent of these cases the general practitioner himself came, in 17 per cent a partner, in 8 per cent someone else acting for him, and in 1 per cent another G.P. In 3 per cent the patient went straight to hospital, in 7 per cent they got advice over the phone, in 3 per cent various other things happened and in 4 per cent the doctor was not available or was not prepared to come out. The time taken before a doctor was seen is shown in Table 30. Roughly a quarter were seen within a quarter of an hour, half within half an hour and three-quarters within an hour. In most instances the general practitioner is thus accessible when approached in an emergency, but many people nevertheless would

[5] McKeown, T., *Medicine in Modern Society*, p. 174.
[6] Cartwright, Ann, *Human Relations and Hospital Care*, pp. 119–34.

go straight to a hospital in certain types of emergency. When asked: 'If you cut your leg while you were at home so that it needed stitching, would you be more likely to go to your own doctor or straight to hospital?', 31 per cent said they would go to their own doctor, 60 per cent straight to hospital and 9 per cent were uncertain and said it would depend on the time of day or whether it was during surgery hours. The most common reason for their choice in both groups was accessibility – those going to the doctor saying he was the nearest or most convenient and those going to the hospital stressing that it was always open or quicker, while the doctor might not be at his surgery.

TABLE 30   *Time taken before doctor saw patient when wanted in a hurry*

	%
Less than 15 minutes	27
15 minutes but less than 30	26
30 minutes but less than 45	10
45 minutes but less than 1 hour	11
1 hour but less than 2 hours	11
2 hours but less than 3 hours	5
3 hours or more	10
NUMBER (= 100%)	163

Although the great majority of patients felt they could get hold of their doctor or someone acting for him in the middle of the night if they wanted to, many, 55 per cent, did not know what arrangements he actually had for night calls. They were also asked: 'Just supposing general practitioners never worked – or were available – at night from six in the evening until nine the next morning – and if you needed a doctor during that time you had to get in touch with an emergency service – how would you feel about that? Would you prefer that arrangement of getting in touch with the emergency service or would you rather go on as you do now?' Just under a fifth, 17 per cent, said they would prefer to have an emergency service, 35 per cent would prefer to go on as they did now but thought an emergency service acceptable, 41 per cent would prefer to carry on as they did now and either would not like an emergency service or made no comment about it, and 7 per cent had no preference or were uncertain. The main reason for wanting to go on as they did now was that their own doctor was familiar, in an emergency they did not want a stranger. The most common reason for preferring the emergency service was that it was better for the doctor's sake – 'He needs his sleep', or 'He will be fresh for the next day's work'.

Doctors were asked a rather similar question – 'If general practitioners were not expected to be available at nights, from 6 p.m. to 9 a.m. and patients who needed a doctor during that time had to get in touch with an emergency service – how would you feel about that?' Fifty-seven per cent said they would prefer to go on as they do now and 43 per cent would prefer an emergency service. Some comments from those who wanted to continue the present arrangement were:

> 'This (an emergency system) is wrong in principle and would further do away with the family doctor status. I prefer to attend my own emergencies over 24 hours.'

> 'We have a private arrangement which provides emergency cover from 7 p.m. to 7 a.m. More than seven or eight practitioners in an emergency service would be too impersonal and it would be impossible if it included any whose judgement was suspect – or their ethics either.'

> 'I think unless a patient is seen by a doctor who has his case sheet – and preferably knows him – serious things can go wrong at emergency calls. The previous surgical history is essential to a correct diagnosis of an acute abdomen and a personal knowledge of the family and psychiatric background may provide a rapid and easy solution to the real nature of many emergency calls.'

And from those who would like an emergency service:

> 'I believe it is wrong, morally and physically, to expect any member of the working community to work such hours as to make him miserable or inefficient, therefore I would be quite agreeable.'

Some had qualifications:

> 'I would prefer an emergency service subject to how it was run – provided doctors doing these calls were sufficiently experienced in general practice.'

As might be expected single-handed doctors more often said they would prefer an emergency service than doctors working in partnerships, 65 per cent against 37 per cent.

Ninety-three per cent of those who would like an emergency service said they would be prepared to be on duty at the emergency service to cover such calls for two nights in a month if that made the arrangement feasible, and 30 per cent of those who would prefer to go on as now also expressed their willingness to do this – so about three-fifths of all general practitioners said they would do so. The actual response would obviously depend on the details of the arrangement.

Another aspect of accessibility discussed at interviews with patients was the evening surgery. They were asked the latest time in the evening when they could get in to see their doctor at the surgery. The replies of those who knew are given in Table 31. Just over half thought they could get in to see their doctor at 7.0 p.m. or later. However only 22 per cent of all patients said they ever went at the latest time.[7] Asked how inconvenient it would be for them if general practitioners all finished their evening surgeries by 5.30, half said it would not be at all inconvenient, a sixth that it would be a little inconvenient and a third definitely inconvenient. But half expressed disapproval of this idea mainly because of the difficulties for people who work.

TABLE 31   *Latest time could be seen at doctor's surgery*

	%
Before 6.0	4
6.0 but before 6.30	11
6.30 but before 7.0	31
7.0 but before 7.30	39
7.30 but before 8.0	11
8.0 p.m. or later	4
NUMBER OF PATIENTS (= 100%)	1,162

'Take a person in employment where there's a chance of redundancy, that person isn't going to ask for time off to go to the doctor.'

[7] This proportion did not vary systematically with the latest time they could go.

'I think they should stay open until 8 p.m. You can't get to a doctor if you finish work at six. You've got to get home first and changed and washed. I think it's right that you do get changed and washed.'

'It would be a bit rough for a lot of people. Sometimes I finish work about six. It would mean getting off from work or going straight from work. I'd rather not do that.'

At the moment some general practitioners may resent their evening surgeries largely because most other professional people and many of their patients finish their formal working day earlier. But as the proportion of married women who work increases this may stimulate a demand for more flexible working hours and availability of services in all sorts of fields. The general practitioner may appear in the vanguard of this trend rather than in the rear of the movement to prevent exploitation of workers by restricting working hours.

Geographical proximity is another part of accessibility and the nearness of the doctor's surgery has already been shown to be important for many people in choosing their doctors. Four-fifths of the patients said it took them less than a quarter of an hour to get to their doctor's surgery. The distribution is shown in Table 32. Just over half, 55 per cent, normally walked all the way, 18 per cent went by public transport, 23 per cent by private transport and 4 per cent said the doctor always came to them.

TABLE 32 *Time taken to get to doctor's surgery*

	%
Less than 5 minutes	29
5 minutes but less than 15 minutes	51
15 minutes but less than 30 minutes	15
30 minutes or more	5
NUMBER OF PATIENTS (= 100%)	1,372

This proximity is only possible because many doctors have branch surgeries,[8] a form of organization which may inhibit the

---

[8] Just over half the doctors studied by Cartwright and Marshall in 'General Practice in 1963' had branch surgeries.

development of health centres. One doctor who was interviewed and would like to work with his partners from a clinic said: 'It's traditional in industrial areas to have branch surgeries so patients don't have to go far. The money spent on these surgeries is really wasted.'

Just under half the patients, 47 per cent, said their doctor was the nearest one to them, but 33 per cent said there were other doctors reasonably near and only 14 per cent felt he was the only reasonably accessible doctor, or group of doctors. There was no evidence that the time it took patients to get to their doctor's surgery was related to the total frequency with which they saw the doctor during the previous twelve months. But it has already been shown (in Chapter V) that the number of home visits was higher for the small group of people living 30 minutes or more travelling time from the doctor's surgery.

Another feature of accessibility – waiting times at the doctor's surgery – is discussed in a later chapter on appointment systems.

Approachability

One of the 'measures' of a doctor's approachability used on this survey was whether patients felt that if they were worried about a personal problem that was not strictly medical they might discuss it with their doctors. Twenty-eight per cent said they would, 12 per cent were uncertain and 60 per cent that they would not. This question followed immediately after one asking whether they thought a general practitioner was a suitable person to talk to about problems such as children getting into trouble or diffi-culties between husband and wife. Forty per cent thought he was, 40 per cent that he was not and 20 per cent were uncertain. So fewer said they would do so themselves than felt it was generally appropriate to do so.

Some comments from people who did not feel a general practitioner was a suitable person to discuss personal problems[9] with were:

'In the old days he used to be but he's not capable of it today. He has too many patients to cope with. It's a full-time job

[9] 'Personal problems' is used here and later as an abbreviation for 'a personal problem that was not strictly a medical one'.

keeping up with new drugs and new medical inventions. He has no time and very little training to be able to deal with social problems of that kind. It would be too time consuming and he's not the only person available if you need anyone. I'm sure I wouldn't ask him. I treat him strictly as a medical adviser – no more and no less.'

'He doesn't want to be bothered with those things. I think people should keep them to themselves anyhow – in the family more. The doctor has enough to do with people who are ill. Now it's different if the thing that worries you is making you sick – then you could see him.'

From those who felt they might discuss their own problems with him:

'Considering you know him and he's got children of his own. He's the proper man used to dealing with human beings. He's had training and they've got to know far more about human beings than a layman or even a vicar.'

'I've been to see him so I've had some experience. My son's wife walked out on him and I talked about it to Dr ————. It was at the time I saw him over gastric 'flu. I had no embarrassment talking to him. I couldn't have told his partner – but you see I know this doctor well enough – and I definitely do think you should consult him if something is worrying you that much.'

And from those with mixed feelings:

'They can help. They have a chance of being a little more intimate with the patients – they get to know them. . . . I wouldn't myself unless it was medical. It's like asking the milkman to be a fireman isn't it?'

Reasons for feeling he was a suitable person varied from the personal: 'Mine's a nice understanding man', 'Mine, yes because I feel relaxed with him'; to the more professional: 'He keeps your confidences – you can be sure they won't go any further', 'His profession puts him in that position of trust'. Reasons given for not asking him about such things ranged from feeling it was unfair to him: 'They've got enough on their plates', to feeling it would be a confession of weakness on their own part: 'If you can't look after yourself it's not going to help much talking to him. You should get over your own problems', 'No, that's private business', 'That's a thing I never discuss with anyone'.

It might be thought that the difference in the proportions who felt a general practitioner was a suitable person to discuss certain personal problems and those who felt they might discuss their own problems with him arose because patients felt they had other people to whom they would turn on such occasions, so although it would be *appropriate* to go to a doctor about such things there would be no *need* for them personally to do so. But the proportion who thought they might discuss such a problem with the doctor was similar for those who would and for those who would not discuss it with relatives or friends, and similarly there was no difference between those who thought they might discuss it with a minister, health visitor or other social worker. However people aged 65 or more were more likely than younger ones to feel they might discuss a personal problem with their doctor – 40 per cent against 26 per cent. This seems contrary to the views aired by some doctors about the comparative dependency of the young.

But some general practitioners themselves do not feel it appropriate for them to be consulted about such things as children getting into trouble or family discord. Thirteen per cent felt that such problems were more appropriately discussed with other people.[10] Comments from these were:

'Only if the child or person at issue is psychotic.'

'Priests, social workers, lawyers are more appropriate. We have *no training* in such matters.'

The 87 per cent who felt it was appropriate obviously varied widely in their attitudes:

'The doctor can listen and in listening help, apart from later suggesting reference elsewhere.'

---

[10] Other studies have shown similar findings. Hadfield, in 'A Field Survey of General Practice 1951–52', found 86 per cent of the general practitioners willing to advise on non-medical problems, while Cooper, in his survey of 'General Practitioners' Attitudes to Psychiatry,' found most of his respondents – who were members of the College of General Practitioners – had a comprehensive outlook on the work of the general practitioner.

'It is appropriate, but under present conditions of service one is under too heavy a burden.'

Some of the difficulties and reactions of general practitioners when confronted by social problems have been described elsewhere.[11] How conscious are patients that their doctor feels inadequate to cope with their personal difficulties? Apparently not at all. The proportion of patients who said they might discuss their personal problems with their own doctor was similar for doctors who did and for those who did not feel it appropriate to be consulted about such things.

Apart from the complex question of social problems and personal difficulties, how approachable do patients feel their doctor is in other ways? They were asked whether they felt their doctor was good, or not so good, about taking his time and not hurrying them, about listening to what they say, and about explaining things to them fully. Replies are shown in Table 33.

TABLE 33   *Various aspects of doctors' approachability*

Doctor felt to be:	About taking his time and not hurrying them	About listening to what they say	About explaining things to them fully
	%	%	%
Good	88	93	75
Not so good	6	3	14
Don't know, doubtful, uncertain	6	4	11
NUMBER OF PATIENTS (= 100%)	1,312	1,310	1,312

The great majority, about nine-tenths, felt their doctor was good about taking his time and not hurrying them and abou listening to what they said. Examples of their appreciation were

'When you're in there, *you're* the patient he's interested in and there no rush to get the next one in – he's not thinking about the long queue outside – and he doesn't leave off for a cup of coffee either.'

[11] Jefferys, Margot, *An Anatomy of Social Welfare Services*, pp. 117–31.

'When you go in he doesn't seem to be in a rushing way. He likes to explain what he thinks up with you, then check you.'

'He sits and talks to you and even if he discharges you he tells you any time you're not feeling well to come in and see him. He's a man I have every confidence in.'

'He doesn't just rush you out. He says, "Come in and have a cigarette. What's the trouble? Let yourself go".'

This seems quite an achievement when the average length of a consultation has been estimated to be about six and a half minutes.[12]

People were more critical of their doctor for not explaining things to them fully. Several of those who felt theirs was good about this went on to make such comments as: 'If you ask the right questions. I don't think any doctor explains things fully unless you ask. I think they rather enjoy leaving you in the dark about what's wrong with you.' 'If you request it – otherwise he's a silent man – but it's up to you, you can know the facts if you ask.'

When general practitioners were asked to indicate their agreement or disagreement with the statement: 'One should try to give patients full explanations about the aetiology of their illnesses and the rationale of treatment', 86 per cent of them agreed (47 per cent of them strongly), 7 per cent were neutral and only 7 per cent disagreed.[13] This suggests that failures of communication may be due more to lack of time or skill or failure to appreciate a particular patient's needs than to a general belief that explanations are unnecessary or unimportant.

Another question throwing some light on the personal nature of the doctor-patient relationship asked patients whether they considered their doctor to be something of a personal friend or whether their relationship was pretty much a business-like one. Equal proportions described it in these two ways – 44 per cent

[12] College of General Practitioners, *Present State and Future Needs of General Practice*, pp. 26–7.
[13] Once again this was not related to patients' views. The proportion who felt their doctor was 'not so good' about explaining things fully was not appreciably higher among those whose doctors disagreed with the statement.

each – the other 12 per cent were uncertain.[14] The proportion who said they liked the relationship as it was rather than preferring it to be more friendly or business-like was high for both groups – but appreciably higher among those who thought the relationship friendly, 98 per cent, compared with 78 per cent of those who said the relationship was more business-like. In addition 36 per cent of the former group against 20 per cent of the latter thought they might discuss a personal problem that was not a strictly medical one with their doctor. Those who described the relationship as business-like were more critical of a number of aspects of their doctor's care than those who described it as friendly. This is shown in Table 34.

TABLE 34   *Patient-doctor relationship and patients' criticisms of their doctor*

	Relationship felt to be:		
	Friendly	*Business-like*	*Uncertain*
Proportion thinking general practitioner 'not so good' about:			
Examining people carefully and thoroughly	2%	7%	4%
Listening to what they say	1%	5%	4%
Explaining things to them fully	9%	21%	9%
Taking time and not hurrying them	3%	8%	7%
NUMBER OF PATIENTS (= 100%)	580	592	156

It would seem that many patients prefer a closer, warmer relationship with their doctor than one where the doctor remains 'objective and affectively neutral'.[15] Chapter IV showed that many general practitioners mentioned the friendship of their patients as one of the things they appreciated, and earlier in this chapter it was shown that the proportion of patients describing their relationship with their doctor as 'friendly' rather than 'business-like' rose with the length of time they had had their doctor. This

[14] This question was taken from an American study, see Davis, Milton S., and Eichhorn, Robert J., 'Compliance with Medical Regimens: A Panel Study' in which 47 per cent regarded the relationship as 'friendly' and 53 per cent as 'business-like'.
[15] Parsons, Talcott, *The Social System*, p. 461.

supports Bynder's theory that 'in those doctor-patient relation-ships which exist over long periods of time . . . the doctor becomes much more emotionally involved with at least some of his patients than would otherwise be the case'.[16] Patients probably have more confidence in a friendly doctor. Some of those who regarded their doctor as something of a personal friend and appreciated this relationship said:

'I look on the doctor as a friend. We have a drink together when he comes. If you make friends with a doctor there's just that bit of confidence about it and confidence goes a long way. I'd sooner a doctor came in and talked to you and at the same time study you – not just write a prescription and bunk off and say ring me if you don't feel better. I don't think any doctor can sum you up without that.'

'The interest he takes makes all the difference. I got to know him quite well when my mother was ill and he was visiting her a lot and he got on Christian name terms with her. He was so nice with her then. So many people really don't have much time for old people, but he was always kind and understand-ing.'

On the other hand, Davis and Eichhorn found a greater degree of 'compliance' with the doctor's advice when patients felt their relationship was businesslike rather than friendly.[17]

Comments from those who liked their more business-like rela-tionship were:

'I'd sooner have it business-like. I like to call a spade a spade and that's it.'

'I don't think it's any good for a doctor and patient to become too involved personally.'

One who would have preferred a more friendly relationship said: 'He's not a friend at all. I don't think today there is that friendliness with a doctor. These young doctors just see you and are gone – they don't stay many minutes. Old doctors would stay and talk to you about things.' Whereas another who felt he was a

[16] Bynder, Herbert, 'Some Problems in the Doctor-Patient Relationship'.
[17] Davis, Milton S., and Eichhorn, Robert L., op. cit.

personal friend expressed some doubts about this: 'I like it that way, but if we didn't have children I would like it to be more business-like as any intimate things are easier to approach if you're on impersonal terms.'

If doctors are both accessible and approachable it might be expected that there would be few unmet demands for medical care in the community. But when people were asked: 'If you could have ten minutes uninterrupted discussion with your doctor or with another doctor you found sympathetic, is there anything particular you would like to ask him about – either for yourself or your family?' – 18 per cent said there was something. For three-fifths of these people it was something about themselves they wanted to discuss, for one-fifth something about their husband or wife, and one-eighth wanted to discuss more general things. One-fifth would prefer to discuss it with another doctor rather than their own, another fifth did not mind, and three-fifths would prefer their own doctor. Only two-fifths had in fact approached their own doctor about this problem. Examples from people who had not approached their doctor about their problem and attributed this to their own diffidence were:

'Now I'm approaching middle-age I'd like to talk to him about contraception and limiting the family. I don't mind talking to him, it's just getting round to it.'

'I've lost a considerable amount of weight in the last few years. I keep thinking there might be something wrong with the bowels because at the slightest excitement I go to the lavatory. It worries me sometimes. I'd rather talk to my own doctor about it because he knows me and he would understand I wasn't imagining things. I've just never got round to it. I'm rather lazy and I'm not terribly doctor conscious. If it goes on I will.'

'I'd just like to ask about the symptoms of cancer. It's just something I'd like to know and he (own doctor) would be the most suitable person. I haven't got much time – if I had any real signs or worries I'd make the effort to go.'

Others had been to see their doctor within the previous year but had not felt it was appropriate to discuss all their problems with him.

'I'd like to ask him about my legs. I have thrombosis. All Dr ——— said was lots of aspirin and lead lotion but other people seem to go to hospital and have different injections and so on. But you can't very well argue with a doctor. Mind you, I haven't said it *to* him. I think if I told him I was so worried – I don't sleep at all with the pain sometimes – but there never seems to be an opportunity. He definitely does not like, if he has come for a specific purpose, to be asked to see something else as well. He would frown on that I know. I miss having the health visitor for all the little things you worry about. The average G.P. doesn't seem to have time – especially in the spring. I think the surgery is just for minor emergencies so I don't like to ask him there.'

'I'd like to ask for a thorough exam for Mrs Y. (wife) and myself. A lot of illness would be caught in time, as it is a lot of cases have gone too far. I wouldn't mind who did it. Doctors have all gone through the same professional training and understand the human body. . . . The occasion has never arisen. If he came here I might ask him then, but when I go to the surgery I know there's other people waiting and when it's my turn I just ask him or tell him my business and think I won't bother asking him anything else. And sometimes doctors seem that way inclined – they want to get on with it like. A doctor should have time on his hands for that sort of thing.'

Those who had discussed their problem with their doctor seemed to feel dissatisfied because the problem was still unsolved, like the woman who wanted a baby and was still not pregnant. Other examples were:

'My mother's been waiting to go to hospital for six months. We're worried. The doctor keeps saying he'll get her in, but I don't know. I'd like a real heart to heart.'

'The monthly business and if there's anything new about migraine. I don't suppose another doctor would know any more than my own doctor. We tried lots of things and he had me go to a specialist. If there is anything new I should think my doctor would think of me. I had tablets and now he's suggesting stretching and scraping.'

'I'd like to know what is the cause of all these general set backs that I can't get on top of, but nothing can necessarily be done about it. It's nothing serious yet it's there. Why? My doctor said: "It's your general surroundings – the particulars of your living and the financial difficulties that are causing it all". My husband has been a patient there so he knows him and he, the doctor, said he's been the cause of it all.'

People who said there was something they would like to discuss with a doctor were more likely to be critical of their doctor about examinations. Ten per cent of them thought he was 'not so good' about examining people carefully and thoroughly compared with 4 per cent of those who had nothing they wanted to discuss with a doctor, and the ones who were most critical were those who would prefer to discuss their problem with another doctor – 23 per cent of them thought their doctor 'not so good' about examinations. So, for various reasons – patients' diffidence, doctors' work-load and on occasions the doctors' attitudes – patients do not always find their own doctor as approachable as they might like. But, if their estimates of the proportion of surgery consultations they feel to be for reasons which are trivial, unnecessary or inappropriate are taken as a guide, many doctors feel they are too approachable. Their answers to this question did not appear to be related to their views on whether it was appropriate for them to be consulted about social problems, nor to their patients' feelings about whether they might do so. Feelings that a high proportion of consultations are for trivial or inappropriate conditions seem to be more related to other feelings of frustration about their job, or to the absence of various ameliorating features.

Two 'case histories'

In this analysis of personal care it may seem that the essential element has eluded description; no feeling has emerged of what it is like to have – or not have – a personal doctor. To try and fill this gap two 'case histories' have been taken from interviews.

The first is from a man of 50, a cashier, in the north of England, a patient of a single-handed doctor. He clearly had a personal relationship with his doctor although his views about this and the organization of the practice were somewhat idiosyncratic.

'A lot of these questions are a matter of taste. You've got the choice of the two – you can't have them both. Either you have everything highly organized and impersonal or you have them a bit disorganized but with personal knowledge. You can't have the two – I'm convinced of that.

'The surgery is just a jumble – it's damned untidy. Probably under some of the junk there's quite a bit of equipment. But he can always find the tackle he wants from somewhere. But there's no showcases with gleaming instruments in them. The waiting room's a shocker – a great gap under the door you could back a barge under. The last time I went there was a *little* electric fire. I'm not sure it's such a good thing to have a comfortable waiting room. I like a doctor's surgery to be a place to get into and get out of. So many people would sit there and talk about their ailments if it was too comfortable.

'It's a disorganized practice because he likes to deal with his patients as human beings. I come away thinking, "He's listened to me, sorted me out to the best of his ability and he's doing what's best for me". To my mind a good doctor must have patience to hear you out; to let you tell your own story in your own way. If you can't get it off your chest you feel he's taken no notice of you. He's dealing with you, not just as a case, but as Charlie C. who's feeling rough – and he thinks, "I'm going to get this bloke better".

'If you go with something unusual he doesn't mind how much time he spends sorting it out. If the surgery is full of people with minor ailments you're no time at all, but if there's one complicated one he won't rush through because the surgery is full. His speed depends on the quality of the ailments. The last time I went, there was a bloke who had had an accident at work. That meant undoing all his bandages and fiddling about with redressing and so on. Then there was an old lady out of breath. She had to sit down and get her breath before she could start talking things over. – You can hear what goes on in the surgery. – This increased the delay but was unavoidable. You can't have things highly organized.

'In hospital I don't mean a thing to them and they don't mean a thing to me. I might be an interesting case or I might be a bloody nuisance. I'd only fall into these two categories. If I

go to hospital I'm feeling sorry for myself. I'm not prepared
to be treated as a number. You get sister's back up and she
turns nasty. That's why I'm all for the G.Ps. If you don't like
him you change.
'It's different to the old family doctors you used to have.
They were little demi-gods. Everybody was on his best
behaviour when the doctor came in. You can talk to him now.
Before, you weren't expected to talk to them. They would
very begrudgingly tell you what was wrong, give you treatment and that was it. In a small place like this the doctor
came here and he stayed here till he was ready for dying.
Because he was the family doctor all kinds used to go to him.
It was a relic of the old days when you touched your cap to
them. They were good doctors; very superior beings – they
knew you – but you didn't enter into conversation with them.
This mental illness – now you can go to him and get things
off your chest. Before you didn't tell them what was wrong
with you. He had a look and then he told you. Here again
this was caused by the fact that everybody paid for treatment.
My parents, like everybody else, they owed him a big bill.
He didn't put pressure on them. He knew he would be paid
eventually. He was the family doctor – friend, counsellor,
etc. It's more near to a men's relationship now. This tends to
better doctoring.
'The old doctors had a bad habit, if you walked in to them and
said: "I've got a shocking cough doctor", they'd say, "He's
had a cough since he was a lad". They'd write a prescription
out – "three times a day, etc." They knew in advance what
was wrong with you. Now they haven't got any idea, but they
get off their bottom and find out what's wrong. Also if you're
not making progress they will bash you away for a second
opinion. To ask for a second opinion before was tantamount
to heresy – it was the biggest insult you could heap on them.
It's a different attitude now.
'In the last ten years there's been a change in the doctor-
patient relationship, but not a loss of prestige. Doctors are
far more approachable – they're one of the people. The old
family doctor was a race apart, but that doesn't necessarily
mean you look up to him. You'd say "Good morning doctor"
and then when you were past you might say, "Oh to hell with

him". Now you say, "Good morning doctor" because you *want* to.

'If you went along with something completely ordinary – that's one thing, but if you went along with something you'd never had before he would give you a damn good examination. He's very fair. He wouldn't examine you for the examination's sake. If it was an ordinary complaint and you were making no headway, after a time he'd say "Get in the examination room" and he'd give you a good sorting out. If it was necessary he'd always do it. If he's at all confused he'll send you to hospital. He won't send you just to get rid of you.

'I go to my own doctor and tell him what's wrong and what I feel and he interprets what I say. He understands how I explain things and knows how to sort the wheat from the chaff. I might completely mislead a strange doctor.'

The second case history is from a housewife living with her husband and young daughter and illustrates the anxieties and concern when people do not feel they have a personal relationship with their doctor.

'They're all alike, doctors. As soon as you walk in they've got their pen on the pad. This one doesn't tell you what you've got he just gives you a prescription – "take this three times a day" before you've even said what's wrong. They're all like that – ready to give you something for it before getting at the cause of it.

'The only good thing I can say for him was when my child had bronchitis, eventually when the temperature was down he gave me a prescription for the cough and said I might have difficulty in getting this as it had just come out. I eventually got it though I had to try a few places. In two days the cough was gone. I thought then, although I didn't find him as efficient as he should be, it proved to me he was keeping up with the times. It wasn't the fact that the medicine was good that impressed me but that I knew he was with it because he's getting on and sometimes when they're getting on they don't keep up to date.

'There's a big difference between him and the lady doctor I had before we moved. I could talk to her about anything and she'd listen and give me advice. This doctor is going deaf and you've got to shout. I think it's about time he packed up, to be quite honest. I've been thinking of changing. He has very bad chest trouble himself and he's always coughing and spluttering. I can't talk to him – even if he could hear better I don't think he's the conversant type. He seems to be good at his job but he just wouldn't come to Vera one evening when we rang him. I don't expect them to come running in the middle of the night but with children they should make an effort. It wasn't the first time. Once I rang him at 5.30 p.m. and he still said he wouldn't come 'til morning. The second time she'd taken a turn for the worse and was very drowsy – she wouldn't stay awake. I realize they were symptoms now but it's very frightening with children.

'He'll send you to hospital rather than examine you himself. Once I went to him with trouble with my eyes watering. He just looked at them and said "You ought to see an optician". I went to the optician and there was nothing wrong with them. The other week I went to him as I had internal trouble. He didn't attempt to examine me – mind you, I didn't want him to, it suited me. He just said: "Go to hospital and get it cleared up". He always gives me the impression he wants to get it over and done with – in and out. I could understand if he had a packed surgery, but he hasn't.

'I have a problem I often want to discuss with a doctor. The week before I have my period I'm so nervy I'm not fit to live with. If you say boo to me I burst into tears and everything annoys me. I know the doctor can give me tablets for it but I can't discuss it with this doctor. I'd have to shout and he wouldn't listen.'

Conclusions

From several points of view general practice under the National Health Service is organized in such a way that general practitioners can give their patients personal care. Most patients have the same doctor for several years, can get to his surgery easily and feel he would be accessible if they needed him in an emergency. Under these conditions something of a personal relationship is built up. Patients seem to identify with their doctor in that few are directly critical of him and, as will be shown later, they express a preference for his type of organization – solo or group practice, appointment system or waiting in turn – although they did not choose him for these reasons. But, from other viewpoints, the patient-general practitioner relationship appears less personal and less satisfactory. That over half the doctors feel that at least a quarter of their surgery consultations are for trivial, unnecessary or inappropriate reasons suggests a certain amount of resentment or scepticism about their present role. And when the patients were asked rather more searching questions about their probable actions and feelings, which did not involve direct criticisms of their doctors, their relationship with their doctor seemed less close and personal. One might describe a 'personal doctor' as having these, admittedly arbitrary, characteristics: (1) Patients feel he would know them by name if he met them in the street, 66 per cent. (2) They regard their relationship with him as friendly rather than business-like, 44 per cent. (3) They feel they might discuss a personal problem that was not a strictly medical one with him, 28 per cent. (4) They feel he is good about explaining things to them fully, 75 per cent. Only 11 per cent of patients have a general practitioner who is a 'personal doctor' on all these criteria, but most people, 88 per cent, have a doctor who meets one or more of them.

VIII

THE GENERAL PRACTITIONER AND
THE HOSPITAL

Discontent and disillusionment among general practitioners is frequently attributed to their isolation from the hospital. McKeown[1] describes three phases of medical practice: 'In the first there is no clear distinction between general and consultant practice. . . . In Australian practice, which is typical of the first phase, the process of referral has not gone far enough, and services which require the attention of the specialist are still in the hands of a general practitioner. In British practice, which is in the second phase, referral has gone too far, with the result that not enough work is left to maintain the interest and prestige of general practice; moreover the exclusion of the general practitioner from hospital has isolated domiciliary from institutional medical care. And in American practice, in the third phase, specialization has gone too far, and it is no longer possible to maintain a personal or domiciliary medical service, or always to make the most efficient use of specialists by a referral system.' One may agree with his diagnosis that the key to a satisfactory general practitioner service lies in the relationship between consultant and general practice, but before accepting his advice on therapy – specialization within general practice – it seems advisable to examine his premise critically. What of his contention that referral in Britain has gone so far that it jeopardizes the prestige and interest of general practice? This chapter starts by considering one aspect of prestige and compares patients' views of hospitals and general practitioners.

Patients' views on hospital and general practitioners

People were asked how they would feel if they did not have a family doctor and they could go straight to appropriate specialists

[1] McKeown, T., *Medicine in Modern Society*, pp. 169 and 172.

when anything was the matter with them. Thirteen per cent said they would prefer that, 5 per cent that they thought going directly to a specialist was a good idea in many ways but they still preferred to have a general practitioner, 79 per cent unequivocally preferred to have a general practitioner and 3 per cent expressed no preference.

The main reason for preferring to have a general practitioner was the need for some preliminary diagnosis. A third of all the people interviewed made comments in this category:

'If you didn't have a doctor to consult first, you wouldn't know if you needed a specialist. If you talk things over with your G.P. and tell him your symptoms he'd know whether you needed a specialist.'

'How would you know who'd be the appropriate specialist? I know because I'm a nurse, but I don't think the average person would know which one to go to.'

A quarter preferred to go to a general practitioner for such reasons as: 'You'd be able to talk to him easier', 'He'd have your case history and he knows you', 'You can explain better to your own doctor. As a middle-man he has a great value', 'They're more homely. You're half way to getting better with a chap like that'. A tenth commented that a general practitioner was necessary for minor conditions.

'If you'd got cancer or T.B. you'd go to a specialist any way but I wouldn't feel like running to him with a boil. A G.P.'s available for the smaller things that need a doctor.'

Four per cent expressed fear of hospitals: 'The fact that a specialist would be at a hospital – that would put me off straight away. I'd feel more in awe of a specialist than of a G.P.' And others foresaw practical difficulties: 'The specialists would be inundated', 'I don't take kindly to waiting for all that time to see the specialists'.

The main reason for preferring a specialist – mentioned by 8 per cent of all people – was that he would be better qualified and have more knowledge or better equipment.

'If I had something serious. I think G.P.s drag on the treatment with you when they don't really know what it is and they should be sending you to a specialist.'

And 4 per cent made such remarks as: 'Your own doctor will send you there anyway nine times out of ten.'

When asked whether they preferred a general practitioner who did a number of tests and investigations himself or one who sent patients to hospital if they needed any investigation, half said the first, a third the second and others were uncertain. Some reasons for preferring the first were: 'You know him well and have more confidence in him', 'Hospitals scare me to death', 'If you trot off to hospital you're there for blooming hours'. Other comments were:

'It shows that he has confidence in his own ability and makes an investigation before passing the buck.'

'It's the easiest thing in the world to unload responsibility. Two or three months ago my wife was badly burnt. He sent her to hospital which lost a lot of time. He should have done something for her. The hospital didn't do any more than the doctor could have done.'

The main reason for preferring to be sent to hospital was 'because they'd be better equipped to do the job'. 'I don't think a doctor can tell you really what's the matter with you, proper'. 'At hospital you see somebody who specializes in that particular complaint.' Other views were:

'They do get into things more thoroughly. If anything is radically wrong it's investigated straight away. You don't have to hang about trying different things.'

'My own doctor knows me too well and sometimes – if it was intimate – I'd prefer a stranger for tests.'

'I had a rash for years. My other doctor gave me tablets but they were no good. He gave me no tests. Eventually he sent me to hospital and they found straight away that I had a metal allergy. I've been all right since, but I was miserable for many years with this rash.'

'In hospital they have everything. They give you a thorough exam. I do believe most people would prefer a hospital investigation unless their doctor was exceptionally well-equipped. Dr ——— certainly wouldn't have the equipment in his tiny surgery.'

And a number of those preferring a general practitioner who did some tests and investigations himself made such remarks as: 'There aren't many who do them themselves, they mostly send you to hospital nowadays', 'You get very few that do'. However when asked directly few were prepared to be definitely critical of their doctor about sending people to hospital when it was not really necessary or not sending them as soon as necessary. (See Table 35.) But about three-tenths of them did not feel they had enough experience to give an opinion about these qualities. The few who were critical believed that they or their families had suffered as a result.

'I had german measles before the last baby. He knew the children had it and that I was pregnant, but he didn't ask if I'd had it or give an injection. Now the baby's very deaf and one eye isn't quite straight. The doctor's a bit backward in his knowledge.'

TABLE 35 *Patients' views on their general practitioner's referral habits, examination procedures and equipment*

	About sending people to hospital as soon as necessary	About not sending people to hospital unless necessary	About examining people carefully and thoroughly	About having a well equipped, up-to-date surgery
	%	%	%	%
Doctor felt to be:				
Good	70	65	81	69
Not so good	3	1	5	15
Don't know/ uncertain/ qualified	27	34	14	16
NUMBER OF PATIENTS (= 100%)	1,312	1,307	1,314	1,314

Sometimes, while saying he was good about sending people to hospital as soon as it was necessary, they paid him a rather back-handed compliment:

'If anything about you puzzles him, he sends you. With National Health the G.P. seems to be rather a clearing house to hospitals. They haven't the time or the skill.'

Patients were slightly more inclined to be critical of their doctor for the way he examined them, although only a small proportion were directly critical, 5 per cent. But some comments from those who said he was 'good' about this suggest that their expectations and standards were not unduly high.

'If you tell him what's wrong then he'll give you something for it. If you don't tell him what you think is wrong then he's compelled to examine you.'

'If he thinks you need it – but he doesn't have to examine you much because he knows you.'

'If I think I've got blood pressure, he'll always take it.'

If a doctor is to examine his patients thoroughly and only send them to hospital when necessary he needs a well-equipped surgery, which 15 per cent of the patients did not feel their doctor had.

'It's a bit ancient. There should be a cubicle of some sort when you go to be examined. I wouldn't know about equipment.'

'He doesn't need a surgery. He gives prescriptions. There's not a lot of palaver about it.'

The sort of criteria on which they were basing their judgements can be assessed from some of the remarks made by those who felt it was adequate.

'So far as I can say – it's not bare. He has a bed and a medicine cabinet.'

'It's got a couch and it's clean.'

'He's all right. He seems to have all the stuff there, weighing machine, couch and lamps.'

Patients' expectations and actions

Patients were asked what they thought their doctor would do if they told him they had had stomach-ache off and on, indigestion and feelings of sickness for the previous six weeks. Over half, 55 per cent, expected to be examined, and for a third this was the only thing they mentioned. Over a third, 37 per cent, expected to be given some medicine or a prescription, and for a fifth this was the only thing they mentioned. A seventh expected to be X-rayed or sent to hospital, and half of these thought this the only thing he would do. A few, 4 per cent, did not expect him to do any of these things and 11 per cent just did not know what to expect. So most patients expected the doctor himself to do something initially rather than refer them to hospital and examinations were expected by more people than medication, but a substantial minority, one-fifth, apparently expected to be given medicine or a prescription without any examination. The only social class difference was that relatively few people in the professional class expected to be given medicine only, 9 per cent compared with 25 per cent in the other social classes.[2]

People were also asked whether if they cut their leg while at home so that it needed stitching they would be more likely to go to their own doctor or straight to hospital. A third thought they would go to their own doctor while three-fifths thought they would go straight to hospital and the others were uncertain, saying it depended on the time of day and whether it was in surgery hours.

The most common reason for going to their own doctor – mentioned by 10 per cent of all patients – was his nearness and accessibility. Four per cent said it was not possible to be seen at the hospital without going to their own doctor first.

Accessibility in another sense was also the main reason given for going straight to hospital. Three-tenths of all patients said the hospital was always open but the doctor might not be in his surgery. Thirteen per cent thought they would get better attention at the hospital, and 12 per cent that the doctor would send them there anyway. Everyone, whatever they thought they would do, was asked whether, if they did go to their doctor first, they thought he would stitch it himself or send them to hospital. People were almost equally divided into three groups – those who thought he would do it himself, those who expected him to send them to hospital and those who were uncertain. Their expectations about this clearly influenced their estimated actions, as can be seen from

[2] Those who did not know what to expect have been excluded from this comparison.

Table 36. But nearly a fifth who expected their doctor to refer them to hospital would nevertheless go to see him first, largely because they felt the hospital would not treat them without a note from their doctor, or just because they felt it was 'the right thing to do'. And two-fifths who thought he would stitch it himself would still go straight to hospital – to avoid possible delays or get better treatment.

TABLE 36 *Patients' expectations about doctors' actions if consulted about a cut leg which needed stitching, and their own probable actions*

	General practitioner expected:		
	To stitch it himself	To refer to hospital	Uncertain
	%	%	%
Patient would:			
Go to own doctor	47	17	30
Go straight to hospital	42	79	57
Uncertain	11	4	13
NUMBER OF PATIENTS (= 100%)	454	462	413

Men were rather more likely than women to say they would go straight to hospital, 65 per cent compared with 54 per cent, but this varied more markedly with age, declining steadily from 81 per cent of those aged 21–24 to 36 per cent of those aged 75 or more. It is not of course possible to tell how far this is an age or a generation effect. There was no difference between people in different social classes in their expectations or probable actions.

Patients' expectations about whether their doctor would cope with certain other things himself or send them to hospital are shown in Table 37.

It has already been shown that four-fifths of the general practitioners reckoned to strap sprains 'more often than not', three-fifths to stitch cuts, three-fifths to do vaginal examinations with a speculum, half to open abscesses, and three-tenths to excise simple cysts. This suggests that patients' expectations are reasonably realistic. And patients who expected their doctor to stitch their cut leg himself more often had doctors who reckoned to stitch cuts 'more often than not' – 73 per cent compared with 57 per cent

of patients who did not know what to expect and 48 per cent of
those who thought he would send them to hospital.

TABLE 37 *Patients' expectations about general practitioners' action or referral
for certain conditions*

	A sprained ankle	A small cyst which needed cutting out	An abscess which needed opening	A blood test	An internal (vaginal) examination*
	%	%	%	%	%
Would expect:					
G.P. to cope with it himself	81	46	67	56	66
Send to hospital	12	37	20	30	18
Uncertain	7	17	13	14	16
NUMBER OF PATIENTS (= 100%)	1,326	1,332	1,329	1,328	696*

* Women only.

Obviously referrals to out-patient departments for specific
treatment of this sort would be much reduced if all general
practitioners carried out the procedures which some of them do
now. Scott and Gilmore in their study of out-patients in Edinburgh
conclude that 'in a substantial number of referrals . . , often for
minor disorders on which the diagnosis is not in doubt, the
patient is being referred on a purely service-providing or therapeutic basis,[3] while Lamont[4] in an analysis of over 3,000 attenders during one month at a casualty department concluded that
'more than half the patients should not be treated in hospital at all'.

Out-patient consultations

Just under a quarter, 24 per cent, of all adults interviewed said
they had been to a hospital as an out-patient at some time during
the previous twelve months. The proportion was rather less for

[3] Scott, Richard, and Gilmore, Margaret, 'The Edinburgh Hospitals'.
[4] Lamont, Daniel, 'The Casualty Dilemma'.

children – 17 per cent. The frequency of consultation is shown in Table 38 for adults. This suggests an annual average somewhat under one. Data from the Ministry of Health[5] give an average of 0·94 outpatient attendances per head in 1964 but this of course includes children and definitions were rather different on the two inquiries.[6] The Ministry has no information about the distribution of attendances and the number or characteristics of the patients involved.

TABLE 38 *Patients' estimates of their number of out-patient attendances in the previous 12 months*

	%
None	76
One	8
Two to four	10
Five to nine	4
Ten or more	2
NUMBER OF PATIENTS (= 100%)	1,392

Young adults, aged 21–24, were the ones most likely to have been to hospital out-patients in the previous year and people aged 65–74 were the least likely.[7] Actual proportions were 40 per cent of the first group, 24 per cent of those aged 25–64, 18 per cent of those aged 65–74 and 23 per cent of those aged 75 or more. Slightly more men than women had been – 26 per cent against 22 per cent – but attendance at hospital out-patients was not related to whether or not people were working.

There was no difference between middle- and working-class patients or between people living in urban and rural areas in the proportion who had been hospital out-patients in the previous twelve months. Nor did this vary with the number of patients a doctor looked after. Forsyth and Logan[8] in their study in Barrow-

[5] Ministry of Health, *Annual Report for the Year 1964*, p. 140.
[6] In this study an attendance was a visit to a hospital no matter how many departments were visited. In the Ministry figures, persons attending different departments on the same occasion are counted in each department.
[7] Scott and Gilmore, op. cit., also found that the age distribution of hospital out-patients did not 'reflect the general practitioners' major preoccupation with the very young and the very old who are relatively unrepresented in the hospital out-patient population'.
[8] Forsyth, Gordon, and Logan, Robert F. L., *The Demand for Medical Care*, pp. 90–1

in-Furness also found no relationship between general practitioners' list size and patient admission rates or use of direct access facilities. Both they and Scott and Gilmore[9] found wide variations between general practitioners in their use of hospitals which were not related to other indices of general practitioner care. On the present study too the proportion of patients who had been to outpatients did not vary with the number of procedures the general practitioner carried out himself, his access to X-ray and other diagnostic facilities or the ancillary help he had in the practice. Forsyth and Logan concluded that their results 'cast doubts on the theories that practitioners who use direct access facilities most send least patients to hospital'.

Earlier in this chapter it was indicated that when doctors carried out certain procedures themselves their patients were less likely to by-pass them and go straight to the hospital, so it would seem that these doctors are using the hospital rather differently from others. They may make more use of the diagnostic and advisory service but less often refer patients for minor therapeutic procedures. Unfortunately there are no further data on this study to substantiate or refute this.

People who went to the out-patients department had an average of about four attendances a year and attended for an average of 1·1 episodes of illness. The general practitioner had referred the patients to the hospital for two-thirds of the episodes, in a quarter they went directly, and a tenth had been referred by dentists, people at work or were recalled by the hospital.[10] Four-fifths of those who went to hospital directly had had some sort of accident. Most of the others just found it more convenient than going to their general practitioner and the hospital apparently raised no objection. '. . . hospital is just over the road. I just popped across from work'. Three people – out of the 17 who went directly but had not had an accident – had gone to their general practitioner first and said they had not been referred.

> 'I had consulted my general practitioner first and he said I had 'flu. When I went into a coma my friend called the police.' (Admitted as in-patient with diabetes, attended subsequently as out-patient.)

[9] Scott, Richard and Gilmore, Margaret, op. cit.
[10] This last answer was only accepted if they had first attended more than five years ago.

'I asked him why I was getting this terrific diarrhoea and said I wanted an exam and he wouldn't so I said I was going up. He was treating me for the wrong complaint – thrombosis and cardiac. When I got to the hospital, they could find nothing of that. It was a cancer, bowels and bladder.'

These two apparently were not getting appropriate treatment from their doctor. But the third, who had asked for an X-ray for bruised ribs, said: 'Now I know that it wasn't necessary for me to go but I wanted to know. It's proved right that I didn't need one – just for my peace of mind.'

About a fifth of those referred by their general practitioner (or a seventh of all hospital episodes) said they had gone to hospital just for a test or X-ray and *not* for a consultation with a doctor. For these patients the hospital was an extension of the general practitioner service.

Nine per cent of hospital out-patients felt it had not really been necessary for them to go to the hospital each time – their own doctor could have done what was done there – another 8 per cent expressed some doubts on this score but the majority, 83 per cent, felt it had been necessary to go to the hospital.[11] Obviously their judgement about this cannot be accepted uncritically but in assessing patients' views it is relevant that 17 per cent felt they might have been sent to hospital or kept on there unnecessarily. One man had gone directly to out-patients with a cut nose and had it stitched, and had been told to return: 'I was pressurized into it. "You must return to O.P.D. on so and so at so and so." I was regimented and when I got there I waited two hours. The specialist I saw must have spent at least one minute of his time with me and I'd waited two hours for nothing.' Another explained:

'I used to go every three months for a check on my blood pressure and tablets. In January I failed to keep an appointment and went to my own doctor instead. It was a drag going to hospital. I get my tablets from my own doctor now.'

The main reasons for feeling it was necessary to go to hospital were the facilities and equipment – about two-fifths of those

[11] The question asked was: 'As far as you can tell, was it really necessary for you to go to hospital (each time), or do you think your own doctor could do what they do there?'

attending had had some type of X-ray – and specialist advice. Scott and Gilmore suggest that hospitals may 'hold on' to some patients too long. The length of time patients had been attending on the present study is shown in Table 39, separately for completed episodes and episodes for which they were still attending.

TABLE 39   *Length of out-patient episodes*

	Completed episodes	*Episodes for which still attending*	*All episodes* *
	%	%	%
First attended out-patients for this condition:			
Less than 3 months ago	19	16	17
3 months but less than 6 months ago	24	11	19
6 months but less than 1 year ago	43	11	32
1 year but less than 2 years ago	9	9	9
2 years but less than 5 years ago	2	23	10
5 years or more ago	3	30	13
NUMBER OF EPISODES (= 100%)	219	134	362†

* Theoretically the number 'less than 3 months ago' should equal the number '3 months but less than 6 months ago' and be half that 'six months but less than 1 year ago'. The observed distribution is similar to the expected which suggests that memory errors are small – or evenly distributed.

† For five episodes the patient was asked to go back and had not done so and for four episodes the question about whether or not they had to go back again was omitted.

Looked at in another way 65 per cent of the episodes starting in the previous three months were completed, 78 per cent of those starting three months but less than six months ago and 84 per cent of those starting six months but less than a year ago. Extrapolation suggests that about nine-tenths of episodes are completed within twelve months, but there is a hard core of 'chronic attenders'. The proportion of episodes involving a single attendance in the study year was 43 per cent of those starting in the previous twelve months.[12] Patients' descriptions of the conditions involved are shown in Table 40.

Accidents accounted for a quarter of all the episodes and a third of the more recent ones. Respiratory conditions and particularly bronchitis are seen less often at hospital out-patients than by general practitioners. (Cf. Table 24, page 71.) Diseases and symptoms of the bones and organs of movement; of the nervous system and sense organs; infective and parasitic diseases (nearly all tuberculosis checks); and allergic, endocrine system, metabolic and nutritional disorders (mainly diabetes and asthma), together accounted for two-fifths of the 'chronic' episodes.

There is no evidence from this survey to suggest that attendance at hospital out-patients weakens the ties between patients and their general practitioners. Those who had been to hospital out-patients in the last twelve months were as likely as those who had not to feel they might consult their doctor about a personal problem not strictly medical, and there was no difference between the two groups in the proportion who would prefer to be able to go straight to a specialist rather than to have a general practitioner. Those who had been to hospital were asked who they found it easier to talk to – the doctors at the hospital, or their own doctor. Half said their own doctor, a tenth the doctors at the hospital and two-fifths said there was no difference. Some comments again illustrate the difficulty patients feel about questioning hospital doctors.

'My own doctor – if there's any choice but there's precious little difference. The hospital doctor didn't give me any advice or tell me what to do. He done his duty and that was all. It was the attitude of that fellow – "You're a very fit person for your age" – and that was all. They don't want to talk to old people.'

Still, for half the patients who had been to hospital the doctors there were felt to be at least as approachable as their own doctor.

[12] All episodes starting in the previous twelve months are of course included, but ones that started more than a year ago are only included here if there was a consultation during the last twelve months.

TABLE 40 *Conditions for which patients attended hospital out-patient departments in the previous year*

	Episodes for which first attended		All episodes
	Within last 12 months	A year or more ago	
	%	%	%
Infective and parasitic diseases	2	8	4
Neoplasms	2	5	3
Allergic, endocrine system, metabolic and nutritional disorders	1	8	3
Diseases of the blood and blood forming organs	2	3	2
Mental, psychoneurotic, personality disorders and nervousness	1	7	3
Diseases and symptoms of the nervous system and sense organs	7	9	8
Diseases and symptoms of the circulatory system	5	7	6
Bronchitis	–	2	1
Other diseases and symptoms of the respiratory system	7	4	6*
Diseases and symptoms of the digestive system	10	8	9
Diseases and symptoms of the genito-urinary system	7	6	7
Pregnancy and complications of childbirth and the puerperium	4	–	2
Diseases of the skin and cellular tissue	5	2	4
Diseases and symptoms of the bones and organs of movement	9	15	11
Other general symptoms, senility and ill-defined conditions	2	3	2
Accidents, poisonings and violence	33	9	26*
Check-up, X-ray – no disease or symptom stated	3	4	3
NUMBER OF EPISODES (= 100%)	243	117	362*

* Two episodes included here could not be classified by when the patients first attended. Two could not be classified by disease – they have been omitted from this table altogether.

To sum up, this survey suggests that there are more referrals than would be necessary if more general practitioners were prepared to carry out procedures themselves. But there is little information from this, or any other studies in this country, about the possibility of inadequate referral. Few patients were directly critical of their doctor for not sending them to hospital when necessary but the wide variations in general practitioner referral rates[13] – which do not seem to be explained by doctors doing more tests themselves – suggest that some are not taking advantage of modern techniques and facilities.

Of course most of the conditions for which the general practitioner is consulted are not referred to hospital. The Annis Gillie report refers to an estimate of 90 per cent of all medical episodes being handled from start to finish by the general practitioner.[14] Such a proportion might seem to belie McKeown's contention that referral in this country has gone too far. But the estimate is of doubtful value in this context since medical episodes can cover everything from colds to cancer. The higher the proportion of simple straightforward conditions about which general practitioners are consulted, the higher the proportion of episodes they look after themselves is likely to be. The estimate reflects this as well as doctors' willingness and ability to care for more complex episodes.

Data which are more relevant to McKeown's argument are first that most people, 79 per cent, prefer to have a general practitioner rather than go straight to a specialist. Referral has certainly not gone so far that most people feel the general practitioner redundant. On the other hand a third of the patients said they preferred a general practitioner who sent patients to hospital if they needed any investigation rather than one who did tests and investigations himself. So a substantial minority regard such things as inappropriate for general practice and the function of the hospital.

In some ways referral may have gone too far, in others not far enough. What of McKeown's other suggestion – that the exclusion of the general practitioner from hospital has isolated domiciliary from institutional care?

[13] Scott and Gilmore, op. cit., found rates varying from 0·6 to 25·8 per 100 patients at risk.
[14] Central Health Services Council, *The Field of Work of the Family Doctor*, p. 12.

Hospital appointments and access to hospital beds

It has already been shown that half the doctors in this study had some form of tie with a hospital – either a part-time appointment (23 per cent) or access to hospital beds where they retained full responsibility for their patients (39 per cent). But there is still an unsatisfied demand for more links of both kinds. The desire for access to beds is shown in Table 41. A third of those who had no access to beds had no desire for any – this amounts to one-fifth of all general practitioners. Several mentioned geriatric or chronic sick beds as the outstanding need. The ways in which hospital appointments and access to beds varied with certain characteristics of the general practitioners are shown in Table 42.

TABLE 41   *Desire for access to hospital beds*

	At present has access to:			All doctors
	Obstetric beds only	Other type of beds	No beds	
	%	%	%	%
Would like access to – or more beds:				
Obstetric only	14	43	16	19
Medical only	20	6	8	11
Obstetric and medical only	22	8	27	23
Other types of bed	30	21	15	19
None – or no more	14	22	34	28
NUMBER OF DOCTORS (= 100%)	112	49	254	415

Older doctors, who qualified before 1925, were comparatively unlikely to have access to beds. A relatively high proportion of those with further qualifications had hospital appointments and more of them had access to beds. But, looking at it another way, less than a quarter of those with access to obstetric beds had a diploma in obstetrics.

Twenty-eight per cent of doctors with lists of less than 2,500 had a hospital appointment compared with 19 per cent of those with lists of 2,500 or more. Those with large lists of 3,000 or more and small ones of less than 1,500 were relatively unlikely to have any beds. Looking at the two types of hospital connection together, the proportion with either an appointment or access to beds, or both, was highest for those with 'medium small lists' of 1,500–2,499, 55 per cent, fell to 44 per cent for those with larger lists of 2,500 or more, but was least, 36 per cent, for those with small lists of under 1,500. These findings suggest that larger lists of 2,500 or more make it difficult for general practitioners to accept or retain such ties with the hospital.

General practitioners who have hospital appointments have direct access to more tests and X-rays than those without one (see

TABLE 42 *Characteristics of general practitioners with hospital appointments and access to beds*

	Proportion with a hospital appointment	*Proportion with access to hospital beds*	*Number of doctors = 100%*
Year of qualification			
Before 1925	13%	21%	30
1925–1934	25%	39%	75
1935–1944	29%	39%	118
1945–1954	21%	41%	137
1955 or later	14%	45%	51
Qualification			
Licentiate only	16%	31%	82
University degree with no further qualification	22%	39%	249
Some further qualification	28%	47%	89
Size of list			
Under 1,500	24%	33%	25
1,500–1,999	32%	46%	37
2,000–2,499	27%	41%	110
2,500–2,999	20%	41%	106
3,000 or more	18%	34%	131

Table 43). This may be due to their hospital connections, but those who would like an appointment but have not got one at the moment fall in between the two groups. It may be that doctors who are attracted to the hospital are more eager to have these facilities. Access to hospital beds is also associated with access to facilities and with the carrying out of more procedures in their own practice.

Neither type of hospital connection was related to the doctors' views on the desirability of cervical smear tests for middle-aged women, although those who had an appointment or wanted one more often than those with no desire for one felt it would be appropriate for general practitioners to collect the smears if the hospital did the cytological examination – 55 per cent compared with 38 per cent.

General practitioners with hospital appointments did not differ from others in the extent to which they said they enjoyed their work as general practitioners but those with access to beds were less likely than others to say they enjoyed their work 'not very much' or 'not at all', 5 per cent compared with 14 per cent. There was no appreciable difference between those with either type of hospital connection in the average number of courses they had attended in the last five years, but those who would like a hospital appointment were more likely to have been on a course than either those who had one or those who had no desire for one – 72 per cent compared with just under 50 per cent in both the other groups.

Doctors who had access to hospital beds less often felt that many of their surgery consultations were for trivial and inappropriate reasons. Only 18 per cent of them thought more than half could be described in this way, compared with 31 per cent of doctors without access to beds. This may be because they feel more tolerant or relaxed or because their patients behave rather differently. When patients were questioned about a specific series of qualities and asked to rate their doctor as 'good' or 'not so good', doctors with hospital appointments and those with access to beds other than just maternity beds were *more* often criticized and classed as 'not so good' about explaining things to people fully (19 per cent and 20 per cent against 13 per cent) but those with hospital appointments were *less* often thought to be 'not so good' about having a well-equipped, up-to-date surgery (11 per

TABLE 43 *Hospital connections and aspects of doctor's work*

	Hospital appointment			Access to hospital beds		
	Has one now	Would like one	No desire for one	Obstetric only	Other beds	None
Proportion with direct access to:						
Full size chest X-rays	87%	78%	74%	83%	84%	75%
Bone and joint X-rays	85%	63%	60%	70%	82%	63%
Bacteriological examination of urine	96%	89%	82%	93%	94%	84%
Glucose tolerance tests	75%	71%	58%	72%	82%	61%
Average number of these	3·4	3·0	2·7	3·2	3·4	2·8
Average score on procedures	4·4	3·8	3·4	3·9	4·5	3·5
NUMBER OF DOCTORS (= 100%)	93	149	170	114	50	256

cent against 17 per cent). It seems reasonable that contact with the hospital may be associated with higher standards in equipment, but it is unfortunate if – as seems possible – general practitioners with appointments or access to beds acquire low hospital standards in relation to communication.

Other aspects of general practitioner-hospital relationships

Data from this study support the indications from other sources that many general practitioners feel dissatisfied with their present relationship with hospitals. There seem to be three main sources of discontent – delays, inadequate communication and lack of esteem.

Many general practitioners who were interviewed on this and on an earlier study[15] expressed concern about delays in both getting out-patient appointments for their patients and in securing admission to hospital.

'Last Monday week I had a girl, 22, who was five months pregnant and breathless. I rang the R.M.O. and asked for an urgent appointment. He said he could fit her in a week on Tuesday. I said, "Can't you do it any earlier?" He said it was the best he could do. She was dead the next day. Nothing could have saved her but it would have been some comfort to the relatives.'

Old people were seen as a particular problem. 'Geriatric patients are the biggest bind to get admitted. Nobody wants them and their social problems are as important as their clinical ones'. Warren and his colleagues have shown that it is difficult in the London area to obtain even emergency admissions for older people.[16]

The problem often seemed to be regarded as intractable – within the existing organizational and financial situation.

'We're always at loggerheads about old people. That's one of the terrible features. There's never enough beds. We had a new geriatrician. At first he was marvellous. He introduced a

15 Cartwright, Ann, *Human Relations and Hospital Care*, pp. 23–6.
16 Warren, M. D., Cooper, Jane, and Warren, J. In preparation.

new system. But time caught up with him. There's too few beds and too many calls on time and resources.'

'They're very short of beds for the long term hopeless case. One geriatric case, I saw a wife beginning to crack. She'd done ten years devoted nursing at home. The hospital does its level best – but they can't put two patients in one bed. They promised me the next bed.'

The hospital and consultants were not generally criticized for what was accepted, almost fatalistically, or regarded as the responsibility of politicians and administrators rather than the medical profession. One doctor who raised another possibility said:

'From the patient's point of view, the waiting list is quite ridiculous. Whether it's feasible to cut it down I don't know. I have a feeling they could if they put their mind to it. There's two months' wait for an orthopaedic appointment here and 18 months to two years for a pelvic repair op. It's certainly true that they get private patients because of it. If you send a patient privately somehow they soon find a bed. Whether the fault is in surgeons or in hospitals who won't let him work the necessary times or sessions, I don't know.'

To some extent, the reason for the delays may lie not so much directly with either administrators, politicians or consultants but with a 'buck passing' interaction between them. Consultants see the cause as inadequate resources. Working in dilapidated hospitals with antiquated equipment and inadequate assistance, some feel discouraged and may adopt an almost 'work to rule' attitude because they feel unable to effect changes. Situations seen as challenges in times of crisis and war become depressants when unduly prolonged and the reasons for them no longer accepted. Administrators on the other hand may blame the rapacity and rigidity of some consultants. Long waiting times ensure private patients; and it has been shown that bed scarcity has much more effect on the numbers of cases treated than on the average length of stay per case[17] – in other words consultants do little or nothing to reduce delays by changing the length of time they keep patients in hospital.

[17] Feldstein, Martin. 'Effects of Differences in Hospital Bed Scarcity on Type of Use'.

When general practitioners directly criticized hospital staff over the delays it was usually because of the trouble it caused them.

'The other week I had a young lady with an acute appendix. I phoned hospital and spoke to the nurse first. She said, "No beds". Then I spoke to the houseman – "No beds". Finally I spoke to the registrar – "Certainly doctor, send her in".'

Another complaint was of a hospital's refusal to arrange an ambulance when the doctor was ringing from a call-box and had no more change.[18]

They also criticized the delays before they received information and the inadequacy of the information they were given.

'Reports are hopeless from some consultants – they expect you to have extra sensory perception. Patients are discharged taking pills but they don't know what pills and there's no note to us.'

'At the moment it's a hit or miss system. You don't know what's happened. We got together socially and they agreed to give discharge notes. That was a big improvement but we often get the notes weeks afterwards.'

Such complaints are the counterpart to those hospitals' criticisms of notes from general practitioners which say 'Please see and treat'. Doubtless when some general practitioners use hospital services in that cavalier manner their colleagues are likely to suffer from some spill over of irritation and contempt. When a general practitioner acquires a good reputation in the hospital he is likely to find things easier.

'Hospital services are good to excellent as they come to regard your treatment of them as good to excellent. In 999 cases out of 1,000 if I explain why I want a bed and show I know what I'm talking about they will find me a bed. I get the maximum help and for my part I keep the maximum out.'

But good reputations take time to build up and depend on a doctor referring people to the same hospital or consultant and not 'shopping around' to find the shortest waiting-time for his patients.

[18] The ambulance service is the responsibility of the local authority not the hospital.

When there is a lack of esteem between hospital staff and general practitioners, patients suffer as well as doctors' pride.

'Students regard general practitioners with a bit of scorn and resentment. I had a patient with a massive haemorrhage. I took blood and dashed to hospital to tell them he's coming and will need pints. – "Here's some so you can find out his group". Half an hour later I went down to see if he'd come in alive. The blood was still untouched. They waited till the patient came in. The bloke wouldn't take my word he needed it. I was so flaming mad I said nothing.'

One way that general practitioners might enhance their prestige with their hospital colleagues would be to develop and enforce professional standards of practice. Lack of any form of quality control makes it possible for the occasional unscrupulous, lazy or inefficient doctor to continue his incompetent practice and endanger the reputation of his colleagues. This is a problem not only for general practitioners. One who was interviewed commented on the 'impossibility of getting rid of inefficient consultants – short of them raping Pat Hornsby-Smith[19]'. But the problem is particularly acute for general practitioners because of their relative, and sometimes extreme, isolation. One young doctor who had just gone into general practice described the situation in this way: 'In hospital everyone asked you "Why? Why? Why?" The whole time you were subject to criticism. In general practice there is no criticism'.

Conclusions

Possibly the most pressing need is to develop a more critical milieu for general practice. Access to hospital beds and part-time hospital appointments are two ways of overcoming the professional isolation of the general practitioner. There is some indication that this affects both the scope of his work and his attitudes towards it, although it may simply be that hospital work attracts different sorts of general practitioners. But the sort of professional contact that general practitioners make with their hospital colleagues under these circumstances may not be the most stimulating and appropriate for them as general practitioners, and if

[19] Parliamentary Secretary, Ministry of Health, 1951–7.

hospital beds are in Cottage Hospitals there may be little or no contact with consultants. Moreover the small number of their patients who would be in hospital at any particular time would mean that their contact with the hospitals and the care they could give their patients there would be sporadic and limited[20]

Fox[21] reasons that the general practitioner will not survive 'unless he concentrates on those things *no* hospital can do as well as he can. And . . . he should give up some of those things *any* hospital can do better.' In other chapters it is argued that general practitioners should give their patients more preventive care. If this and the personal care, which most of their patients so appreciate, are regarded as the appropriate specialities of general practice, then the general practitioner will look more to his colleagues in general practice, in community medicine and in the social welfare services for professional stimulation, encouragement and constructive criticism.

This is not to underrate the importance of effective links between general practitioners and hospitals. One doctor described their relationship in this way: 'We're the forwards in a scrum. We've got to get the ball out to the consultant, otherwise they don't score any tries.' This emphasizes the need for collaboration and the division of skills and labour and puts them on an equal footing.

[20] Leeson, Joyce 'Medical Care Tomorrow'.
[21] Fox, T. F., 'Personal Medicine'.

IX

PARTNERSHIPS AND PRACTICE ORGANIZATION

When general practitioners work together in partnerships or groups how does this effect the doctor-patient relationship and the working conditions and professional contentment of the doctors? Obviously it will depend partly on how their collaboration is organized. Some groups may simply share premises and ancillary help while other partnerships may co-operate closely in their work. This study has no information about the organization within practices.[1] It is only possible therefore to look at both patients and doctors in different sizes of practice.

Fifteen per cent of the patients felt certain their doctor worked on his own and another 4 per cent believed he did. Thirty-four per cent said he worked with one other doctor, 22 per cent with two, 13 per cent with three and 6 per cent with four or more. Another 6 per cent thought he worked with other doctors but were uncertain how many. When compared with their doctors' statements the two agreed completely in three-quarters of the cases and were 'right' or only 'one doctor out' in 93 per cent. Most of the discrepancy arose when doctors worked with three or more others and this may be partly because the terms were inadequately defined. For example two of the doctors interviewed were found to be working in the same premises as two other doctors and sharing ancillary help but not seeing each other's patients; one had recorded that he worked on his own and the other that he worked with three other doctors.[2]

---

[1] Doctors were just asked whether they worked single-handed, or with an assistant' or with one partner, or with two others or with three or more others. Patients were asked whether their doctor worked on his own or with another doctor or doctors, and if the latter how many other doctors there were.
[2] Patients' descriptions of their doctor's type of practice have been taken for analysis with patients' characteristics and views, and the doctors' statements for analysis with their characteristics and views.

Older patients, aged 65 or more, were more likely to have doctors who worked on their own – 28 per cent, compared with 18 per cent of people under 65. People in rural areas also more often had single-handed doctors – 29 per cent against 18 per cent of those in urban areas, but the proportion with doctors in large groups of four or more was similar for people in urban and rural districts. Large groups of five or over were relatively common in designated areas, where the Ministry of Health – through the Medical Practices Committee – encourages more doctors to work.[3] Fourteen per cent of the patients in these areas had doctors in such groups, 5 per cent of those in open areas and 1 per cent of those in restricted and intermediate ones. The social class of patients was unrelated to the doctor's type of practice.

When asked which they preferred, a doctor working on his own or one in a partnership, 27 per cent of the patients said one on his own, 37 per cent one in a partnership, and 36 per cent thought it did not matter or had no feelings about it. Their own doctor's type of practice was important in forming their views, as can be seen from Table 44. Such an association could arise because patients who preferred a certain type of practice chose that initially, but it has already been shown that few patients selected their doctors on such grounds.

The proportion who said they preferred a doctor who worked

TABLE 44   *Type of practice and patients' preferences*

	Doctor on own	Doctor believed to be on own	Doctor believed to work with:				
			One other	Two others	Three others	Four or more others	Unknown how many
Patient prefers:	%	%	%	%	%	%	%
Doctor on own	59	50	19	21	21	14	25
Doctor who works with others	15	15	37	43	51	58	34
Does not mind, uncertain	26	35	44	36	28	28	41
NUMBER OF PATIENTS (= 100%)	197	54	443	287	173	76	71

[3] This is described in more detail in Appendix 1, p. 233.

with others rose from 37 per cent of those whose doctor worked in a group or partnership of two to 58 per cent of those with doctors in groups or partnerships of five or more. Possibly the latter group of patients find it relatively difficult to envisage a doctor working on his own today.

All patients, whatever their views, were asked what they thought were the advantages and the disadvantages – if any – from the patient's point of view, of a doctor working on his own. The most frequent advantage mentioned was that the patient always saw the same doctor. Fourteen per cent stressed that this meant better, more consistent, medical care because 'he knows your case'; 12 per cent that it created a closer personal relationship, and 21 per cent did not enlarge on their view that it was an advantage to see the same doctor. The main disadvantages were that the doctor was rushed, tired or overworked, 43 per cent; that it was not always possible to get hold of him, 25 per cent, that there was no second opinion available – the doctor had no colleagues to consult and the patient no choice of doctor, 16 per cent; and if the doctor was away the patient had to see a complete stranger, 9 per cent.

A third of the people mentioned both advantages and disadvantages while 11 per cent did neither. The points they stressed were again related to the type of practice in which their own doctor worked. Those with single-handed doctors mentioned disadvantages as well as advantages rather more often than the others mainly because they were aware – almost as often as others – that a single-handed doctor might get tired, rushed or overworked. But they less often felt that a doctor who worked on his own might not be available in an emergency – 19 per cent of them mentioned this possibility, 27 per cent of those with doctors in groups of two to four and 36 per cent of people with doctors in large groups of five or more.

How do people feel when they cannot see their own doctor? The circumstances will be rather different if their doctor works on his own or with others, so patients with a single-handed doctor were asked how they would feel if they went to the surgery and found a strange doctor there because their own was away ill or on holiday. Patients whose doctor worked with others were asked about their reactions if they went to the surgery and found unexpectedly that their own doctor was not there. The same choice of answers was offered to the two groups. Their responses are shown in Table 45.

TABLE 45 *Type of practice and patients' reactions when own doctor not at surgery*

	With single-handed doctor	With doctor who works with others
	%	%
Not mind in thel east	35	45
Feel quite prepared to see other doctor although would have preferred to see own	53	42
Feel quite put out because can't see own doctor	4	7
Prefer to see other doctor	1	2
Uncertain – depends on doctor/illness etc.	7	4
NUMBER OF PATIENTS (= 100%)	245	1,039

Those with doctors in groups or partnerships were more likely not to mind in the least and this proportion was highest when the doctor worked with just one other one – presumably because they were more likely to know the other doctor and not to feel that the absence of their doctor meant they would be seeing a stranger.

Three-fifths of the patients whose doctor worked with others said they usually knew when they went to the surgery whether their own doctor would be there, but two-fifths did not know this. (This did not vary with the size of group or partnership.) Asked what they would usually prefer to do if they could see another doctor in the group straight away or wait about half an hour and see their own, 53 per cent would wait to see their own doctor, 39 per cent would see the other doctor and 8 per cent said it would depend on various circumstances. The proportion who would wait for their own doctor rose from 46 per cent of those whose doctor worked with one other doctor to 62 per cent of those whose doctor worked in a larger group or partnership of four or more doctors.

Identification with an individual doctor obviously persists in many partnerships. Eight per cent of those with doctors in partnership felt another doctor in the partnership – not the one whose list they were on – was *their* doctor. Fifty-five per cent said they knew their doctor much better than others, 16 per cent knew him a little better, 19 per cent knew him no better and 2 per cent knew him less well but did not feel another doctor in the partnership was theirs.

Peoples' relationships with and opinions about their doctor appeared to vary remarkably little with the number of doctors he worked with. There was no difference between patients with doctors who worked on their own and patients with doctors in a group or partnership in the proportion who thought they might consult him about a personal problem, nor in the proportion who felt their relationship was friendly rather than businesslike, nor in those who thought their doctor good about listening to what they said and explaining things fully, nor in the way they ranked a general practitioner compared with people in other professions. Neither did the size of group or partnership affect these things. But the proportion of patients who thought their doctor would know their name if he met them in the street declined from 76 per cent of those with single-handed doctors to 60 per cent of those whose doctors worked with four or more others. The proportion critical of their doctor's surgery, saying it was not so good about being equipped and up-to-date, was highest for single-handed doctors – 21 per cent, and fell to 8 per cent of patients of doctors working in groups of three or more.

But while working in a partnership apparently made little difference to their patients, doctors in partnerships enjoyed their work more than doctors working on their own. This is shown in Table 46.

TABLE 46   *Size of partnership and enjoyment of general practice*

	Size of partnership or group				All doctors
	Single-handed	Self and partner	Self and two others	Self and three or more	
	%	%	%	%	%
Enjoys general practice:					
Very much	41	49	56	62	52
Moderately	37	37	38	35	37
Not very much or not at all	22	14	6	3	11
NUMBER OF DOCTORS (= 100%)	86	110	94	122	414

Part of the explanation almost certainly lies in the relative amount of free time the doctors had. Table 47 shows the variation in the nights a week on call and amount of weekend duty. Half the single-handed doctors were on call every night and on more than half their week-ends. At the other end of the scale, two-fifths of those in groups or partnerships of four or more were on call for not more than two nights a week and three-quarters were on for less than half their week-ends. But obviously if a doctor is on call for a large group the frequency with which he is actually called out will be greater than for a single-handed doctor on call for just his own patients. And there may be other disadvantages:

'The formation of a group (of four) far from making things flexible has imposed a rigid time-table which is impossible to vary without a great deal of discussion. When there was just my brother and I in practice it was more free and easy and there was more give and take.'

TABLE 47 *Size of partnership and leisure*

	Size of partnership or group				All doctors
	Single-handed	Self and partner	Self and two others	Self and three others	
Week-ends on call	%	%	%	%	%
More than half	51	14	7	12	20
One in two	14	51	22	14	26
Less than one in two	35	35	71	74	54
Nights a week on call	%	%	%	%	%
Every night	48	18	2	8	18
Five or six	30	19	11	25	21
Three or four	12	54	61	28	39
Two or less	10	9	26	39	22
NUMBER OF DOCTORS (= 100%)	88	112	92	121	415

A relatively high proportion of the single-handed doctors qualified before 1925 – 13 per cent of them compared with 6 per cent of other doctors – while more of those in larger groups or partnerships qualified after 1955 – 18 per cent compared with 10 per cent of those in smaller groups and 5 per cent of the single-handed doctors. Single-handed doctors had access to an average of 2·4 out of the four tests and X-rays asked about compared with 3·1 for other doctors.[4] Their score on procedures was also relatively low – 3·2 compared with 3·9 for the others. Some other variations are shown in Table 48.

TABLE 48   *Type of practice and other working arrangements*

	Single-handed	*With one partner*	*With two others*	*With three or more others*
Proportion with a hospital appointment	19%	22%	23%	26%
Proportion with access to hospital beds	33%	41%	51%	32%
Proportion who had been on at least one course in the last five years	54%	51%	57%	65%
Proportion with some ancillary help	72%	74%	88%	98%
Appointment system:	%	%	%	%
All surgeries	6	4	14	15
Some sessions	20	36	33	23
None	74	60	53	62
NUMBER OF DOCTORS (= 100%)	88	113	95	124

Although there was some variation with type of practice in access to beds, attendance at courses, ancillary help and appointment systems – it is perhaps surprising that the relationships were not stronger. Neither were there any strong relationships between a doctor's attitudes and his type of practice. Whether he worked

[4] The difference persists when date of qualification – also related to the number of tests and X-rays they have access to – is taken into account. The averages for those who qualified before 1935 were 1·9 for single-handed doctors, 2·8 for those in partnership, and for those who qualified later 2·7 for single-handed, 3·2 for those in partnership.

on his own or with one other doctor or with three or more others did not appear to affect his views on the proportion of consultations for trivial, inappropriate or unnecessary reasons. Nor apparently did it affect his attitude to cervical smear tests. There was however some indication that single-handed doctors were rather less inclined than others to feel it was appropriate for them to be consulted about such things as children getting into trouble or family discord – 21 per cent of them thought such problems were more appropriately discussed with other people, but only 12 per cent of doctors working in groups or partnerships felt this.[5] Single-handed doctors also appeared to be rather more likely than others to feel that 'patients nowadays tend to demand their rights rather than to ask for help and advice': 68 per cent of them agreed with this statement, 54 per cent of the doctors working with others. In addition when confronted with the statement: 'One should try to give patients full explanations about the aetiology of their illnesses and the rationale of treatment' more of the single-handed than the other doctors disagreed – 14 per cent compared with 6 per cent. *If* these questions give any indication of doctors' abilities to accept and understand their patients' needs, social pressures and foibles, there is some suggestion that working with other doctors slightly increases their tolerance and sympathy.

There was also some difference between single-handed and other doctors on whether patients should be encouraged to stick to one doctor when general practitioners worked in a partnership (see Table 49), but no difference on whether patients 'should nearly always be able to see the doctor of their choice'. Fifty-nine per cent of all the general practitioners 'strongly agreed' with this last statement and only 7 per cent disagreed with it.

It is not unexpected that single-handed doctors should feel more strongly than others that patients' attachment to a particular doctor is important in establishing satisfactory personal relationships. Table 49 also suggests that doctors in larger working groups may put more stress on the importance of this than doctors working with just one partner. In larger partnerships the likelihood of patients feeling no particular attachment to any

---

[5] Again the difference remains when date of qualification is taken into account. The proportions for those qualifying before 1935 were 22 per cent of single-handed, 11 per cent of those in partnership and for those who qualified later 19 per cent of single-handed, 12 per cent of those in partnership.

doctor is possibly greater and the dangers more easily recognized. At the same time one advantage of a larger working group is that when either patient or doctor find their relationship unsatisfactory it is possible, if the system is not too rigid, for the patient to see another doctor who may be more compatible – and even if that relationship is not more satisfactory this can relieve the strain.

TABLE 49 *Type of practice and views on importance of encouraging patients to stick to one doctor*

If general practitioners working in partnerships are to establish satisfactory personal relationships with their patients it is important that patients should be encouraged to stick to the same doctor		Size of partnership or group				All doctors
		Single-handed	With one partner	With two others	With three or more others	
		%	%	%	%	%
Strongly agree	2	50	34	40	46	43
	1	29	33	26	24	28
	0	11	12	16	14	13
	1	5	12	11	11	10
Strongly disagree	2	5	9	7	5	6
NUMBER OF DOCTORS (= 100%)		86	112	94	123	416

For these reasons it might be thought that doctors who agree – but not strongly – with the statement in Table 49, might work in practices which encourage the development of a personal relationship but are relatively flexible if it does not work out well. This of course assumes that their views are related to the way in which they work. In fact patients of doctors in groups of three or more were less likely to feel they might consult their doctor about a personal problem if the doctors disagreed with the statement that patients should be encouraged to stick to the same doctor. Only 18 per cent of these patients thought they might do so compared with 30 per cent of patients with doctors in this type of practice who either agreed or felt neutral about the statement. But there was no variation according to the strength of the agreement about it. It is perhaps not surprising that in larger partnerships, where most doctors feel it is increasingly important to encourage a patient to identify with an individual doctor, the relatively small group – 5 per cent of all doctors – who do not regard this as important should have patients who do not feel their doctor (or doctors) would be very interested in their personal problems. As the trend towards larger partnerships continues this small group might increase, but apart from them there seems to be no danger that the trend will affect patient-doctor relationships adversely.

Appointment systems

Fifteen per cent of the patients interviewed said their doctor ran an appointment system. When asked what they thought of this system and whether they preferred such an arrangement or would rather wait in turn, 72 per cent of them liked the appointment system, 21 per cent would rather wait in turn and 7 per cent were uncertain. Patients whose doctor did not have an appointment system were asked whether they would like him to have one, provided they could always see him the same day as they wanted to, or whether they would rather go on without one. Thirty-five per cent said they would prefer an appointment system, 60 per cent that they preferred to go on without one and 5 per cent were uncertain. So a majority prefer their present arrangement – whether with appointments or without – though the proportion is some-what greater when their doctor has an appointment system than when he has not.

Waiting times were much less when the doctor ran an appoint-ment system (see Table 50), and this appears to account for much of their popularity. Table 51 shows how people's attitudes to appointment systems and the lack of them varies with the length of time they are kept waiting.

Another study[6] showed that a quarter of the general practi-tioners without a full appointment system felt their patients would find it difficult or would not like it. In practice the great majority of patients appreciate it when it works well and although most patients express a preference for the system they know this does not hold if waiting times are three-quarters of an hour or more.

The proportion of patients who said they would like an ap-pointment system although their doctor did not have one de-creased with age from 41 per cent of those under 25 to 19 per cent

[6] Cartwright, Ann, and Marshall, Rosalind, 'General Practice in 1963'.

of those aged 75 or more. But among those with an appointment system there was no variation with age in the proportion expressing appreciation. Older people may be more resistant to the idea of such changes but apparently adapt to them and accept them just as well as others. Rather surprisingly, possession of a telephone made no appreciable difference either to people's appreciation of an appointment system or to their desire for one.

TABLE 50 *Waiting times at doctor's surgery*

| | Patients whose doctors have | | All patients* |
	An appointment system	No appointment system	
	%	%	%
Time had to wait last time went to doctor's:			
Less than 10 minutes	49	18	23
10 mins. but less than 20 mins.	25	30	29
20 mins. but less than 30 mins.	10	19	17
30 mins. but less than 45 mins.	10	15	14
45 mins. but less than 1 hour	2	8	7
1 hour but less than 1½ hours	3	7	7
1½ hours but less than 2 hours	1	2	2
2 hours or more	–	1	1
NUMBER OF PATIENTS (= 100%)	179	989	1,196

* Sixteen patients whose doctors had a 'queue-ticket system' and 12 who gave inadequate information about their doctors' arrangements are included in this column but not in either of the other two.

Middle-class patients were rather more appreciative of appointment systems when their doctors had one than working-class, 81 per cent of the former liked them compared with 68 per cent of the latter. They were also slightly more likely to say they would like one when their doctor did not have one, 39 per cent compared with 33 per cent. But there was no difference between the middle and working-class patients in the proportion whose doctors ran one, nor did they differ in the time they were kept waiting the last time they went to the doctor's surgery.

It is sometimes argued that an appointment system creates a useful barrier between patients and doctor, discouraging the

TABLE 51   Length of time kept waiting and attitudes to appointment systems

| | Less than 10 minutes | Time had to wait last time went to doctor's surgery | | | | | | All times |
		10 < 20 minutes	20 < 30 minutes	30 < 45 minutes	45 < 60 minutes	1 < 1½ hours	1½ hours or more	
Those with an appointment system:	%	%			%			%
Likes appointment system	80	71			52			72
Would prefer to wait in turn	15	23			40			21
Uncertain	5	6			8			7
NUMBER OF PATIENTS (= 100%)	85	62			25			188
Those without an appointment system:	%	%	%	%	%	%	%	%
Like it as it is	72	69	59	54	39	39	28	60
Would prefer appointment system	23	27	37	39	54	54	72	35
Uncertain	5	4	4	7	7	7	–	5
NUMBER OF PATIENTS (= 100%)	173	297	185	150	76	70	29	1,071

trivial consultation but at the same time removing a sense of pressure so that when patients see the doctor they feel more relaxed, more able to tell him what is really bothering them because they do not feel they are keeping him from a roomful of other, waiting, patients. There was no evidence from this survey that patients felt their doctor better at taking his time and not hurrying them when there was an appointment system. But when patients were asked to describe the qualities of their general practitioner that they appreciated, more of those whose doctor had an appointment system said he was good at listening – 20 per cent compared with 14 per cent – and at explaining 7 per cent against 3 per cent. In addition, when detailing qualities they thought a general practitioner ought to have that theirs had not, only 20 per cent of patients whose doctor had an appointment system mentioned something – for 3 per cent it was an ability to listen – compared with 27 per cent of those with doctors without one – 6 per cent of whom mentioned an ability to listen. There is therefore some indication that an appointment system helps both patients and doctors to feel relaxed and able to discuss things more fully, although of course it may be that doctors who run appointment systems differ from the others anyway.

An appointment system does not seem to reduce the doctor's work load in terms of the number of consultations; rather the reverse. There was no difference between doctors with and those without appointment systems in the proportion of patients who had consulted them at all in the previous twelve months, but patients appeared to consult their doctor rather more frequently if he had an appointment system. Thirty-seven per cent of patients whose doctor ran a full appointment system said they had consulted him five or more times in the previous twelve months compared with 25 per cent of patients whose doctors did not have one. In addition 62 per cent of patients whose doctors had an appointment system said they thought they would consult their doctor about a constant feeling of depression for three weeks, compared with 53 per cent of other patients.

It seems plausible that an appointment system might encourage some patients to attend and discourage others, and it is likely to give the doctor – and his receptionist – opportunities for controlling and influencing patients in their attendance. The number of consultations reported in the two weeks before interview were too few to allow many conclusions to be drawn from them, but it appeared that when the general practitioner had a full appointment system a higher proportion of the consultations were regarded by the patients as being initiated by the doctor – two-thirds against just over one-third.

The doctors who had an appointment system themselves felt that they were less often consulted about trivial things than did other doctors. The proportion who regarded a quarter or more of their surgery consultations as trivial, unnecessary or inappropriate was 60 per cent of those with no appointment system, 51 per cent of those who had one for some sessions and 43 per cent of those who had one for all surgeries.[7] Those who ran an appointment system differed in a number of ways from the others. As has already been shown they more often worked in partnerships of three or more. They also qualified more recently – the proportion with an appointment system at any surgery session rose from 17 per cent of those who qualified before 1925 to 44 per cent of those who qualified in 1945 or later. They were more likely to employ ancillary help and to carry out certain procedures themselves. These differences are shown in Table 52.

TABLE 52 *Some characteristics of doctors with and without appointment systems*

	Appointment system for all surgeries	Appointment system some sessions	No appointment system
Proportion with a secretary or receptionist	93%	82%	71%
Average score on procedures	4·1	4·1	3·5
NUMBER OF DOCTORS (= 100%)	41	118	261

Probably associated with these differences, patients of doctors who had an appointment system more often thought their doctor was good about having a well equipped, up-to-date surgery, 82 per cent compared with 69 per cent of other patients, and about having a pleasant, comfortable waiting room, 83 per cent against 68 per cent.

[7] Four out of the 65 doctors who filled in the later questionnaire about trivialities said they had introduced an appointment system since they had completed the first questionnaire and had found this had cut down the number of trivialities.

But although doctors with appointment systems appear to work under more attractive, efficient conditions they were not apparently any more likely than other doctors to enjoy their work.

Ancillary help

Eighty-four per cent of the doctors said they had some ancillary help in the practice. Most, 66 per cent, had just a secretary or receptionist, 12 per cent had a nurse (nearly all of these also had a secretary or receptionist), 3 per cent a dispenser, 7 per cent a health visitor and 5 per cent some other type of help. There is no information about the number of people employed or the hours they worked.

What effect does the employment or attachment of ancillary help have on the work the doctor undertakes, on his feelings of satisfaction with his job and on patients' reactions? These questions cannot be answered categorically because obviously other things are related to the employment of ancillary help. For example, it has already been shown that doctors who work with others and those who run appointment systems more often have some help in the practice. Associated with this, the more recently qualified doctors more frequently worked in practices with some ancillary help. Eighty-five per cent of those who qualified in 1955 or later had a secretary or receptionist compared with 60 per cent of those who qualified before 1925 and 77 per cent of the intermediate group. And whereas 84 per cent of those who looked after 2,500 or more patients had such help, only 66 per cent of those looking after fewer patients had a secretary or receptionist.

There was some suggestion that doctors with a nurse in the practice felt they had fewer trivial consultations than other doctors – 43 per cent of them thought at least a quarter of surgery consultations fell into that category, compared with 58 per cent of other doctors. Those with a nurse also carried out more procedures – their average score was 4·5 compared with 3·7 for those with a secretary or receptionist and 3·2 for those with no help at all. The patients seemed aware of this difference – 43 per cent of those whose doctor employed a nurse would expect him to stitch a cut leg himself rather than send them to hospital, compared with 32 per cent of other patients. Few of the doctors with no ancillary help had many private patients, 9 per cent of them had 20 or more compared with 26 per cent of those with some help.

Whether or not they had a secretary or receptionist made no difference to their views on the *ideal* number of patients for them to look after, but more of those who had a nurse felt the ideal number was less than 2,000 – 52 per cent of them compared with 34 per cent of those without one. At first sight this may seem surprising but another study of the work of a nurse employed in a general practice[8] concluded that the main effects were to extend the range of care given to patients, to ease the sense of isolation experienced by some general practitioners and reduce the amount of use made by these doctors of the hospital, local authority and pharmaceutical services, but that it did not enable doctors to increase their size of list. The present study tends to confirm this – at least as long as the nurse is not used as a filter for patients before they see the doctor. There was no indication either that having a nurse – or other ancillary help – increased the doctor's enjoyment of his work.

Size of list

It has already been shown how the number of patients the doctors looked after varied: one in seven of the doctors had less than 2,000 patients, one in three 3,000 or more. The variation in the estimates of the number of patients they looked after with the type of partnership is shown in Table 53. The group of doctors looking after 3,000 or more patients contained a relatively high proportion of both single-handed doctors and those in groups of four or more and relatively few in groups of two or three. 'Younger' doctors who qualified since 1944 were less likely to have large lists of 3,000 or more – 26 per cent compared with 37 per cent of older doctors.

It has also been shown that doctors with relatively small lists were more likely to have hospital appointments and less likely to employ ancillary help. In addition they were less likely to have attended any courses in the last five years. The proportion who had been on at least one course was 28 per cent of those with less than 1,500 patients, and 35 per cent of those with 1,500–1,999,

[8] Cartwright, Ann, and Scott, Richard, 'The work of a nurse employed in general practice'.

and 62 per cent of those with 2,000 or more. Over 2,000 there was no appreciable variation with list size.

TABLE 53   *Type of practice and number of patients*

Estimated number of N.H.S. patients doctor looked after	Single-handed	Self and partner	Self and two others	Self and three or more
	%	%	%	%
Under 1,500	11	5	4	5
1,500–1,999	7	16	7	5
2,000–2,499	19	35	31	22
2,500–2,999	25	24	33	25
3,000 or more	38	20	25	43
NUMBER OF DOCTORS (= 100%)	88	113	94	124

Although two-thirds of the doctors looked after more patients than they felt would be ideal under their existing practice arrangements, there was no evidence either that doctors with larger lists were more frustrated than others or that they were giving a less comprehensive service to their patients. The proportion who enjoyed general practice 'very much' was comparatively low, 35 per cent, for those with lists of under 2,000 but did not vary significantly from 55 per cent, for the other three groups. (Those with small numbers of patients were also more likely to be on call every night – 30 per cent of those with under 2,000 patients, 15 per cent of others.) But when their actual size of list is compared with their 'ideal', this does seem to be related to their enjoyment. Sixty per cent of those whose present list size was in the same group as their ideal, enjoyed general practice very much compared with 55 per cent of those who looked after about 500 more patients than they thought was ideal, and 48 per cent of those who looked after over 1,000 more than their ideal. Still, the least happy ones were those who looked after *less* patients than they thought ideal. Only 32 per cent of them said they enjoyed general practice very much, but they did not mention pay any more often than the others as one of the things they found frustrating about their work, so it does not seem as if they were simply regarding a small list as unsatisfactory because it did not provide a large enough income.

Their estimates of the proportion of consultations they felt to be trivial was not related to their present number of patients, but those with large lists of 3,000 or more were more likely than others to 'strongly agree' with the statement: 'patients nowadays tend to demand their rights rather than to ask for help and advice', 31 per cent of them compared with 18 per cent of doctors with fewer patients.

If anything, those with lists of 2,500 or more carried out rather more procedures themselves than did doctors with smaller lists. The average score for the former group was 3·9 compared with 3·5 for the others. For tests and X-rays the group that stood out were those with small lists of under 1,500. They had access to an average of only 2·2 out of four compared with 3·0 for the others.[9] There was no variation with list size in the proportion who thought it appropriate for general practitioners to be consulted about such things as children getting into trouble or family discord, nor was there any difference in their views on cervical smear tests. But the proportion who thought that *ideally* general practitioners should carry out some (other) regular check-ups on middle-aged people increased from 41 per cent of those with lists of under 1,500 to 58 per cent of those with lists of 2,500 or more. Possibly those with larger lists are more likely to have come across conditions which might have been picked up by such check-ups.

If the size of the doctor's list seems to make comparatively little difference to the doctor's own perception of his role, is it related in any way to patients' attitudes and behaviour? There was a tendency for the proportion of patients who consulted their doctor (or his representatives) in the last twelve months to decrease as the doctor's size of list increased.[10] This is shown in Table 54.

Such a trend might arise because patients of doctors with large lists are discouraged from consulting their doctor when he is busy and has many other patients waiting, because doctors with small lists encourage their patients to come back to see them rather more frequently, because chronically ill patients seek out

[9] Hitchens, R. A. N., and Lowe, C. R., in 'Laboratory Services in General Practice' found 'large partnerships in which the partners have an average list of between 2,000 and 3,000 are most active in use of laboratory services'.
[10] Similar results were observed in a study of prescribing in general practice carried out by the Medical Research Council's Social Medicine Research Unit, see Last, J. M., *Objective Measurement of Quality in General Practice*.

doctors with small lists, or because doctors whose patients do not consult very frequently on the average are able to take on a larger number of patients. These possibilities are looked at in turn.

TABLE 54   *Number of patients and frequency of patient consultation*

	Number of patients				
	Under 1,500	1,500– 1,999	2,000– 2,499	2,500– 2,999	3,000 or more
	%	%	%	%	%
Consultations in previous twelve months					
None	29	23	31	35	35
One to four	40	54	40	39	43
Five or more	31	23	29	26	22
Estimated annual average consultation rate (from consultations in previous two weeks)	5·6	5·7	3·8	4·6	4·2
NUMBER OF PATIENTS (= 100%)	42	90	269	261	379

On the first, it would seem that patients of doctors with larger lists wait rather longer on the average to see their doctor at the surgery. The proportion waiting 20 minutes or more increased from 33 per cent when the doctor looked after under 1,500 patients to 53 per cent when he looked after 3,000 or more. But there was no evidence that the time a person had to wait in the surgery was related to the frequency with which he consulted the doctor. There was little or no variation with the doctor's list size in patients' expressed opinions about their doctors nor, rather surprisingly, in the proportions who thought their doctor would know them by name if he met them in the street. Slightly more patients of doctors with lists under 2,500 regarded their relationship as friendly – 49 per cent compared with 42 per cent of those with doctors with larger lists. But the proportion who said they might discuss a personal problem not strictly medical with their doctor did not vary with the number of patients. These data suggest that the variation in consultation rates with size of list cannot be explained by patients of doctors with large lists being discouraged from consulting their doctor. Nor was there any indication, from the details of the consultations occurring in the previous two weeks, that doctors with small lists initiated consultations themselves more frequently. The proportion of consultations said by the patients to be for the first time for that episode or at the suggestion of the doctor did not vary with the number of patients the doctor looked after. This does not support the 'Parkinson's Law' theory, put forward by Last[11] in explanation of this trend.

It may be that some patients – possibly particularly people who are mentally disturbed – seek out doctors who are prepared to listen and spend time with them. The data on choosing and changing doctors suggest that the number of people who do this is probably small. There was no indication either, from this study, that doctors with small lists were regarded by their patients as being more sympathetic listeners, more prepared to take time and not hurry them, more willing to explain things, or more appropriate people with whom to discuss personal problems that are not entirely medical.

The other hypothesis, that doctors whose patients consult relatively infrequently take on larger numbers – or those whose patients consult frequently recruit more doctors into their partnership – seems at the moment to be the most plausible explanation for the difference.

Summing up

The single-handed general practitioner is, from many points of view, an anachronism, and in any case is disappearing. In 1952 43 per cent of principals in general practice worked on their own, in 1965, 24 per cent and many of these now remaining are older doctors – a third qualified before 1935. But the image of the single-handed family doctor dies hard. Patients were asked if they had to choose between these two doctors, which they would prefer:

'The first doctor has his surgery attached to his house. He works mainly on his own, but he has an arrangement with a

[11] Last, J. M., op. cit.

nearby doctor for some weekends and some night calls. His waiting room is comfortable, which is a good thing because patients often have to wait a long time. He knows his patients and their families well, and when you do see him, he takes his time, doesn't hurry you and listens to what you say. He prescribes well established drugs and sends patients to hospital if they need anything more complicated.'

'The second doctor works in a partnership. There are four of them altogether and they share a well equipped surgery where they have a nurse and a secretary. This doctor takes turns with his partners to be on duty for surgeries and for weekend and night calls. They all examine you carefully, and are very up to date, and only send patients to hospital if they need very complicated investigation or treatment.'

The first description was intended to emphasize the better aspects of the old fashioned single-handed doctor and the second the better aspects of more modern, general practice in a partnership. The patients were almost equally divided in their preferences; 50 per cent chose the first, 47 per cent the second and 3 per cent were undecided. But this choice does not simply reflect a hankering for the general practitioner of the past. When asked which of the two doctors their own was most like, 51 per cent felt he was more like the first, 38 per cent the second and 11 per cent could not say. Moreover an analysis of which they preferred by which they thought their doctor most like, showed that the great majority (83 per cent of those making the choices) preferred the one they thought their doctor most like. Since few people chose their doctor for reasons which differ in these two stereotypes, these data emphasize the adaptability – and conservatism – of most patients.

If general practice changes radically in the next few years and, for example, many health centres are built, it seems probable that most patients will adjust their picture of the ideal doctor and come to see him as one who practises at a health centre; just as patients whose doctor has an appointment system come to prefer that. And there is no evidence from this survey to suggest that the doctor-patient relationship will either deteriorate or improve if doctors work more together and the single-handed practitioner finally disappears. But the demand for such a change will certainly not come from the patients.

The doctors themselves are more likely to benefit directly from working in partnerships than are their patients. Certainly those in larger groups or partnerships enjoyed their work more than single-handed doctors. They also had more leisure and more opportunities to attend courses and take on work outside their practices. It is perhaps disconcerting that these increased opportunities for outside stimulation and more organized ways of working do not apparently lead to a greater appreciation of the importance of preventive care, a wider view of their own activities or a very much more understanding or tolerant attitude to their patients' difficulties. Partnerships by themselves are clearly no panacea for the present malaise of general practice but they can relieve some of its more onerous burdens.

Appointment systems were generally appreciated by patients and certainly cut down waiting times. They did not reduce consultation rates but they probably had some influence on which patients came. Certainly doctors who had appointment systems were less likely than others to feel that a high proportion of their surgery consultations were trivial, inappropriate or unnecessary. There was also some suggestion that they helped patients to feel able to discuss things fully.

If anything, doctors with relatively large lists appear to give their patients a slightly wider service than those with small lists. There is no clear suggestion from this study that patients whose doctors had large lists found their doctors less sympathetic, less interested in their problems or that they less often did examinations. Similarly Hitchens and Lowe in their study of the use of laboratories services[12] found no support at all for the arguments advanced in favour of much smaller lists than are now common. Nevertheless slightly more patients seem to consult their doctor if he has fewer patients to look after and this might suggest that those on large lists are, in some way which has not been possible to demonstrate, discouraged from consulting their doctors. An alternative explanation, supported by the expressed views of patients and the fact that doctors with large lists did not seem any more frustrated or enjoy their work any less, is that list size is more determined by the patients' consultation rates than the other way round.

[12] Op. cit.

X

SOME VARIATIONS BETWEEN DOCTORS

The last chapter looked at the way patients' and doctors' views and habits varied with some of the ways in which the doctor organized his practice. This one again considers variations in the opinions and behaviour of doctors and patients, this time in relation to some characteristics of the doctor.

Year of qualification

Three-tenths of the doctors approached in this study qualified before 1935, but this proportion was higher – over two-fifths – among those who did not fill in the questionnaire than among those who did – one-quarter. A comparatively high proportion of patients living in rural areas had a doctor who qualified before 1925 – 11 per cent against 7 per cent of patients in urban areas. It may be that doctors in country areas find it easier to go on working after they are 60.

In the 'designated' areas, where list sizes are large and the Ministry tries to attract more doctors, a relatively high proportion had doctors who qualified since 1955 – 13 per cent compared with 8 per cent in other areas – presumably as a direct result of this policy. Older doctors, who qualified before 1925, had a comparatively high proportion of elderly patients. The proportion of patients aged 65 or more was 26 per cent for doctors who qualified before 1925, 17 per cent for those who qualified between 1925 and 1954, and 14 per cent for those who qualified more recently. There was some suggestion that, as a result of this, patients of doctors who qualified before 1925 had a slightly higher consultation rate than others – an estimated annual average of 4·4 compared with 3·7. In addition the proportion of home visits was higher – 38 per cent of all consultations for the older doctors and 28 per cent for the others. It is ironic that as a general practitioner gets older the demands of his patients are likely to increase.[1]

There was some indication that people in the professional class had rather younger doctors than patients in the other classes – 57 per cent of them had doctors who qualified in 1945 or later compared with 39 per cent of other patients. But this is probably because of the patients' greater mobility – 34 per cent of them had lived in the same district 20 years or more compared with 57 per cent of others and this proportion was in turn related to the doctor's date of qualification. Sixty-four per cent of patients with doctors who qualified before 1925 had lived in the same district for at least 20 years compared with 49 per cent of those whose doctors qualified in 1945 or later. Patients with older doctors were more likely to say their relationship with their doctor was friendly than people with doctors who qualified more recently. The proportion describing their relationship as friendly rather than businesslike declined from 58 per cent of patients whose doctor qualified before 1925 to 35 per cent of those whose doctor qualified in 1955 or later. This again is partly – but not entirely – because of the different lengths of times these patients had known their doctors – 68 per cent of the patients of doctors who qualified before 1925 had had their doctor for 15 years or more and this fell to 16 per cent of those whose doctor qualified between 1945 and 1954.

Patients with older doctors were somewhat more critical of them for not explaining things. Eighteen per cent of the patients whose doctors qualified before 1935 felt their doctor was 'not so good' about explaining things to them fully compared with 12 per cent of the patients whose doctors qualified more recently.

A number of variations between doctors who qualified in different periods have already been discussed. Older doctors were more likely to work on their own, less likely to have access to hospital beds and in a number of other ways appeared more isolated. This is summarized in Table 55.

Surprisingly, since isolation in general seemed to be associated with the feeling that a high proportion of consultations were for trivial or unnecessary reasons, older doctors were no more likely

---

[1] The Review Body on Doctors' and Dentists' Remuneration in its *Seventh Report* proposes that the standard capitation fee in respect of patients over 65 should be higher than for other patients, (p. 51).

to feel that a high proportion of consultations fell in that category. It may be that while older doctors are more isolated they are also further away in time from their hospital oriented training. With increasing experience of general practice doctors are likely to replace hospital attitudes to ill-health with views more attuned to the community in which they are living.

TABLE 55 *Year of qualification and aspects of the doctor's work*

	Year of qualification				
	Before 1925	1925– 1934	1935– 1944	1945– 1954	1955 or later
Proportion:					
Working single-handed	38%	26%	26%	20%	10%
With access to hospital beds	21%	39%	39%	41%	45%
With a hospital appointment	13%	25%	29%	21%	14%
Who had attended at least one course in last five years	33%	48%	58%	66%	58%
Average:					
Number of tests and X-rays has access to (out of four)	2·2	2·7	3·0	3·2	3·3
Score on procedures	3·9	4·2	3·5	3·9	3·1
NUMBER OF DOCTORS (= 100%)	30	75	113	137	51

The variation – or mainly lack of variation – in the score on procedures with year of qualification is unexpected. Those who qualified since 1954 are the ones who stand out as doing fewer procedures themselves – this although they had access to relatively more tests and X-rays and in general this is positively correlated with procedures carried out in the practice.[2] Analysis by the individual procedures shows the proportion saying they used a laryngoscope falling from 48 per cent of those qualifying before 1925 to 28 per cent of those qualifying in 1955 or later and the proportion opening abscesses 'more often than not' from 68 per cent to 38 per cent. On the other hand the proportion doing vaginal examinations with a speculum rose from 39 per cent to 75 per cent. There was no consistent trend with year of qualifica-

[2] The relationship between year of qualification and access to tests was rather similar to that found by S. L. Morrison and M. Mary Riley in their study of 'The Use of Hospital Diagnostic Facilities by General Practitioners'.

tion for the other procedures. Clute, in his study of general practice in Ontario and Nova Scotia, found that with increasing age there was a tendency for practice to be of poorer quality.[3] On this study there is no clear measure of quality, and what indices there are do not suggest that there is any marked variation in the type of work undertaken with age.

However more of the doctors who qualified comparatively recently thought that middle-aged women should have regular cervical smear tests – 86 per cent of those who qualified since 1954, 55 per cent of those who qualified before 1925 and 75 per cent of the intermediate group. Younger doctors also expressed a greater interest in obstetrics or midwifery – 46 per cent of the more recently qualified mentioned this as a special interest and this proportion declined steadily to 10 per cent of those who qualified before 1925. This interest was reflected in the amount of obstetrics they did: the proportion who had 50 or more cases in the last twelve months rose from 10 per cent of those who qualified before 1925 to 31 per cent of those qualifying since 1955. As doctors get older they probably find the night work associated with obstetrics increasingly irksome. When the things they found frustrating about their work are considered, late calls were mentioned most often by the oldest and the youngest groups (Table 56).

Possibly the younger doctors also have their nights disturbed by their own young children. Inadequate leisure was regarded as one of the frustrations more often by younger than by older doctors although, mainly because they worked with other doctors, younger ones were on call for fewer nights and weekends than older doctors. The proportion on call every night fell from 39 per cent of those who qualified before 1925 to 8 per cent of those who did so in 1955 or later, and the proportion on call more than half their weekends fell from 35 per cent to 15 per cent. When asked about the things they enjoyed about their work younger doctors put more stress than their older colleagues on their freedom and independence and on the variety of the work.

The 'middle-aged' doctors qualifying between 1935 and 1955 recorded their dissatisfaction with their pay more frequently than either younger or older doctors, and they were the ones least likely to say they enjoyed their work as general practitioners 'very much'. This can be seen from Table 57.

[3] Clute, K. F., *The General Practitioners*, pp. 319–20.

TABLE 56   *Year of qualification and frustrations and enjoyment*

	Year of qualification				
	Before 1925	1925– 1934	1935– 1944	1945– 1954	1955 or later
Mentioned as frustrating:					
Late calls	18%	13%	7%	9%	17%
Inadequate leisure	4%	4%	11%	14%	11%
Trivial conditions	25%	27%	34%	38%	36%
Pay	4%	6%	18%	16%	4%
Mentioned as something they enjoy:					
Variety	14%	13%	8%	22%	41%
Freedom, independence	7%	1%	4%	15%	25%
NUMBER OF DOCTORS (= 100%)	28	71	121	129	51

TABLE 57   *Year of qualification and enjoyment of work*

	Year of qualification				
	Before 1925	1925– 1934	1935– 1944	1945– 1954	1955 or later
	%	%	%	%	%
On the whole enjoys general practice:					
Very much	77	54	47	48	57
Moderately	13	32	38	45	35
Not very much or not at all	10	14	15	7	8
NUMBER OF DOCTORS (= 100%)	31	74	119	137	52

There are various possible explanations which probably con-tribute in some way to the relatively high level of dissatisfaction among general practitioners in their thirties and forties. One possibility is that during the nineteen thirties and forties, when these doctors were training, medical education was particularly oriented towards the hospital. Another is that it is during this period of life that people's family and financial responsibilities are greatest. If people feel their job is undervalued financially they are likely to feel most resentment about this when their commitments are heaviest. One doctor who was interviewed said:

'On remuneration – I'm now 50. I qualified in 1937 and have 27 years experience. I'm married and I have three children. Rightly or wrongly I sent them to boarding school. I can't afford to entertain or to go away for holiday. It's unfair that we're not paid for holidays. If your partner has one before you, by the time you get back he's ready for another one. I feel that comparing myself with people in other walks of life – and the only valid comparison is medicine – but with staff of I.C.I. with a university degree and people in families like mine who send their children to boarding school – they can live better than I do. I admit that if I was not sending children to boarding schools . . .' (enjoys his work as a general practitioner 'moderately').

It is doctors in this age-range too who are likely to be most conscious of the present lack of any career structure in general practice. One doctor who qualified in 1953 and said he did not enjoy his work at all under present conditions said:

'I'm not a frustrated consultant. I like treating people. It's not the money – but you're not treated as a professional now. I'm 34, and at a dead end. I've a full list – lots of drive – nothing left to live for. I could sit on my backside, not investigate things. We don't do this. But the better work you do the less you have to spend on your family. – If anyone showed a film of us you would laugh – answering the phone, the front door, filling in prescriptions, and in the middle of this all sorts of social problems. We could pass the buck but we get fed up seeing nothing done for them if we do, so we try to do it ourselves. There's no encouragement to run an efficient medical service. In no other profession as he grows older is a man tied to the same amount of work. We're doing a favour now for a man of 60 who cannot get a satisfactory locum. He's crippled with arthritis and needs a holiday. There are no increments of pay for seniority. As you grow older you should get seniority pay so you can cut down – or, alternatively a salaried service and make general practice a proper career.

We'd like to work from a clinic. We tried to organize this but only three out of seven or eight local doctors were interested.'

Yet another possibility is that there is a cycle of enthusiastic idealism followed by disillusionment then adaptation, common to all professions. My view is that such a cycle probably exists in the medical profession but is generally completed while the individual is still at medical school. It will only be repeated after they leave, if their training has left them unprepared for realities, or if they encounter particularly frustrating conditions. At the time of the study the hospital orientation of most medical training and the absence of a career structure in general practice seemed to create a sense of disillusionment after doctors had been practising a few years.[4]

Further education

That over half of the general practitioners working in 1964 had qualified 20 or more years earlier indicates the obvious need for continuing medical education. The doctors were asked to rank the importance to them of various methods of keeping up-to-date. Their replies are shown in Table 58. A low number indicates a high importance.

There was little difference in the importance attached to the

TABLE 58   *Relative importance of various ways of keeping up-to-date*

	Rank
Professional meetings	2·6
Journals, books, other publications	2·6
Informal discussions with doctors	2·7
Courses	2·9
Drughouse literature or representatives	4·2
NUMBER OF DOCTORS	412

[4] Possibly the proposals in the *Seventh Report* of the Review Body (op. cit.) about additional allowances for seniority and the reimbursement of up to 70 per cent of expenditure on ancillary help, will overcome some of this.

first four methods – professional meetings, journals and publications, informal discussions and courses. Drug house literature or representatives were recorded as the least important; 3 per cent of the general practitioners said it was the most important method for them. One who ranked drug house literature or representatives as the third most helpful way of keeping up-to-date said at the interview: 'I get the B.M.J. but very rarely have time to read it because I've no free time at all. Representatives are quite good and helpful. It saves reading pamphlets about things.' As might be expected informal discussions with other doctors were more important for doctors working in partnerships: the proportion regarding this as the most important method rose from 10 per cent of the single-handed doctors to 32 per cent of those working in groups of four or more. In contrast the proportion regarding publications as most important fell from 37 per cent to 21 per cent. Associated with this, older doctors less often than younger ones felt that informal discussions were their most important way of keeping up-to-date: 15 per cent of those who qualified before 1925 felt this, 38 per cent of those who qualified during or after 1955 and 20 per cent of the intermediate group.

Naturally doctors who found courses their most important way of keeping up-to-date had been on more than other doctors – an average of 2·9 in the last five years compared with 1·2 for other doctors. What is less expected is that doctors who found journals and periodicals most helpful had been on fewer courses (0·9) than either those who found informal discussions or professional meetings most important (1·4 and 1·6 respectively). This again is partly related to their type of practice. Doctors working in groups of four or more were rather more likely to have been on a course in the last five years than other doctors, 65 per cent compared with 54 per cent, but there was no difference between single-handed doctors and those in small groups of two or three.

Is there any truth in the gibe that doctors most in need of further education are the ones least likely to go on courses? The variation with year of qualification is shown in Table 59. Doctors who qualified between 10 and 20 years previously were the ones most likely to have been on a course. Beyond that there was a fall off, with the older ones less likely to have been on any. Part of the reason for this appears to lie in their practice arrangements and amount of free time. The proportion who had been on any courses in the last five years declined from 63 per cent of those on call for less than half their weekends to 50 per cent for the others. Similarly, it declined from 62 per cent of those on call for two nights or less on the average to 43 per cent of those on call every night. But again, as with the year of qualification, the number of courses per attender varied in the opposite direction. Doctors who were on call every night and had been to any courses averaged 3·8 compared with 2·3 of attenders on call for two or less nights. It would seem that those who overcome such difficulties are exceptionally keen. Rather surprisingly there was no difference in the course attendance of doctors in urban and rural areas, and it has already been shown that doctors with a relatively large number of patients were more likely to go on courses than those with small lists.

TABLE 59   *Year of qualification and attendance at courses*

	Year of qualification				
Course attendance in previous five years	*Before 1925*	*1925– 1934*	*1935– 1944*	*1945– 1954*	*1955 or later*
Proportion attending any	33%	48%	58%	66%	58%
Average number attended	1·2	1·6	1·6	1·7	1·3
Average number of courses per attender		3·3	2·8	2·6	2·3
NUMBER OF DOCTORS (= 100%)	30	71	116	138	52

Attendance at courses was related to a wider scope of work. Those who had not been on any course in the last five years carried out fewer procedures themselves: their score was 3·4, compared with 3·7 for those who had been on one or two courses, 4·3 for those who had been on three or four and 4·4 for those who had been on five or more. There was some indication that having been on a course was also related to the number of tests and X-rays the doctors said they had direct access to – 2·7 out of 4 for those who had not been on any, 3·2 for those who had – but there was no increase with the actual number of courses. Doctors who had a hospital appointment were no more or less likely to have been on courses than doctors who neither had one nor had any desire for one, but 72 per cent of those who wanted a hospital appointment had been on a course compared with 51 per cent of the others. There was no difference between those with and those without access to hospital beds but attendance at courses was positively correlated with the number of obstetric cases they had had in the previous twelve months. The proportion who had been on any courses rose from 33 per cent of those with no obstetric cases to 66 per cent of those with 50 or more, and was 58 per cent for the intermediate group. The average number of courses rose from 0·7 to 2·0. On the other hand those with 50 or more private patients were comparatively unlikely to have been on a course, 36 per cent against 60 per cent of those with none or less than 50.

Course attenders more often enjoyed their work, regarded fewer consultations as trivial, were more concerned about cervical smear tests and more often expressed a special interest in psychiatry than other doctors. These findings are shown in Table 60.

Obviously it is not possible to say how far some of these views have been influenced by attendance at courses or how far doctors take courses because of their prior attitudes and interests. Almost certainly both causes contribute to these associations. The relationship between course attendance and belief in the usefulness of cervical smear tests is shown also by the variation in attitudes to these tests with their most important way of keeping up-to-date. The proportion believing that middle-aged women should have such tests regularly ranged from 86 per cent of those whose most important way of keeping up-to-date was courses, to 65 per cent of those who found informal discussions with other doctors the most helpful. Informal discussions may harden resistance to change. Among those who found informal discussions the most helpful way of keeping up-to-date, there was no difference between those who had and those who had not attended any courses in their views on cervical smear tests. Among other doctors the proportion approving of them rose from 72 per cent of those who had not been on any course to 82 per cent of those who had. This last proportion compares with 64 per cent of those attending courses but regarding informal discussions the most useful way of keeping up-to-date.

TABLE 60 *Association between attendance at courses and various opinions and attitudes*

	Proportion attending any courses	Average number of courses	Number of doctors
Enjoys work as general practitioner:			
Very much	64%	1·8	212
Moderately	55%	1·5	149
Not very much or not at all	31%	1·0	39
Estimated proportion of surgery consultations felt to be trivial. etc.:			
Less than 10%	67%	1·8	64
10% < 25%	58%	1·6	117
25% < 50%	58%	1·6	120
50% < 75%	54%	1·4	76
75% or more	34%	1·1	29
Views on cervical smear tests:			
Middle-aged women should have, and appropriate for G.P. to collect	63%	1·7	190
Middle-aged women should have, but *not* appropriate for G.P. to collect	53%	1·5	108
Does not think middle-aged women should have regular tests	48%	1·3	97
Regards it as appropriate to be consulted about children getting into trouble or family discord:			
Yes	59%	1·7	338
No	45%	1·0	53
Special interest:			
Psychiatry	72%	2·4	43
Other	56%	1·5	288
None	50%	1·1	62

Is a doctor's course attendance related in any way to the characteristics and views of his patients? Apparently not. It did not seem to be associated with patients' social class, their views on general practitioners' prestige, their opinions about his premises, or whether they found him good about explaining things or listening to what they had to say. Neither did patients' views on whether or not they would consult their doctor about personal problems vary in relation to the courses he had attended. But it seemed as if the doctors who had been on five or more courses in the previous five years had a relatively high proportion of patients who had not been to see him in the previous twelve months: 43 per cent compared with 32 per cent of patients whose doctor had been on one, two, three or four courses and 28 per cent of those who had not been on any. Possibly doctors with a relatively high proportion of non-attenders can more easily find the time to go on courses.

Another characteristic related to attendance at courses was membership of the College of General Practitioners: members had been on an average of 2·8 courses in the previous five years, non-members on 1·2. Further differences between members and non-members are considered next.

Membership of the College of General Practitioners

Twenty-one per cent of the doctors who replied to the postal questionnaire were members or associates of the College.[5] Once again[6] it seemed that College members were a fairly representative sample of general practitioners in relation to the number of patients they looked after, the type of practice (single-handed, etc.) they worked in, hospital appointments, access to beds and the areas where they worked.

The proportion of College members was highest, 27 per cent, among those qualifying between 1945 and 1954, and lowest, 9 per cent, for those qualifying before 1925. Associated with this College members were rather better qualified: the proportion of members was 12 per cent of those with licentiate qualifications

---

[5] The proportion among those who did not respond was lower, 13 per cent. Among all those approached it was 19 per cent. Information about membership was obtained from current lists of members supplied by the College.
[6] Cartwright, Ann, and Marshall, Rosalind, 'General Practice in 1963'.

only, 20 per cent of those with a university degree but no further qualifications, 25 per cent of those with an obstetric diploma and 26 per cent of those with other qualifications.

There was quite a lot of evidence that College members carried out a rather wider range of activities in their practices than non-members. The average 'procedure scores' in the two groups were 4·4 and 3·5 respectively; College members said they had direct access to an average of 3·4 out of the four diagnostic facilities asked about, non-members 2·9. Ninety-one per cent of members had had ten or more obstetric cases in the previous year, compared with 81 per cent of non-members. Sixty-four per cent of members against 43 per cent of non-members felt that middle-aged women should have regular cervical smear tests and that it was appropriate for general practitioners to collect the smears. And 80 per cent of members had been on a course in the last five years, 51 per cent of non-members.[7]

College members did not apparently enjoy their work as general practitioners any more than non-members, but more of them said they had a special interest in medicine – 92 per cent against 81 per cent. The difference in the interests of members and non-members was most marked for psychiatry: 21 per cent of members mentioned this, 8 per cent of non-members. This interest is possibly reflected in their attitudes to their patients and their views on the social aspects of their work. Members were more inclined to feel it was appropriate for them to be consulted about such things as children getting into trouble or family discord, they less often felt that patients demanded their rights rather than ask for help or advice and they did not feel so many of their surgery consultations were for trivial, unnecessary or inappropriate reasons. These differences are shown in Table 61.

Presumably related to these different attitudes, a rather higher proportion of the patients of College members felt that they personally might consult their doctor if they were worried about a personal problem (that was not a strictly medical one), 34 per cent compared with 27 per cent of people whose doctor was not a member of the College. There was no difference between the two groups who thought that a general practitioner was an appropriate person to discuss such things with. There was no other difference

---

[7] Clute, Kenneth F., op. cit. pp. 318–19, found that the quality of care by members and non-members did not differ significantly.

between these two groups of patients – their social class, views on general practitioners' prestige, their estimates of whether their doctor was good about explaining things, listening to what they had to say – except that patients of members were rather more critical of their doctors' waiting rooms: 26 per cent of them felt he

TABLE 61 *Membership of the College of General Practitioners and doctors' views*

	Members	Non-members
Feel it is appropriate to be consulted about such things as children getting into trouble or family discord:	%	%
Yes	95	84
No	5	16
Proportion of surgery consultations estimated to be for reasons they feel are trivial, unnecessary or inappropriate:	%	%
90% or more	–	2
75% < 90%	3	6
50% < 75%	11	21
25% < 50%	30	30
10% < 25%	31	28
Less than 10%	25	13
Agreement with statement: 'patients nowadays tend to demand their rights rather than ask for help or advice':	%	%
Strongly agree 2	17	23
1	31	36
0	8	16
1	28	17
Strongly disagree 2	16	8
NUMBER OF DOCTORS (= 100%)	90	332

was 'not so good' about having a pleasant, comfortable waiting room compared with 20 per cent of patients of non-members. It might be argued that members spend more on equipment and ancillary help and therefore can afford less on what they might feel are more marginal or more purely decorative features of their practice. And it has been shown that they do more procedures themselves and may therefore have somewhat greater expenses for equipment; but on this study, unlike the earlier one[8], there was no suggestion that they were more likely to employ ancillary help.

Qualifications

Twenty-two per cent of the general practitioners had licentiate qualifications only, 58 per cent had a university degree with or without licentiate qualifications but no further qualifications, 11 per cent had a diploma in obstetrics, 4 per cent had some other diploma, 4 per cent M.D.s[9] and 2 per cent specialist qualifications. (A few – less than 2 per cent – had more than one 'further qualification').

Doctors who qualified since the last war were less likely to have licentiate qualifications only than doctors who qualified before or during the war – 16 per cent compared with 25 per cent. This probably reflects a change in the policy of medical schools rather than in standards. More of the younger doctors had a diploma in obstetrics, 32 per cent of those who qualified in 1955 or later, 17 per cent of those qualifying between 1945 and 1954 and 4 per cent of the others. Associated with these age differences, doctors who were less well qualified were more likely to work on their own. The proportions working single-handed were 35 per cent of those with licentiate qualifications only, 22 per cent of those with a university degree but no further qualification, 17 per cent of those with a diploma in obstetrics, and 11 per cent of those with other additional qualifications. Another difference was that the better qualified doctors had more private patients. The proportions with 50 or more rose from 2 per cent of those with licentiate qualifications only to 18 per cent of those with further qualifications other than an obstetric diploma.

Patients' opinions of their doctors did not appear to be related to the doctors' qualifications in any way. Nor did the doctors' own views on the scope of their work vary appreciably.

---

[8] Cartwright and Marshall, op. cit.
[9] Doctors who qualified abroad were not included here.

Sex

Five per cent of the doctors in our sample were women. With such a small number – only 21 women doctors completed the question-naire – differences between men and women doctors would only show up if they were very large. The most obvious difference between them was in the proportion of their patients who were women – three-quarters for the women doctors and half for the men. Another difference was that the women doctors did rather more obstetrics than the men – 76 per cent of them had had 25 or more cases in the previous twelve months, compared with 53 per cent of the men. (Sixteen per cent of the women and 11 per cent of the men had a diploma in obstetrics). Men and women had the same score on the procedures they carried out in their own practices and there was no difference between them in the pro-portion reckoning to do vaginal examinations with a speculum. Comparatively few of the women doctors' patients had been to out-patients in the past twelve months – 14 per cent against 25 per cent of the men's. This may be partly because of the sex dis-tribution of their patients, or because male doctors refer their women patients to hospitals when they feel the need for a 'chaperone'.

Another difference, less expected, was in the proportion of patients who regarded their relationship with their doctor as friendly rather than businesslike – 42 per cent of men doctors' patients and 63 per cent of the women's – although there was no over-all difference between men and women patients in their response to this question.[10]

Conclusions

In this century of unprecedented scientific and technological advances, continuing education for professional people is ob-viously essential. This is generally recognized; many forms of education and stimulation are available, and doctors are en-couraged to make use of the opportunities. Nevertheless the impact of further education programmes appears to be somewhat

---

[10] The proportions saying their relationship with their doctor was friendly were 43 per cent of men with a male doctor, 59 per cent of men with a female doctor, 42 per cent of women with a male doctor and 64 per cent of women with a female doctor.

haphazard and there is a real danger that they fail to reach those in most need of education. Since just over two-fifths of the doctors had not been on any formal courses for general practitioners in the last five years, and only 9 per cent had averaged at least one a year or more in that time, there would appear to be ample room for extending this form of further education.

TABLE 62 *College membership, course attendance and various practices and attitudes*

	Not a member of the College of General Practitioners		Member of the College of General Practitioners	
	0 or 1 course in previous 5 years	*2 or more courses in previous 5 years*	*0 or 1 course in previous 5 years*	*2 or more courses in previous 5 years*
Average number of tests and X-rays has access to	2·8	3·0	3·3	3·4
Average score on procedures	3·3	4·0	4·6	4·4
Proportion feeling less than a quarter of surgery consultations trivial	40%	45%	48%	60%
Proportion disagreeing that patients demand their rights	21%	34%	40%	48%
Proportion feeling it appropriate to be consulted about family discord	82%	89%	97%	95%
Proportion with a special interest in psychiatry	8%	9%	10%	28%
Proportion enjoying their work as a general practitioner 'very much'	49%	58%	48%	65%
Proportion thinking middle-aged women should have regular cervical smear tests	42%	49%	70%	62%
NUMBER OF DOCTORS (= 100%)	228	92	31	57

Doctors who have been on such courses and those who are members of the College of General Practitioners differ from their colleagues in a number of ways which might suggest they are better general practitioners, though it is of course impossible to say what is cause and what effect. The two characteristics – attendance at courses and membership of the College – are themselves linked, but Table 62 suggests they are also independently related to a number of the variables discussed.

It is to be hoped that the influence of the College of General Practitioners will grow and its membership increase, and that the courses offered to general practitioners will develop in interest and scope and attract more people. The question raised by this study is whether present forms of further education are adequate for present needs.

XI

SOME VARIATIONS IN PATIENTS' ATTITUDES AND CARE

Throughout this report some variations between patients have been discussed in relation to their use of services, their attitudes and their doctors. This chapter brings these variations together and discusses the differences between men and women, between people of different ages and particularly the needs of older people, between people in different social classes and between those living in different types of area.

Men and women

Men and women differ in many ways in their attitudes to their doctors. One reason for this is probably that women know their general practitioner better than men. Although there was no difference in the length of time they had had their doctor 28 per cent of the women reckoned they had consulted him at least 50 times compared with 18 per cent of the men. Part of this difference arises because they were asked to include occasions when they consulted the doctor about their children, but women are also more likely to consult the doctor about themselves. Ten per cent of the men had consulted their doctor 10 or more times in the previous twelve months against 17 per cent of the women. Age and sex variations are shown in Table 63.

As expected, differences are most marked in the reproductive age groups. One interesting feature, which has been noted on another study of general practice,[1] is that men aged 55–64 have a relatively high proportion of consultations. It is in this age range that their mortality rates are increasing rapidly and show the greatest excess over those of women.

Probably because they see more of their doctor, a higher pro-portion of women, 70 per cent, thought their doctor would know

[1] Anderson, J. A. D., *A New Look at Social Medicine*, p. 35.

Some Variations in Patients' Attitudes and Care

TABLE 63   *Age, sex and frequency of consultation with general practitioner*

	Men						
	21–24	25–34	35–44	45–54	55–64	65–74	75 and over
	%	%	%	%	%	%	%
Number of consultations in previous 12 months:							
None	39	38	42	40	31	39	17
One	37	18	17	25	12	14	13
Two to four	20	31	27	20	24	26	40
Five to nine	2	10	6	5	10	12	10
Ten or more	2	3	8	10	23	9	20
NUMBER OF MEN (= 100%)	41	131	145	136	117	69	30

	Women						
	21–24	25–34	35–44	45–54	55–64	65–74	75 and over
	%	%	%	%	%	%	%
Number of consultations in previous 12 months:							
None	17	17	36	37	31	32	32
One	10	20	16	10	11	5	11
Two to four	43	29	30	26	29	18	15
Five to nine	17	17	8	12	11	23	15
Ten or more	13	17	10	15	18	22	27
NUMBER OF WOMEN (= 100%)	30	133	130	138	143	95	53

them by name if he met them in the street. Sixty-one per cent of the men thought this, but if the frequency of contact is held constant there is no difference between them.

More frequent contact with their general practitioner may explain why women seem to be more attached to him as a person and less willing to consult someone else. Fifty per cent of the men whose doctor worked with others said they knew their own doctor much better than others, compared with 59 per cent of the women. When asked whether, if faced with a choice, they would either see another doctor in the group straight away or wait about half an hour and see their own doctor which they would prefer to do, 45 per cent of the men but 60 per cent of the women said they would rather wait.[2] In addition women less often said they would 'not mind in the least' seeing another doctor if theirs was not available. Half the men said this compared with a third of the women, and whereas a quarter of the men felt there were some circumstances when it might be helpful to see another general practitioner rather than their own doctor, only a sixth of the women felt this. Presumably because they cared about it more, a higher proportion of the women than men with doctors working in groups said usually they knew before they went to the surgery whether their own doctor would be there – 65 per cent compared with 54 per cent of the men.

While women consult their general practitioner more frequently than men, it has already been shown that men are slightly more likely to attend hospital out-patient departments – 26 per cent of them had been in the previous year compared with 22 per cent of women. Whether this different pattern of use stems from convenience, inclination or different types of morbidity or whether their more frequent use of the hospital makes them more 'hospital oriented' than women it is not possible to say. But certainly on a number of issues men were more inclined towards the hospital and slightly less towards the general practitioner than women. More men than women said it was more convenient for them to go to the hospital out-patient department than to their own doctor, and more of them said that if they cut their leg while they were at home so that it needed stitching they would be more likely to go straight to hospital than to their own doctor. More men than women stressed the good attention they would receive at hospital, while of those who would go to their own doctor, men mentioned the convenience more than women did, and more women than men said they preferred going to their own doctor. When asked if they preferred a general practitioner who did a number of tests and investigations himself or one who sent people to hospital if they needed any investigation both men and women more often chose the first rather than the second but the men were more

[2] It might be argued that this simply reflects the low value women put on their own time, but they were no less likely to regard the time they were kept waiting as unreasonable. Neither was there any difference between men and women in their views on appointment systems.

Some Variations in Patients' Attitudes and Care

TABLE 64 *Sex and attitudes to hospitals versus general practitioners*

	Men	Women		Men	Women
	%	%		%	%
Which more convenient:			*Action if cut leg:*		
Hospital out-patient	10	6	Own doctor	25	37
Own doctor	80	85	Straight to hospital	65	54
No difference	10	9	Uncertain	10	9
			Reasons for going to own doctor:	%	%
			Ease of access	41	29
			Prefer to	7	16
			He can do it – he's qualified	13	10
Which prefers:	%	%	Don't like hospitals	2	4
Hospital out-patient	8	5	You can't go to hospital without going to doctor first	10	15
Own doctor	81	86			
Don't mind	11	9	Vague – no reason	29	31
			Reasons for going straight to hospital:	%	%
			Better or good attention	29	16
			Accessibility – hospital always open	49	48
			Doctor would send you there anyway	15	24
Prefer to have G.P. as at present or go straight to specialist:	%	%	Vague – no reason	15	18
			Prefers:	%	%
Prefer G.P.	82	87	G.P. who does tests and investigations himself	46	54
Prefer to go to specialist	16	11	One who sends to hospital if need investigation	40	31
No preference	3	2	Don't know	14	15

NUMBER OF PEOPLE
(= 100%) 672 725

evenly divided. These differences are given in Table 64 which also shows that while the great majority of people said they preferred to go to their own doctor than the hospital and would prefer to have general practitioners as at present rather than go straight to specialists, more men than women expressed the opposite points of view.

Men seem slightly less conservative and more prepared to think of different types of organization. Twenty-two per cent of them compared with 12 per cent of women said they would prefer to have an emergency service that they could get in touch with at night instead of going on as they did now. Men were also more likely to disapprove of private patients – 20 per cent of them expressed some disapproval compared with 12 per cent of women, while 4 per cent of the men and 8 per cent of the women expressed envy or approval.

But women's conservatism was not simply a question of always preferring existing arrangements. They do not believe as frequently as men in the advantages of a doctor working in partnership. Forty-three per cent of the men compared with 31 per cent of the women said they would prefer a doctor who worked in a partnership. Equal proportions, 27 per cent, preferred one working on his own and more women than men felt it did not matter. But men's relatively greater preference for a doctor working in a partnership existed for all sizes of their own doctor's present partnership, as can be seen from Table 65.

TABLE 65   *Sex, type of practice and preference for partnership*

	Proportion preferring partnerships	
	Men	Women
Doctor works:		
on own	19% (99)	11% (98)
with one other	42% (196)	33% (247)
with two others	52% (137)	34% (150)
with three others	59% (86)	43% (87)
with four or more	68% (37)	49% (39)

The figures in brackets are the numbers on which the percentages are based.

When asked whether their own doctor was more like an 'old-fashioned type' single-handed doctor or a more up-to-date one in a partnership, slightly more women than men said the first, although the difference might have occurred by chance. But asked which they preferred 43 per cent of men said the first and 56 per cent of women. If their own doctor was most like the first 'old fashioned' single-handed one 25 per cent of men and 13 per cent of the women would prefer the second; if he was more like the second in an up-to-date partnership 11 per cent of men and 18 per cent of women would prefer the first.

One reason for women's preference may be the greater importance they attach to having a doctor who is approachable and who listens. Men on the other hand more often mentioned 'straight-forwardness' as one of the qualities they appreciated about their general practitioner and they more often than women mentioned some aspect of his medical care (see Table 66). Men were also more critical of their doctor's surgery for not being well-equipped and up-to-date, 18 per cent of them said this against 12 per cent of the women.

TABLE 66 *Sex and some of general practitioners' qualities appreciated*

	Men	Women
	%	%
Listens, takes time, doesn't hurry you, has patience	12	18
Straight-forward, blunt, frank, talks 'man to man'	15	8
Approachable, 'homely', 'puts you at ease', 'you can talk to him'	14	22
Good with children	6	11
Some reference to medical care	71	64
NUMBER OF PATIENTS (= 100%)*	609	697

* The percentages add to more than 100 as several qualities might be mentioned.

If women seem to set rather more store on their personal relationship with their general practitioner and men on their efficiency and clinical competence, this is probably not because women do not regard the latter as important, but because they take it slightly more for granted.

Differences in their desires for a regular check-up have already been discussed. But if women were not so enthusiastic as men about the idea of regular check-ups they may be more prepared to try other preventive actions. When asked: 'If you were going on a journey and thought you might be travel-sick, do you think you would go to the doctor to get some pills to prevent it or would you buy them yourself from the chemist or don't you believe in taking pills for that sort of thing?', there was no difference between the sexes in the proportion who would go to the doctor but 66 per cent of the women compared with 54 per cent of the men said they would go to the chemist, and 31 per cent of the men and 17 per cent of the women that they did not believe in taking such pills. Possibly men felt the idea that they might be sea-sick reflected on their manhood, but in general women consume more medicines than men.[3]

Data about their action and predicted action on various conditions are summarized in Table 67. There was no difference between men and women in the average number of conditions they said they would consult their doctor about.

Obviously the evidence here is very slight, but there is much more information from the Survey of Sickness to support the contention that differences in consultation rates between men and women are explained by differences in perceived morbidity.

Table 68 shows the number of consultations per reported illness for various conditions. The only two for which women had appreciably more consultations per condition than the men were tuberculosis of the lungs and ulcers of the stomach and duodenum. Both these conditions were more prevalent among men than women. These data do not suggest that women are more dependent on their general practitioner than men – given their different morbidity pattern.

When asked whether they thought a general practitioner was a suitable person to talk to about family problems there was no difference between men and women in the proportion who said yes – 40 per cent – but men more often gave a categorical 'no' – 44 per cent compared with 37 per cent of the women, and women were more often uncertain. However, asked whether if they were

[3] Jefferys, Margot, Brotherston, J. H. F., and Cartwright, Ann, 'Consumption of Medicines on a Working-Class Housing Estate'.

TABLE 67 *Sex variations in prevalence, action and predicted action on various conditions*

| | Feeling tired | | Depression | | Difficulty sleeping | | Dandruff | | Loss of voice | | Boil on neck | |
	Men	Women	Men	Women	Men	Women	Men	Women	Men	Women	Men	Women
	%	%	%	%	%	%	%	%	%	%	%	%
Predicted action:												
Would consult G.P.	67	61	58	51	49	42	9	7	51	46	33	48
Would *not* consult G.P.	30	34	34	38	46	54	87	87	43	46	54	38
Uncertain	3	5	8	11	5	4	4	6	6	8	13	14
Had had condition in last 12 months	Not asked		5%	15%	11%	29%	16%	15%	5%	8%	4%	1%
Proportion with condition who had consulted doctor	Not asked		50%	50%	38%	42%	5%	8%	42%	35%	Numbers too small	

worried about a personal problem they thought they might discuss it with their doctor, a third of the women thought they might compared with a quarter of the men. This difference does not arise because women are less likely to have other people to discuss such problems with. They were more likely than men to say they might discuss such problems with relatives (other than husbands or wives) 42 per cent compared with 27 per cent of the

TABLE 68   *Consultations per reported illness for selected diagnoses. Data from the Survey of Sickness 1951. Adults 21–64**

	Men	Women
Tuberculosis of lungs	1·14	1·51
Psychoneurosis and mental disorders	·77	·75
Eye infections	·19	·19
Ear and mastoid	·22	·22
Rheumatism	·25	·21
Heart and arteries	·89	·60
Infections of veins	·33	·22
Colds and influenza	·39	·34
Sore throat	·72	·63
Other respiratory	·37	·36
Dental disorders	·03	·04
Ulcer of stomach and duodenum	·95	1·25
Other stomach	·19	·14
Other digestive	·24	·16
Disease of skin	·69	·60
Other defined illnesses	·57	·60
Ill-defined symptoms	·19	·17
Injuries	2·01	1·71
ALL CONDITIONS	·36	·30

* Logan, W. P. D., and Brooke, Eileen M., *The Survey of Sickness 1943–1952*, p. 52.

men, and just as likely to say they might discuss it with friends or neighbours. More men than women mentioned a solicitor or lawyer as a possible confidant, 8 per cent against 2 per cent.

Although the differences between men and women that have

been discussed in this section are 'significant' in that they are unlikely to have occurred by chance, most of them are not large. They seem to stem from four sources – first the higher morbidity and consequently greater use of doctors among women, second the slightly greater orientation of men towards the hospital, third the greater conservatism of women, and fourth the somewhat stronger emphasis women put on personal relationships.[4]

Age and the needs of older people

As people become older and more frail, their increasing ill-health may be aggravated by problems of isolation, unsatisfactory accommodation and inadequate means.[5] All these are likely to affect their relationship with their general practitioner. As greater morbidity and isolation increase their dependence on their doctor, difficulties about treatment may be accentuated by inappropriate housing and low incomes. The increase in consultation rates has already been noted, nevertheless a sizeable proportion even of those aged 75 or more have little or no contact with their doctor. As Table 63 showed (p. 187) 30 per cent of men and 43 per cent of women in this age range reported less than two consultations in the previous year.[6]

Age variations in the people with whom they might discuss a personal problem are given in Table 69. Older people of 65 and over were more likely than younger ones to discuss such problems with their doctor. Just over two-fifths of those aged 75 or more would talk their problems over with their children, and it was the oldest and youngest (21–24) who were most likely to discuss such things with relatives or friends.

---

[4] This is in line with the suggestion, made by Parsons and his colleagues, that the role of men in the family is 'instrumental', and that of women 'expressive'. See Parsons, Talcott and Bales, Robert F., *Family, Socialization and Interaction Process*, pp. 12–24.

[5] See Cole, Dorothy, and Utting, D., *The Economic Circumstances of Old People*; Townsend, Peter, and Wedderburn, Dorothy, *The Aged in the Welfare State*, and Tunstall, Jeremy, *Old and Alone*.

[6] One difficulty here is that people's memories may deteriorate with age and more consultations be forgotten. Data from the G.R.O. and College of General Practitioners study (Logan, W. P. D., and Cushion, A. A., op. cit.) are not subject to this error as the information was collected by the doctors. They found 42 per cent of men and 37 per cent of women over 65 with less than two consultations. Comparable figures from this study are 46 per cent of men, 39 per cent of women.

TABLE 69   *Age and the people with whom a personal problem might be discussed*

	Age						
	21–24	25–34	35–44	44–54	55–64	65–74	75 and over
Might discuss with general practioner*	19%	23%	24%	29%	28%	41%	37%
Friends or relatives:†	%	%	%	%	%	%	%
Parent(s)	57	35	20	6	–	–	–
Child(ren)	–	–	1	6	12	16	43
Brothers or sisters	12	8	11	11	17	9	14
Other relatives	9	9	5	6	7	5	5
Neighbours	–	1	–	3	1	3	1
Friends at work	7	7	8	5	2	–	–
Other friends	27	14	15	16	19	18	8
No friends or relatives	22	42	53	59	54	54	37
Other professional sources:‡	%	%	%	%	%	%	%
Minister	19	22	27	28	33	37	33
Health visitor or district nurse	6	7	6	2	6	4	4
Other social worker or agency	9	15	13	9	12	7	6
Lawyer/solicitor	3	3	3	6	5	8	3
Teachers	1	–	1	–	–	1	–
Others	–	4	7	6	6	4	1
Uncertain	1	5	3	5	4	3	6
No one at all (except husband or wife)	7%	13%	19%	17%	12%	8%	4%
NUMBER OF PATIENTS (= 100%)	68	253	265	264	249	156	72

* 'If you were worried about a personal problem that wasn't a strictly medical one do you think you might discuss it with your doctor?'
† 'Who (else) do you think you might discuss such problems with (apart from your husband/wife)?'
‡ 'Is there anyone such as a minister, health visitor or social worker you think you might ask about such things? Who?'

When older people live alone or are otherwise fairly isolated, what part does their general practitioner play in their lives? If anything people living alone saw rather less of their general practitioner than other older people and the ones who saw him most frequently were those living with people of a younger generation (Table 70). This is no doubt partly because as people get more frail and in need of care they are more likely to live with their children. Half the older people living with people of a younger generation were aged 75 or more compared with a quarter of those living on their own or just with their husband or wife. Those living with younger people were also less likely than others to say they could get to their doctor's surgery easily, and it seemed that more may be visited regularly by their general practitioner. These differences too are shown in Table 70.

TABLE 70 *Family circumstances of older people and contact with general practitioner*

	Lives alone	Lives with spouse only	Lives with people of a younger generation
Number of consultations in last 12 months:	%	%	%
None	40	28	28
One	16	10	7
Two to four	18	27	18
Five or more	26	35	47
Proportion of those with any consultations who were visited in own homes in previous 12 months	45%	48%	67%
	%	%	%
G.P. visits regularly	12	11	20
Can get to surgery easily	78	82	63
Cannot get to surgery easily:			
Would like G.P. to drop in	5*	–	5
Would not like G.P. to drop in	5	7	12
NUMBER OF PEOPLE AGED 65 OR MORE (= 100%)	45	93	66

* Tunstall in his study found that 4% of isolated old people would like to see more of their doctor. Op cit. p. 210.

When all the people aged 65 or more were asked whether their general practitioner visited them regularly, 13 per cent said he did. Seventy-six per cent said he did not but they could get to the surgery fairly easily, and the remaining 11 per cent were not visited and had some difficulty getting to the surgery. However, only a fifth of this last group felt they would like him to drop in about once a month, the others felt either that it was unnecessary or would be putting too great a strain on the doctors.

'I don't think there's any need. It's a busy life for him and I wouldn't like to trouble him when there's no need.'

'He comes whenever I ask him to. There's no need for regular visits.'

Some comments from the few who said they would appreciate regular visits were:

'It would be nice to have him drop in occasionally just to see everything is all right, but it takes him 20 minutes to get here. It sort of bucks me up after he's been.'

'I think they should for the age I am. Dr ———— used to call on me every month when I turned 85 and when these two new ones came they did for a while. Then one day Dr ———— said there was no need for him to come again – that I was all right. I say if he says he won't come again I won't ask him to. Last night I was awful sick with my ulcer. My grand-daughter says she'll get the doctor to me this morning, but I say, "No, Dr ———— says he won't come again so I won't have him." So she went up to the chemist and got some salts and paraffin. I don't like bothering no doctors.'

One of the problems, particularly for older people living alone, may be getting in touch with the doctor when they are ill. Only one in ten of them said it was difficult for them to do this,[7] but three-quarters relied on neighbours, 5 per cent on relatives living elsewhere, 5 per cent on a nearby public telephone and less than a fifth on their own phones. These arrangements must be a bit haphazard on occasions. Some comments here were:

[7] 'When you are ill is it at all difficult for you to get in touch with your doctor?' 'How do you do it?'

'It has been. If the neighbours aren't in we have to wait till they come back.'

'My neighbour's mother-in-law would get in touch with him, but I pray I won't be a trouble to anybody.'

Even if people living alone have rather less frequent contact with their doctor than other older people, it might still be that they are more likely to turn to him in emergencies, to use him as a confidant and to feel their relationship is fairly close. Evidence from this study does not support these propositions. Compared with other older people, those living on their own were no more likely than others to regard their general practitioner as a suitable person with whom to discuss personal problems, and they were less likely to say they might consult him about such things – 17 per cent compared with 41 per cent. There was no difference in the proportion who regarded their relationship with their doctor as friendly rather than businesslike, but those living alone were less likely to think their doctor would know them by name if he met them in the street, 69 per cent compared with 81 per cent of other older people.

But if older people living on their own did not appear to be unduly dependent on their general practitioner, several doctors expressed concern that they were unable to visit older, isolated people as much as they would like and a number felt that trained ancillary help could be used for routine visiting.

'I would like to see a health visitor and two midwives permanently attached to this practice. A health visitor would be very useful as we've got a lot of old patients. It's unnecessary for a doctor to visit the old, chronic sick. Old people don't really want to see a doctor – just someone to chat to. At the moment I have no contact at all with health visitors. One partner has – two health visitors are patients of his,' (working in 'purpose built' premises where eight doctors practise and have a total list of 25,000).

Doctors may feel they do not have the time to visit all the older people who need or would appreciate it, but how far are general practitioners aware of the needs of their older patients?

A recent study[8] of old people in three general practices in

[8] Williamson, J., *et al.*, 'Old People at Home. Their unreported needs.'

Edinburgh and district concluded that 'the amount of unmet need for general practitioner care was high', and that 'most old people do not report their complaints to their doctor until the condition is advanced'.

In the present study older people were asked whether they had any chronic trouble with their feet, their eyesight, their hearing or with backache. Chronic was 'defined' as being a continuing or recurrent condition that they first had at least three months before and which was still bothering them or they felt was likely to recur. They were asked whom they had consulted about any conditions they reported. Replies are shown in Table 71.

TABLE 71 *Chronic conditions reported by older people and advice sought for them*

	Feet	Eyesight	Hearing	Backache
Proportion having chronic trouble with	27%	19%	20%	30%
Proportion of those having chronic trouble who had consulted:	%	%	%	%
General practitioner	31	47	48	46
Chiropodist/Oculist	34	60	—	—
Other	10	26	20	15
No one	36	12	41	46
NUMBER OF PEOPLE AGED 65 OR MORE (=100%)		227		

The proportion of people reporting difficulties were somewhat smaller than those observed in the Edinburgh inquiry, in which older people were medically examined. Just over a third of the Edinburgh sample were found to have visual defects and a similar proportion some degree of deafness. A higher proportion, 43 per cent, had some form of disability associated with their feet. A fifth had trouble with eyesight, a similar proportion with hearing, just over a quarter with their feet and nearly a third with backache. Two-fifths reported no chronic trouble with any of these.

Their general practitioner was consulted by slightly less than half those suffering with their eyesight, hearing or from backache and less than a third of those with foot troubles. But people had alternative sources of help for their eye conditions – only 12 per cent with eyesight problems had not consulted anyone. Those with foot problems fall into three roughly equal groups, those seeing their doctor, those consulting a chiropodist and those not seeking any help. (Five per cent had consulted both their doctor and a chiropodist). Townsend[9] in his study found just under a third feeling a need for chiropody treatment, and of those, three-fifths were receiving some treatment either privately or through the National Health or welfare services.

When people have open access to a general practitioner, why do they not consult him about such conditions? One reason is that acceptance of pain and disability, prevalent at all ages, increases with age. 'I think it (backache) is natural at my age.' 'I'm not troubled about it (trouble with hearing). It's just getting old, isn't it?' In the latter instance the interviewer reported that the person was almost completely deaf. She had not seen anyone about it, yet her disability might of course be due just to wax in the ears. Another person reporting that she no longer had hearing difficulties said 'My G.P. syringed my ears last week. My hearing's much better now.'

Doubtless older people are aware of the increasing likelihood of becoming seriously ill. Paradoxically this may make them chary of taking their symptoms to the doctor when they first develop, and might be more responsive to treatment, as they are anxious to avoid consulting the doctor for supposedly trivial conditions.

'I use Sloane's liniment (for backache). I don't want to go to see my doctor unless I'm really ill.'

'I don't want to trouble the poor man.'

Sometimes people had sought advice but not found it helpful.

'Years ago I saw my doctor (about fibrositis). He sent me to a specialist who told me to come up when I was bad. But I can't go out then. The pain's too great. So I've got a lamp here and use that.'

'He told me (when consulted G.P. about foot trouble) "You can't have two forenoons in one day. When you're old you've got to put up with it".'

[9] Townsend, Peter, and Wedderburn, Dorothy, op. cit. p. 51.

Others recalled their treatment with gratitude.

'I used to have it (backache) very badly. It's quite better since I had a blood test and Vitamin B12' (from her general practitioner).

Those with foot conditions may not have thought their general practitioner an appropriate person to consult about them.

'It's only corns and bunions. I don't think there's a cure for them. I put a little plaster with holes on them so that I can walk, or I have a foot bath and scrape the hard skin. I'm all right.'

If there was no free chiropody service available in their area, or they were unaware of it, cost was sometimes a deterrent in seeking help from that source.

'I can't afford it. I do it myself.'

'I used to go to a chiropodist, but not since I left work.'

Townsend[10] found that three-fifths of the older people on his study who were having chiropody treatment paid for it privately.

For one reason and another many older people were suffering from chronic conditions which might have been alleviated by treatment but for which they had not sought any advice. It is likely that some others also had these conditions but did not report them at the interview, and of course people were only questioned about four conditions. The results of this study support the conclusion of the Edinburgh one that 'a general practitioner service based on the self-reporting of illness is likely to be seriously handicapped in meeting the needs of old people'. This reinforces the plea, made earlier in this report, that general practitioners should be encouraged to carry out regular systematic check-ups of their older patients.

But if they did this and identified further needs for care, more resources for meeting these needs would have to be mobilized. Several of the doctors were eloquently indignant about the inadequacy of present resources for older people.

'We look after our old people disgracefully – the worst in the world next to the Germans. The geriatric ward here needed a

[10] Townsend, Peter, and Wedderburn, Dorothy, op. cit. p. 51.

new lav. but they spend thousands on elaborate equipment for one or two interesting cases first. Politicians aren't interested. It's not a medical problem, it's a national one. In China an old person is revered. Here when you stop working you are looked on as a liability. "Can you get my father into hospital?"' (at interview).

Once again[11] 'trying to find hospital or other accommodation for the elderly and chronic sick' and the delays involved were seen as one of the frustrations of their work and was their most frequent criticism of the hospital service. The division of responsibility between local authorities and the hospital service gives opportunities for avoiding action and 'passing the buck'.

'There are too few beds and too many calls on time and resources. We went to the M.O.H. He sent us to the hospital. They told us we did not make enough fuss. So we made more fuss, and the hospital sent us back to the M.O.H.' (at interview).

This last general practitioner went on to complain about 'the alleged services that aren't – laundry, bedding collected, laundered and brought back – you just try and get hold of it.'

Certainly the general practitioner bears the brunt of the domiciliary service at present given to old people. Table 72 shows the various services used by older people in the previous twelve months.[12] And it was the general practitioner who often arranged for the district nurse to visit or instigated the home help services for the few recipients of these types of care. Another study[13] showed that the great majority of general practitioners, 81 per cent, thought the home-help service inadequate, so it does not seem surprising if one of their frustrations is 'the inadequate facilities for dealing with the social problems of geriatric patients'.

Other studies too[14] have suggested that the present basis on which services for the old are organized do not encourage a rational division between hospital, other institutional and domiciliary care. And a group of doctors and sociologists professionally

[11] See also Cartwright, Ann, *Human Relations and Hospital Care*, pp. 23–5.
[12] See also Tunstall, Jeremy, op. cit. p. 208.
[13] Cartwright, Ann, and Marshall, Rosalind, 'General Practice in 1963'.
[14] Edge, J. R., and Nelson, I. D. M., 'Survey of Arrangements for the Elderly in Barrow in Furness'.

TABLE 72   *Use of various services by older people in previous 12 months*

Had home help	4%
Visited by district nurse	3%
Other welfare services*	4%
Consulted general practitioner	68%
Visited by general practitioner	36%
Attended hospital out-patients	20%
NUMBER OF OLDER PEOPLE (= 100%)	229

* Six people, 3%, had been visited by a health visitor or welfare officer, and four, 2%, mentioned here visits from the National Assistance Board.

concerned with the care of the elderly recommended that public health nurses should be attached to groups of family doctors in a variety of areas 'to ascertain the medical and social needs of over-seventy-year-olds and to take the necessary action'. They also proposed that a new *duty* to care for infirm old people living in their homes should be placed upon welfare authorities by amendment of the National Assistance Acts, since permissive services are often inadequate.[15] They suggest that services should be co-ordinated at national level by a committee concerned with the health welfare and housing of old people, and that in addition each major local authority should set up a standing committee 'to identify local needs; to plan services; to relate them to each other; to define responsibilities; and to advise on the allocation of resources'.

Such steps should promote better co-operation between general practitioners and local authority services and stimulate the development of more adequate domiciliary care. The doubt is whether they would ensure adequate co-ordination with the hospital service.

The influence of social class

One of the hypotheses formulated when this project was conceived was that middle-class patients were receiving rather better

[15] Morris, J. N., and Warren, Michael, *et al*, *Our Old People: next steps in social policy.*

care from their doctors than working-class patients. It was expected that doctors of middle-class patients would be found to have smaller lists, to be better qualified, to carry out more procedures themselves, to attend more courses and to be more aware of the need for preventive care. At the same time it was thought that middle-class patients were likely to have higher expectations so that they might still be more critical of their doctor than working-class patients. One reason for putting forward this hypothesis was that in another earlier study[16] a number of differences between general practitioners in working- and middle-class areas had been found. Those in the former had larger lists, were less well qualified, and had less access to various hospital facilities. In addition, 14 per cent of the middle-class patients were visited by their general practitioner while they were in hospital, but only 4 per cent of the working-class patients had a visit from theirs.

Another reason for believing that working-class people have doctors with larger lists than middle-class patients was based on data for different areas published by the Ministry of Health. The Medical Research Council's Social Medicine Research Unit has correlated the proportion of people on doctors' lists of 3,000 or more in the 83 largest county boroughs with various social data about these districts. They found it correlated with education, social class, industrialization and wages in the ways which substantiate the hypothesis that working-class people are more often on large lists. These correlations are rather crude in that they are related to large county boroughs, and cannot take into account any variation within these broad areas. It might be thought that within large towns there would also be a tendency for doctors in middle-class areas to have smaller lists than those in working-class areas.

If this were so the relationship between the social class of individuals and the size of their doctor's list would be closer than that observed between social characteristics of towns and the average size of doctor's list in those towns. But, in the present study, the size of their doctor's list did not differ significantly for middle- and working-class patients, although those in the professional class only[17] were rather more likely to be on small lists of

[16] Cartwright, Ann, op. cit. p. 191.
[17] See Appendix 8.

under 2,000 – 25 per cent of them compared with 13 per cent of people in other classes.

TABLE 73 *Areas and size of list*

Size of list (Ministry of Health data)	Middle class urban			Working-class urban			Mixed urban		Partly-urban			Rural
	Newcastle North	*Wandsworth Streatham*	*Kingston*	*Sheffield Hillsborough*	*Ashton-under-Lyne*	*Bristol South-East*	*Luton*	*Southampton Test*	*Nantwich*	*Worcester*	*Conway*	*Cambridgeshire*
	%	%	%	%	%	%	%	%	%	%	%	%
Under 1,500	16	25	15	4	4	19	6	18	16	9	19	7
1,500–1,999	6	1	3	4	8	7	3	4	8	12	19	20
2,000–2,499	11	10	22	12	10	7	6	15	17	15	15	19
2,500–2,999	32	10	13	31	14	15	9	25	30	15	13	15
3,000 or more	35	54	47	49	64	52	76	38	29	49	34	39
Proportion of middle-class patients on lists of 3,000	24%	61%	41%	39%	55%	53%	86%	46%	40%	38%	37%	46%
Proportion of working-class patients on lists of 3,000	44%	41%	55%	52%	65%	51%	72%	36%	24%	57%	29%	33%
NUMBER OF PATIENTS	99	89	101	118	106	123	117	107	121	116	112	122

Neither was there any straightforward relationship between list sizes and social characteristics of the areas as shown in Table 73. More patients in the partly rural and rural areas were on small lists of under 2,000. In the urban areas population expansion between 1951 and 1961 appeared to be positively correlated with the proportion of patients on lists of 3,000 or more ($r = $ o·67, $p = $ o·o5). Thus at one end of the scale in Luton, a town which *expanded* by 19·2 per cent between 1951 and 1961, three-quarters of the patients were on lists of 3,000 or more, while at the other end only one-fifth of patients in Newcastle North were on such large lists, Newcastle's population having *declined* by 7·6 per cent during that period. This difference is rather similar to the variation in hospitalization rates found on an earlier study.[18] Areas which are furthest away from this regression line are Ashton-under-Lyne, a working-class area in the north, with a high proportion of patients on large lists in spite of a declining population, and Southampton, a more mixed area in the south, with an expanding population but relatively few patients on large lists. Unfortunately the number of areas included in the present study is too small to make multiple regression analysis feasible. But it is clear from the bottom two rows of Table 73 that there is within areas no consistent pattern of working-class people being on larger lists than middle-class. However, it has already been shown in an earlier section that, when the frequency of consultation was taken into account, doctors in working-class areas had greater work-loads than doctors in the middle-class ones. It has also been shown that professional people were comparatively likely, probably because of their greater mobility, to have doctors who qualified since 1945. In addition, middle-class people were comparatively likely to have doctors with hospital appointments – 27 per cent compared with 21 per cent. There was no difference, however, in the proportion whose doctors had access to hospital beds or other facilities, in the number of procedures the doctors carried out in their own practices, nor in their membership of the College of General Practitioners, their views on preventive care, or their enjoyment of general practice.

Patients' reactions to their doctors and their opinions of them also varied surprisingly little with social class. When asked what they appreciated about their doctor, if anything professional people put more emphasis on his medical or professional qualities than did patients in other social classes. Seventy-seven per cent of the professional group mentioned his skills in this field compared with 67 per cent of the other group, but this difference could have occurred by chance. Their descriptions of the personality

[18] Cartwright, Ann, op. cit. p. 245.

characteristics of their doctor that they appreciated – his willingness to listen, to explain things, to give them confidence, his
approachability, his straightforwardness – did not vary to any
significant extent with social class.

When they were asked whether there were any other qualities a
general practitioner ought to have but theirs had not, the middle-
class patients emerged as more critical than the working-class ones.
Thirty-five per cent of the former mentioned something here,
compared with 23 per cent of the latter, and within the working
class the proportion fell from 24 per cent of the skilled manual
group to 16 per cent of the unskilled.

TABLE 74 *Social class trends in criticisms of general practitioners*

	Patient's social class					
	I Profes- sional	II Inter- mediate	III Skilled non- manual	III Skilled manual	IV Semi- skilled	V Un- skilled
Proportion feeling their G.P. 'not so good' about:						
Having a well equipped, up-to-date surgery	20%	16%	17%	16%	13%	10%
Having a pleasant, comfortable waiting room	34%	22%	18%	23%	20%	10%
Explaining things to them fully	18%	15%	17%	14%	12%	6%
NUMBER OF PATIENTS (= 100%)	55	237	158	508	233	79

Patients were asked whether they thought their general practitioner was 'good' or 'not so good' about a number of things.
There were no appreciable differences between middle-class and
working-class patients in the proportions feeling their doctor was
not so good in several spheres, but there was some evidence of a
trend – with professional people being the most critical and unskilled people the least critical over the doctor having a well

equipped, up-to-date surgery, his having a pleasant comfortable waiting room and explaining things to them fully (see Table 74).

Over three other things – sending people to hospital as soon as necessary, not keeping people waiting long in his surgery, and not sending people to hospital unless necessary – there was also a trend with professional people being the least likely and unskilled the most likely to describe their doctor as good. But these trends arose not because professional people more often said their doctor was not so good but because they more often said they did not know or were uncertain. Unskilled people on the other hand seemed more prepared to give their doctor the benefit of any doubt: if they did not know, they apparently assumed he was good (see Table 75). There was no social class variation in patients' views about their general practitioner's willingness to visit when asked, to examine people carefully and thoroughly, to take his time and not hurry them and to listen to what they say.

When asked whether they would consult their doctor about various conditions if they had them, working-class people said they would consult him about an average of 2·7 conditions – out of six – middle-class about 2·4. The difference between them was most pronounced for 'difficulty in sleeping at nights for about a week' which varied from 50 per cent of working-class people to 38 per cent of middle-class, and 'a constant feeling of depression for about three weeks' which was 58 per cent and 47 per cent. It may be that working-class people are more likely to consult their doctor about problems that might not be thought of as strictly medical. There was no difference between middle and working-class people in the proportion who thought a general practitioner a suitable person to talk to about family problems, but more working-class people thought they might discuss a personal problem with their doctor, 32 per cent compared with 22 per cent of middle-class people.

For the most part, this survey suggests that the differences between middle- and working-class patients' perceptions of their doctors' skills and their relationships with him are relatively small. Professional patients were, if anything, more likely to mention their doctors' professional competence as one of the qualities they appreciated but this seems to be because they did not take it for granted as people in other social classes seemed more inclined to do. In addition, there were few differences between the practices

TABLE 75 *Further social class trends in opinions about their general practitioner*

	I Profes- sional	II Inter- mediate	III Skilled non- manual	III Skilled manual	IV Semi- skilled	V Un- skilled
			Patient's social class			
Sends people to hospital as soon as necessary:	%	%	%	%	%	%
Good	45	72	63	70	78	80
Not so good	4	1	4	4	2	1
Uncertain, don't know	51	27	33	26	20	19
Does not keep patients waiting long in surgery:	%	%	%	%	%	%
Good	54	63	67	69	76	78
Not so good	13	16	15	14	13	8
Uncertain, don't know	33	21	18	17	11	14
Does not send people to hospital unless it is necessary:	%	%	%	%	%	%
Good	49	64	62	66	66	70
Not so good	4	1	2	1	1	1
Uncertain, don't know	47	35	37	33	33	29
NUMBER OF PATIENTS (= 100%)	55	237	158	508	233	79

and habits of the doctors of middle-class and working-class patients,[19] but because of the different consultation rates doctors in working-class areas had a greater work load and may therefore have been more hurried. Although there is some evidence that professional people had slightly 'better' doctors in a number of ways, they were the most critical group of patients, but even so few of them were at all severely critical of their doctor and most expressed a great deal of appreciation.

The initial hypothesis – that middle-class patients would be

[19] Obviously nearly all doctors will have both middle and working-class patients but, mainly because of class concentrations in areas, the proportions are likely to vary widely and it might be thought that the practices and attitudes of doctors in working-class areas with nearly all working-class patients would differ from those in more middle-class areas.

receiving rather better care from their doctor but would tend to be more critical of him – would now be modified to cover just professional patients rather than all middle-class ones. But in view of the conflicting data from other sources and the few areas included in this survey, this conclusion is obviously tentative. Social class differences are likely to be related to differences between the areas and these are now looked at in more detail.

Differences between areas

The twelve study areas are described in Appendix 1. This section is mainly concerned with two attributes of these areas: their urban or rural nature,[20] and whether they are in the north or the south of England and Wales.

Doctors in rural areas tended to look after rather fewer patients than those in urban areas. Fifty-five per cent of them looked after less than 2,500 or more patients compared with 39 per cent of those in urban areas. They seemed less able to make arrangements with other doctors for covering night calls or weekends on a rota. Thirty-eight per cent of them were on call for more than half their weekends compared with 16 per cent of those in urban areas, and 33 per cent were on call every night against 15 per cent. In spite of this, there was no difference between them in the amount they enjoyed their work but other things related to enjoyment varied between the two groups in ways which 'favoured' those in rural areas. They carried out more procedures – their average score was 4·8 compared with 3·5 for those in urban areas. There was no difference between them on hospital appointments, access to hospital beds, number of diagnostic facilities they had access to, courses attended or number of obstetric cases. But they varied in their estimates of the proportion of surgery consultations they felt to be trivial, unnecessary or inappropriate. Thirty-six per cent of doctors in rural areas felt a quarter or more fell in this category, 60 per cent of urban doctors. At the same time, they did not differ in their views on patients demanding their rights, or on the appropriateness of being consulted about family problems, or on the desirability of cervical smear tests.

[20] Patients were classified simply by whether they were living in rural districts or other urban-administrative districts; doctors by the type of area in which the first patient who told us about the doctor was living.

The difference in their views on 'trivialities' did not seem to be explained by any observed variation in their patients' behaviour. People in urban and rural areas did not apparently differ in the frequency with which they consulted their doctor, in the proportion of home visits, nor in their views about whether they would consult a doctor about various things, including personal problems that were not strictly medical except that those in rural areas were *more* likely to go to their own doctor rather than straight to hospital if they cut their leg and it needed stitching. Rather more of those in rural areas had had the same doctor for five or more years – 77 per cent compared with 67 per cent. Possibly associated with this, more of the rural patients felt their doctor would know them by name if he met them in the street – 79 per cent compared with 63 per cent. This also probably reflects the anonymity of urban compared with country areas.

Another way in which patients in urban and rural areas differed was in their preference for the two stereotypes of doctors they were asked to choose between. Nearly two-thirds of those in rural areas preferred the single-handed, relatively old-fashioned one, against less than half those in urban areas. This was no doubt largely because they felt their own doctor was more like this – 68 per cent compared with 47 per cent.

In a country so small and densely populated as England and Wales it is not surprising that there are relatively few differences between urban and rural areas, nor that, in the occasional differences that do emerge, people in the country are rather more conservative than those living in towns.

What of the differences between north and south? Of the eight purely urban areas in the study three are well to the north of the line between the Bristol Channel and the Wash – Newcastle, Sheffield and Ashton. The other five are in the south – Wandsworth, Kingston, Bristol, Luton and Southampton.

Predictably, a rather higher proportion of people in the south than in the north were middle-class – 40 per cent compared with 30 per cent, and more people in the north had lived in the same area for 20 years or more – 65 per cent against 49 per cent. Because of the differences in mobility that are related to class more people in the north had had the same doctor for at least ten years – 57 per cent compared with 43 per cent in the south. There was no difference between the two groups in the frequency with which they had seen their doctor in the last year nor in the proportion who had been to a hospital out-patient department. Neither was there any difference between them in the conditions they thought they would consult their doctor about – including personal problems.

These findings are rather different from the results of an analysis of incapacity for work made by the Ministry of Pensions and National Insurance.[21] They found both higher inception rates and higher numbers of days of incapacity in the north than in the south. But their study showed that two of the areas in our study had atypical characteristics: Bristol in the south had higher than average incapacity rates in their analysis whereas Sheffield in the north had lower than average rates.

On the present study a relatively high proportion of people in the south were registered with doctors who looked after less than 2,500 patients – 34 per cent compared with 27 per cent of those in the north – but in addition more of those in the south were with doctors who looked after 3,000 or more – 48 per cent compared with 38 per cent. In the north a comparatively high proportion, 35 per cent, were with doctors who had medium large numbers of 2,500–2,999. Only 18 per cent of people in the south were on 'lists' of that size.

Rather more doctors in the south worked in groups of four or more, 32 per cent against 22 per cent, and rather more of them had qualified since the last war – 48 per cent compared with 37 per cent. They did not differ appreciably in their attendance at courses or the procedures they carried out but those in the north were more in favour of cervical smear tests and regular check-ups on middle-aged people. Sixty-eight per cent of the doctors in the south thought middle-aged women should have regular cervical smear tests and 39 per cent that it would be appropriate for general practitioners to collect the smears. The comparable proportions in the north were 89 per cent and 57 per cent. Half the doctors in the south thought that ideally general practitioners should carry out (other) regular check-ups on middle-aged people, two-thirds of those in the north. This high level of concern about preventive care existed in each of the three areas in the north and was not explained by extreme differences in a single area. It was not

---

[21] Ministry of Pensions and National Insurance, *Report on an Enquiry into the Incidence of Incapacity for Work*, Part II.

reflected in the proportion of patients who said they had had some sort of check-up in the last two years – 45 per cent in the north, 53 per cent in the south.

At the same time doctors in the north were more inclined to feel that 'patients nowadays tend to demand their rights rather than ask for help and advice' – 69 per cent of them agreed with this statement compared with 51 per cent of the doctors in the south.[22]

Another indication that the relationship between patients and doctors is rather less mutually satisfying in the north than in the south came from the patients. In the north people more often preferred a general practitioner who sent them to hospital if they needed any tests or investigations – 44 per cent compared with 30 per cent in the south – and more of the people in the north said they would prefer to go straight to a specialist rather than have a general practitioner – 20 per cent against 11 per cent in the south.

Summary and conclusions

Women consult their doctor more often than men but this seems to be simply because they have, or see themselves as having, more illnesses. They are more appreciative of the personal aspects of the general practitioner service than men and less inclined to see advantages in hospital care.

This study adds to the accumulating evidence from other inquiries that there is a lot of disability among old people, some of which is preventable and some of which could be alleviated by suitable treatment. The gradual onset of many chronic conditions encourages the feeling among older people that such tribulations are inevitable at their age, and because there is no dramatic or even clear beginning to their symptoms they defer, or perhaps do not even consider, seeking help and advice. An earlier chapter showed that preventive care for adults is infrequent and haphazard, and almost non-existent for elderly people whose need is probably

[22] This difference was not explained by the different medical schools of the doctors. Doctors who qualified in the north were just as likely as others to feel their patients were demanding, and although too few doctors who qualified in the north practised in the south and vice versa to make comparisons possible for these groups, when those who qualified in Scotland are considered 73 per cent of those who practised in the north agreed that patients tended to demand their rights, 44 per cent of those who practised in the south.

greatest. If general practitioners gave elderly people preventive care and regular check-ups this would almost certainly be more acceptable to them than a service based on hospitals or clinics. But at the moment a few local authorities are fulfilling their traditional role of initiating services for unmet needs. For example the London Borough of Richmond-upon-Thames runs 'A Clinic for Preventive Medicine for Older People'.[23] If the general practitioner continues to be inactive in this field it is to be hoped that more local authorities will take on this role, but from several points of view it would appear preferable to stimulate and encourage general practitioners, possibly in collaboration with the local authorities, to take on this vital task.

Turning to differences in social class, the main observations from this study were:

(i) Consultation rates were higher among the working- than the middle-class and among the unskilled manual workers than among the skilled. The differences were reduced but not eliminated when age was taken into account.

data?

(ii) Consultation rates were higher when the doctor's list size was small.

(iii) There was no relationship between doctors' list size and patients' social class.

The first two observations are supported by data from other sources, the third is not. Yet the combination of the first two might lead one to expect that working-class people would have doctors with relatively small lists. That they do not shows that doctors with mainly working-class patients have relatively heavy work loads.

[23] See Maddison, John, 'Maintaining the Health of Older People'.

XII

IN CONCLUSION

If a plebiscite was held on whether patients wished to retain the general practitioner service or to change to a system in which front-line care was based on specialists and hospitals, there is little doubt that the result would be overwhelmingly in favour of the present arrangement. But behind the satisfaction of most patients there lies an uncritical acceptance and lack of discrimination which is conducive to stagnation and apathy. At the same time the data from the general practitioners themselves suggest that general practice has in a number of ways failed to adapt to new scientific and medical techniques and the social conditions of a National Health Service.

In attempting to put the points of view of both patients and doctors in perspective, this concluding chapter ventures beyond the interpretation of data from the present study and draws upon material from other sources to make suggestions about innovations.

Present achievements

Most people in this country have a general practitioner they have known for some time, who is accessible, comes to their homes when needed, cares for other members of the family, and gives them what might be described as a semi-personal service. Few people are directly critical of their doctor, most have confidence in his decisions and care, and many have a friendly and satisfying relationship with him. These conclusions are based on such findings as:

Two-thirds of adults have had the same doctor for at least five years.

Four-fifths take less than 15 minutes to get to their doctor's surgery and over half normally walk all the way.

About a fifth of general practitioner consultations are in the patients' homes. Only 2 per cent of patients felt their doctor was 'not so good' about always visiting when asked; and the willingness of doctors to come to their homes was one of the main points mentioned spontaneously by patients as one of the things they appreciated about their doctor's care.

Eighty-five per cent of patients had a family doctor in that at least one other relative had the same doctor.

Two-thirds thought that if they met their doctor in the street he would know them by name.

Ninety-three per cent felt their doctor was good about listening to what they had to say, 88 per cent that he was good about taking his time and not hurrying them, 75 per cent that he was good about explaining things to them fully.

Twenty-eight per cent thought that, if they were worried about a personal problem not strictly medical, they might discuss it with their doctor.

These are the not inconsiderable achievements of general practice at the moment.

Limitations

The most obvious flaw in the present organization of the general practitioner service that emerges from this study is the uncertainty about the doctor's role. There have been many descriptive studies of the work undertaken in different practices, but the amount and type of work vary so much – and opinions about what should be done probably even more – that the Committee set up 'to advise on the field of work which it would be reasonable to expect the family doctor to undertake in the forseeable future'[1] made few specific recommendations about what procedures the doctor might be expected to carry out or what equipment he would need. This lack of job definition bedevils the relationship between general practice and hospital, hinders effective collaboration with local authority services and adversely affects the relationship between doctors and patients. Some detrimental

[1] Central Health Services Council, Standing Medical Advisory Committee, *The Field of Work of the Family Doctor.*

consequences of this failure to define the area, scope and limits of the general practitioners' work are:

Hospitals do not know what to expect of general practitioners. They resent it when some doctors refer patients for procedures they feel the doctors could undertake themselves. On other occasions hospitals retain patients unnecessarily, uncertain whether the general practitioner is prepared to accept responsibility once a diagnosis or treatment regime has been established. Both are prejudicial to mutual respect and understanding.

Friction and resentment between local health authorities and general practitioners are aggravated by overlapping and ill-defined responsibilities.[2] This is clearly demonstrated by the arrangements for child-care, which can also be confusing to mothers.

Patients suffer because responsibilities between the three branches of the National Health Service are not clear-cut. Old people particularly are likely to be bandied round from one part of the service to another, a responsibility each part is unable or unwilling to accept.

Some important facets of medical care are neglected because no one accepts responsibility for them. Changing patterns of disease and developments in medical science are making a medical service based simply on overt medical need obsolete and inefficient, yet general practitioners give little or no preventive care to their adult patients, and what service there is from other sources is haphazard and generally unco-ordinated.

Patients do not make the best use of the service when they are uncertain about its potentialities: they may accept disabilities that could be cured or alleviated by proper treatment. There is a considerable amount of treatable morbidity, among elderly people at any rate, which is never brought to the notice of general practitioners. Two-fifths of the elderly people on this study who had trouble with their hearing had never consulted anyone about it.

Some general practitioners feel insecure because they are

[2] See Warren, Michael D., and Cooper, Jane, 'Medical Officer of Health: The Job, the Man and the Career'.

uncertain what is expected of them; others are resentful because they regard their job as inappropriate. Over half the doctors estimated that a quarter or more of their surgery consultations were for reasons they felt to be trivial, inappropriate or unnecessary.

The tri-partite division of the National Health Service contributes to many of these difficulties but co-ordination under a single authority[3] would not necessarily resolve them. The complexity of modern medical care makes some division of responsibility inevitable and it is at these boundaries that precise and accepted definition of responsibility and the job to be done is most essential.

An inappropriate medical education and the consequent unrealistic expectations of many general practitioners may contribute to their disillusionment. Post-graduate vocational training can help to prevent the development of cynicism and isolation among general practitioners – the proportion feeling that half or more of their surgery consultations were trivial, unnecessary or inappropriate fell from 31 per cent of those who had not been on any courses in the last five years to 18 per cent of those who had been on five or more. But two-fifths of the doctors had not been on any course for general practitioners in the last five years. For a few there seems to be a barrier of incomprehension which prevents them from recognizing their patients' needs. Confronted by an apparently trivial condition, they feel resentful and fail to recognize the underlying need for help. This seems the most plausible explanation for the fact that general practitioners who feel a high proportion of their surgery consultations are trivial carry out relatively few procedures themselves, while some of their patients are apparently discouraged from coming to consult them again.

Another problem is the absence of quality controls, incentives and any career structure. Incentives which reward professional achievements and skills, controls on professional ineptitude, and a career structure in which promotion depends on the approbation of professional associates – these are three ways by which professions regulate and stimulate their members. The absence of any one of these might be tolerable but when none exist the

[3] As suggested by the 'Porritt Committee' in *A Review of the Medical Services in Great Britain*, p. 20.

profession is open to strain and abuse. Members become cynical and discouraged when they feel financial rewards are greatest for those who do least for their patients and there are no restraints on the misuse of hospital referral, no recognition for particular talents. Here again a clear definition of the scope and content of general practice would help curb inefficiency, could encourage the proper uses of scarce resources and might stimulate the profession to extend its frontiers in such a way that the service offered was more closely related to peoples' needs and demands.

Lack of capital investment during the first 18 years of the National Health Service has also contributed to the disenchantment of general practitioners. Minimal equipment with little or no ancillary help in dreary 'surgeries' has led many patients to regard them as inappropriate places for any tests and investigations, and some feel the general practitioner is now little more than a signpost to the hospital. Over a third of the patients on this study said they preferred a general practitioner who sent them to hospital if they needed any investigations to one who did a number of tests and investigations himself. From the doctor's viewpoint, the lack of equipment and facilities reduce the scope and interest of his job, while inadequate organization creates an inhibiting environment with little professional stimulation and uncertain leisure.

These flaws are all related. They also produce undesirable side-effects, notably a high emigration rate among practitioners,[4] low morale, concern about prestige and periodic but intense discontents about pay.

Some suggestions

Diagnosis indicates treatment – a clear definition of the role of the general practitioner, a revision of medical education so that it is more directly linked with the form and content of medical practice, a career structure with recognition and rewards for professional expertise, professional sanctions to safeguard against incompetence, and greater capital investment. The details of the prescription are harder to work out, and it may be even more difficult for the remedy to be accepted. But two basic ingredients seem to be a critical evaluation of the job to be done and experiments with different forms of organization. Both these are

[4] Abel-Smith, Brian, and Gales, Kathleen, *British Doctors at Home and Abroad.*

relatively long-term projects, although many studies and experiments are already under way. Immediate relief of some of the more distressing symptoms should be obtained once the proposals of the Review Body[5] are implemented.

It has been suggested elsewhere that general practice needs a Beeching type of inquiry.[6] But in the same way as a general transport study would have been more fitting than one restricted to the railways, so it is only by a study of all the health services that the most efficient and appropriate developments for general practice can be determined. Essentially, what we need to know is what general practice does at the moment, how this relates to the hospital and local authority services, what are the deficiencies of the service and how these can best be remedied with the resources of manpower, materials and money available. While the social aspects of the doctor's work have been investigated in this study and others[7] and there have been many descriptive studies of his work[8] there has been no critical and systematic appraisal in this country of the quality of his clinical care – apart from the early studies of Collings, Hadfield and Taylor[9] only one of which was based on anything approaching a representative sample.[10] Studies in America[11] and Canada[12] have tended to apply hospital standards of investigation to general practice without demonstrating the need for them. Methods of evaluating standards of care need to be developed which count as good care the *non*-investigation of symptoms which clear up quickly and spontaneously as well as the adequate investigation of conditions which need it. General practice should be assessed in terms of what it achieves and what it actually overlooks (not what it might be overlooking) rather

[5] Review Body on Doctors' and Dentists' Remuneration *Seventh Report*.
[6] Fry, John, 'General Practice Tomorrow'.
[7] Jefferys, Margot, *An Anatomy of Social Welfare Services*, pp. 117–31.
[8] See The College of General Practitioners, *Present State and Future Needs of General Practice*, with list of references.
[9] Collings, J. S., 'General Practice in England Today. A Reconnaissance'. Hadfield, S. J., 'A Field Study of General Practice 1951–2'. Taylor, S., *Good General Practice*·
[10] Hadfield's study was of a sample of B.M.A. members.
[11] Peterson, O. L., Andrews, L. P., Spain, R. S., and Greenberg, B. G., 'An Analytic Study of North Carolina General Practice, 1953–54'. In this study doctors were observed and awarded a possible total of 107 points; 30 for clinical history, 34 for physical examination, 26 for use of laboratory aids, 9 for therapy, 6 for preventive medicine, 2 for clinical records.
[12] Clute, K. F., *The General Practitioner*. In this study 15 per cent of points were for prevention and treatment (p. 271).

than by its conformity to standards of care developed for hospital patients. Such assessment would involve difficult equations of cost, manpower and delays in obtaining suitable treatment, but every general practitioner must make decisions of this sort several times a day. An analysis of present achievements and short-comings would help them to make their decisions on a more rational basis.

At the same time we need to know more about the relationship between general practitioners and hospital out-patient depart-ments under different conditions. Some studies have been made[13] and others are under way but the nature and methods of referral, means of communication and outcome need to be compared in different circumstances. When general practitioners have rotating hospital appointments, or there are special units attached to hospitals where general practitioners and hospital staff can meet both socially and professionally, does this stimulate co-operation and engender mutual understanding and respect? We need to assess the changes in referral and discharge habits, in the use of diagnostic facilities and in domiciliary consultations.

The relationship between general practice and local authority services has been looked at in a number of ways. The studies suggest that the present relationship is inefficient and unsatisfactory for all three participants – the public and the members of the two services. Jefferys[14] found many general practitioners ignorant of the local authority services available and the local health authority insufficiently aware of the obstacles to adequate co-operation. Rehin, Houghton and Martin[15] in their study of community mental services concluded that 'if doctors recognized the potential of social casework . . . it might be possible to deploy the social workers in the local authority more effectively'. A study of general practitioners[16] showed that many general practitioners are still hostile to health visitors, and contact and co-operation between them consequently often non-existent. More effective co-operation between health visitors, social workers and general practitioners

[13] Nuffield Provincial Hospitals Trust, *Casualty Services and their Setting. A Study on Medical Care*, and Scott, Richard, and Gilmore, M., 'The Edinburgh Hospitals.
[14] Jefferys, Margot, op. cit. pp. 128–31.
[15] Rehin, G. F., Houghton, H., and Martin, F. M., 'Mental Health Social Work in Hospitals and Local Authorities: A comparison of two work situations'.
[16] Cartwright, Ann, and Marshall, Rosalind, 'General Practice in 1963'.

might be achieved if they worked together in home-based health units as Jefferys has suggested.[17] This might also break down the relative isolation of some general practitioners. There have been a number of reports – some descriptive eulogies rather than critical assessments – of schemes in which health visitors and general practitioners work together apparently to their mutual satisfaction and the benefit of their clients. We need to know the problems of setting up such schemes in different types of area, the changes in the work undertaken by both doctors and nurses when they work together in this way, the modification in their outlook and use of other services, ways in which they reconcile their somewhat disparate aims, and, once again, the reactions of patients. An American study[18] found that patients tended to 'reject' the social-worker member of a family health maintenance team but of course the British reaction might be different.

Research into present organization is only a preliminary. It should lead to clear definitions of the content and scope of the work most appropriately undertaken by the different parts of the health services. It can also point the way to possible reforms, but these in turn must be evaluated. Experiments with different types of organization are needed.

Already we know enough about the shortcomings in present medical care services to suggest ways in which the organization might be changed. But it would be sensible to try out some of the changes on a small scale and evaluate them before introducing them generally. Examples of other possible changes which might be studied experimentally and have been discussed earlier in the book are check-ups for older people, a car service to reduce home visiting by general practitioners and the use of ancillary help for some home visiting. It was also suggested, in Chapter IV, that if machinery was available for dealing with doctors' grievances when they felt patients were making inappropriate demands, this might remove the sense of injustice from which some doctors suffer and so improve doctor-patient relationships. The hypothesis that it would seldom be necessary to use such machinery could

[17] Jefferys, Margot, op. cit. The ratio suggested was three general practitioners working with one health visitor, one state enrolled nurse and a part-time social worker (p. 312).
[18] See Silver, G. A., *Family Medical Care. A Report on the Family Health Maintenance Demonstration* and Freidson, Eliot, *Patients' Views of Medical Practice.*

also be tested by the introduction of such a scheme in a limited number of areas.

Another possibility is that more informed and discriminating public attitudes might be developed by improved education about health and health services. Pamphlets exhorting people to help their doctor probably make little impression. Certainly there has been no convincing demonstration of their efficacy. A more ambitious programme involving schools, radio and television could be mounted and the results assessed by before and after studies of the frequency and nature of calls to general practitioners, the extent of self-medication, and people's ability to distinguish between trivial and possibly serious symptoms.

Specialization within general practice has been advocated by McKeown as a 'means of reconciling the personal and intellectual interests of medicine'.[19] His suggestion involves four types of doctor – an obstetrician, paediatrician, adult physician and geriatric physician – working in groups, each functioning as a personal doctor, and each responsible for hospital as well as home care. Although family care did not emerge, on the present study, as an aspect of the existing service that was particularly valued or important its demise might cause concern among patients and doctors. Since its abolition is intended to improve the quality of care and the satisfactions of the practitioners, evaluation of these should obviously be built in to any assessment of such a scheme. And once again it would be important to consider hospital as well as general practitioner care. It might be that if the four 'specialist general practitioners' were responsible, as McKeown suggests, for much hospital care, clinical standards in general practice might improve while those in hospital deteriorate. This survey has indicated another danger – that communications between doctors and patients might deteriorate if general practitioners were more hospital-oriented.

Many of the changes listed are already being tried out in one or two areas. But it is clearly important that they should be assessed with proper critical detachment; that they should be, as far as possible, genuine experiments. Only too often changes are made and subsequent achievements observed without comparable measurements beforehand. There are some experiments which cannot be made within the existing structure of the National

[19] McKeown, T., *Medicine in Modern Society,* p. 177-8.

Health Service, and some changes already being tried out depend on a greater flexibility among local participants than is likely to be possible in other areas with more rigid adherents to conventional arrangements. Others involving statutory changes are different methods of payment for general practitioners, the introduction of a career structure of the type described by Crombie[20] and the integration of general practitioner, hospital and local authority services. It is essential to break through the rigid administrative barriers of the Health Service which inhibit the experiment and change vital to successful adaptation.

Another important area for experiment and change is medical education. A vocational training for general practice lasting at least five years from qualification has been proposed by the College of General Practitioners,[21] and continuing post-graduate courses over one and two years started at Winchester-Southampton and Canterbury.[22] Again these need critical evaluation and the great variety of alternative forms of post-graduate education should also be studied. Changes in the undergraduate curricula are also needed. More emphasis on the study of the medical needs of society and on the behavioural sciences should develop attitudes which would enable general practitioners to find greater satisfaction and challenge in their job.

If the different constituents of this prescription seem unacceptable, the combination may be more bland and palatable. If doctors work together from adequately equipped and staffed premises it is easier to envisage a career structure dependent on professional recognition. Clear definition of the job to be done should lead to more appropriate education and training at both undergraduate and post-graduate level. It should also help patients to make more appropriate use of the service. At the same time, experiments with different types of organization and their critical evaluation should create a stimulating atmosphere and encourage the development of more effective ways of organizing medical care.

[20] Crombie, D. L., 'A Career Structure for General Practitioners'.
[21] College of General Practitioners, *Special Vocational Training for General Practice*.
[22] Information about the Winchester–Southampton course obtained from George Swift and about the Canterbury one from J. Lipscomb.

STUDY AREAS

To choose the twelve study areas, all the 547 parliamentary constituencies in England and Wales were listed in two main groups: purely urban constituencies and those containing some rural districts. Each of these two groups was divided into eleven regions[1] and within each region the purely urban constituencies were listed in order of the proportion of jurors on the electoral register,[2] and the partly rural constituencies were listed in order of the proportion of electors living in rural districts. In order to choose constituencies with a probability proportional to the number of electors, the numbers of electors in each constituency were listed cumulatively, and the grand total divided by twelve to give the sampling interval. A number less than this was taken from a book of random numbers, and the constituencies in which this number and subsequent additions of the sampling interval fell were taken as the study areas.

Those chosen were Newcastle-upon-Tyne North, Sheffield Hillsborough, Ashton-under-Lyne, Bristol South-East, Wandsworth Streatham, Kingston-upon-Thames, Southampton Test, Nantwich, Cambridgeshire, Worcester, Conway, Luton. Details of these areas are shown in Table A. Eight were purely urban areas and these have been divided into three groups, relatively middle-class areas, working-class areas and a mixed or intermediate group.

[1] The ten standard regions used by the Registrar-General and the Greater London area.
[2] See Gray, P. G., Corlett, T., and Jones, P., *The Proportion of Jurors as an Index of the Economic Status of a District.*

Type of Area	Constituency and County	Proportion in rural districts	Proportion voting left 1964	Proportion of Jurors on Electoral list 1954	Population 1961	Population change 1951-1961	Survey data Proportion in social classes: I, II and III non-manual	IV and V	Proportion of G.P.s describing patients as mainly or nearly all working-class
Middle-class urban areas	Newcastle-upon-Tyne North, Northumberland	—	39%	7%		(−7·6%)	46%	16%	57%
	Wandsworth Streatham, London	—	32%	5%		(5·1%)	65%	11%	36%
	Kingston-upon-Thames, Surrey	—	30%	18%	83,033	−3·2%	50%	16%	10%
Working-class urban areas	Sheffield Hillsborough, Yorkshire W. Riding	—	62%	2%		(−3·6%)	20%	30%	76%
	Ashton-under-Lyne, Lancashire	—	55%	3%	85,391	(−4·5%)	27%	30%	93%
	Bristol South-East, Gloucestershire	—	60%	5%		(−1·3%)	27%	21%	75%
Mixed urban areas	Luton, Bedfordshire	—	50%	6%	131,583*	19·2%*	33%	23%	70%
	Southampton Test, Hampshire	—	50%	10%		(7·9%)	28%	31%	67%
Partly rural areas	Nantwich, Cheshire	37·8%	30%	3%	72,354*	3·4%*	36%	30%	45%
	Worcester, Worcestershire	15·6%	36%	7%	87,971	7·8%	33%	22%	53%
	Conway, Caernarvonshire	17·3%	41%	3%	65,309	2·7%	36%	32%	45%
Purely rural	Cambridgeshire	100·0%	34%	1%	94,857	11·1%	37%	27%	63%

Figures in brackets relate to the administrative area of which the constituency is part. Newcastle-upon-Tyne North is one of four, Wandsworth Streatham one of four, Sheffield Hillsborough one of six, Bristol South East one of two constituencies in the large administrative districts for which Census Data are available.

* These figures include parts of administrative districts not included in the constituency.

227

Middle-class urban areas

The three constituencies of this type are Newcastle-upon-Tyne North, in the Tyneside conurbation and Wandsworth Streatham and Kingston-upon-Thames, both part of the London conurbation. All three constituencies had Conservative majorities of 7,000 or more in the 1964 election and 46 per cent or more of the people in the sample were classified as middle-class.

The Royal Borough of Kingston-upon-Thames lies about twelve miles upstream from central London, on the eastern bank of the Thames as the river curves down from Kew to Hampton Court. The northern boundary is formed by Ham Common and Richmond Park and the river shapes the western limit, but to the east and south the suburbs of Kingston merge imperceptibly into those of Wimbledon, Surbiton and Esher. Kingston is believed to have originated as a Roman settlement and the town had strategic value for many centuries afterwards, originally because it was a convenient fording-point, later because it possessed one of the few bridges across the Thames. Many of the buildings are of historic interest and the Market Place has stalls selling everything from haddock to old lace every day of the week but Sunday. Kingston is still important as a trading centre today; the market and large department shops attracting many shoppers from the surrounding area. Around the beginning of this century it became popular as a residential area for prosperous Londoners, and although their mansions are not in themselves particularly beautiful, most of them are set in large tree-planted gardens or estates. There is a feeling of spaciousness about the Kingston suburbs and there seems little monotonous building of semi-detached houses. Canbury ward, just behind the commercial centre, is the only densely built-up district; here rows of little houses crowd against each other, their low straight lines broken only by the occasional bleak warehouse. There are few industries in the area, apart from small light engineering and plastics firms. A high proportion of the workers probably commute to London, but Kingston has retained its market town atmosphere and seems in no danger of becoming an anonymous suburb of London.

Wandsworth Streatham, on the other hand is unequivocally part of London. It too is mainly a residential area, with pleasant open spaces – in this instance Streatham Common – typical of London.

Newcastle North also has a large open common – the Town Moor – which lies in the more prosperous part of the area between Jesmond and Westgate. In other parts of the constituency, Arthur's Hill and Elswick there are a number of back-to-back terrace houses built at the end of the 19th century. To one of our interviewers who had always lived in the South, Newcastle appeared: 'chaotic, grimy and ugly, in a bleak mountainous countryside'. The heavy industry, coal mining, shipbuilding and iron around the industrialized riverside are certainly a contrast to the more gentle landscapes of the South. But the study was done in the most prosperous quarter of the City – the only one of the four to return a Conservative member to parliament in 1964.

Working-class urban areas

Sheffield Hillsborough, Ashton-under-Lyne and Bristol South-East are all 'safe' Labour seats with majorities, in 1964, of over 4,000. Between 20 per cent and 27 per cent of the people interviewed in these areas were middle class.

Sheffield lies between the dales and moorlands of Yorkshire and the Peak district of Derbyshire. Its heavy industry, based mainly on steel, is concentrated in the centre of the city especially along the banks of the Don. One of the four wards in the study constituency covers part of the city centre with shops, offices, an area of large pre-war blocks of flats, a newly developed area and part of an industrial area along the banks of the Don. The other three wards include the original river valley developments of small houses and shops with few social amenities, also new housing estates on the outskirts which verge on to moorlands.

Ashton-under-Lyne is part of the great industrial belt of South-East Lancashire, six miles from Manchester. Adjoining towns of Droylsden and Mossley make up the parliamentary constituency. Droylsden is flat, smoky and thickly populated, Mossley lies in a valley of the Pennines and has more open spaces. The three towns were part of the cotton industry area and were badly hit by the depression in the 1920s. People there recall the bad old days of unemployment.

By contrast *Bristol*, in the South-West, with its diverse industries and commerce, was largely protected from long or heavy unemployment. The south-eastern constituency, where the study was done, extends from older wards near to the city with their mixture of old shabby houses and new blocks of flats, to new estates just north of the Somerset downs. Although many people commute to the centre of town to work several large firms have established branches in the district and the area is included in the future development plans for Bristol.

Urban areas of mixed or intermediate class

Luton and Southampton Test are marginal constituencies. In 1964 Labour had a majority of 723 in Luton and the Conservatives one of 348 in Southampton. The proportions of middle-class people on the survey were 33 per cent and 28 per cent respectively.

Luton is a town of 132,000, which lies in a fold of hills 30 miles from London and linked to it by main line railway and the M.1 motorway. Since the seventeenth century, when the first straw-plaiters came from Lorraine, Luton has been a centre for the hat making industry. It is better known today as the home of Vauxhall Motors, which employs 19,000 people at its Luton factory, and is reputedly known as the 'turnip patch' because of its lack of industrial disputes. Although Vauxhall is by far the biggest source of employment in Luton, there are a number of other engineering companies as well as Laporte chemicals and a flourishing aircraft industry. Vauxhall estimates that 75 per cent of its employees are immigrants to Luton and there has been a continuing rapid growth of population for many years. Between 1951 and 1961 it expanded by 19·1 per cent; it is an 'overspill' town for London. The town centre has barely kept up with the growth of the population – the main streets look more characteristic of a town half its size, and are a jumble of traffic and shoppers. The two most imposing buildings are both very new ones, the College of Technology and the Central Public Library. There is a great deal of new housing on the outskirts of the town, both council estates and privately built.

In *Southampton* – 'the gateway to England' – the survey constituency covered the Royal pier, part of the dock area and the city centre. The bombed area and slum clearance has now made way for many new blocks of flats – yellow and grey brick boxes with balconies and a touch of orange, set amongst grass and flowering shrubs. There are many reminders of the sea and the docks. The scarlet funnel of a liner and rows of cranes rise black against the sky at the end of a side street. We had a number of stewards amongst our informants, one stewardess, two riggers, a tally clerk with Union Castle, a boilermaker and the widow of a berthing officer. Merchant seamen away at sea increased our failure rate here. We had stevedores and men who worked in the Pirelli General Cable Works.

Their homes were in Georgian terraces which recalled the days when Southampton was a fashionable spa and Jane Austen danced at the Assembly Rooms, big Victorian houses, prosperous surburban houses, and on the large inter-war council estate at Flowerland. On the outer margin there is a post-war housing estate, and the low trim flat-roofed brick and glass factories of the Millbrook Industrial Estate face the pleasant well-placed new blocks of flats, the 20-storey tower and the big new secondary school of the Millbrook Housing Estate.

Partly-rural areas

The three areas – Nantwich in Cheshire, Worcester, and Conway in North Wales – all returned Conservative members of parliament in 1964, with majorities of between 3,000 and 7,400. But in partly-rural areas this is not so indicative of affluence and high economic status as it is in towns. Between 33 per cent and 36 per cent of the people on the survey in these areas were classified as middle-class, and between 3 per cent and 7 per cent of people on the electoral register were jurors. In these respects the areas are more like the intermediate urban areas. Less than a fifth of the people in both Conway and Worcester live in rural districts, two-fifths in Nantwich.

Worcester constituency covers Worcester C.B., Droitwich M.B. and the rural district of Droitwich. Worcester city centres on a much restored cathedral, the cricket field and a single bridge over the Severn from which each day at peak hours the traffic blocks spread back along every road right through the town. A considerable area in the city centre is in the process of demolition and redevelopment, and the usual ring of housing estates are spreading on the edge. With its livestock markets, Worcester is the main market and shopping centre of a large agricultural area specializing in soft and hard fruit and hop growing, market gardening, pasture, largely dairy and some arable farming. The traditional industries of the town are gloving, printing and the manufacture of sauce (Lea & Perrins) and porcelain (The Worcester Royal Porcelain Co. Ltd.). Nowadays the main industry is engineering, the manufacture of machine tools, underground conveyors and valves (James Archdale & Co. and H. H. Ward & Co.). Droitwich, with a population of 8,100, is a spa town, whose salt springs provide baths for the treatment of rheumatism and the rehabilitation of paralytic patients. It has the large expensive hotels and the recreation facilities typical of a watering place. There are a few light industries in the north of the town and it is scheduled to receive in the near future some of the Birmingham overspill, but the official county guide states that Droitwich 'has no intention of becoming an industrial townlet or dormitory town, preferring to be its unique self with its unique service to the community'. Droitwich Rural District, of 50,437 acres and 22 parishes, is almost entirely agricultural, primarily devoted to fruit growing and pasture with some arable farming.

The parliamentary constituency of *Conway* covers the municipal boroughs of Conway and Bangor, the urban districts of Bethesda, Betws-y-coed, Llandudno, Llanfairfechan and Penmaenmawr and the rural districts of Nant Conway and Ogwen. From the popular sea coast resorts with their day trippers from Manchester and Merseyside to lake Ogwen in the National Park of Snowdonia, the main industry is tourism.

Nantwich includes the urban districts of Middlewich, Winsford and Nantwich and the main parts of Tarvin and Nantwich rural district. The area is predominently agricultural, producing the famous Cheshire cheese as well as butter and milk. The old salt industry has now been superseded by the chemical industry, which is based on the production of salt and is one of Cheshire's most important industrial assets. At Winsford plans are being made for further industrial development as an overflow from Manchester. There are firms of constructional and agricultural engineers. Middlewich was an ancient market town but now no markets are held and salt and chemicals are the staple industries. In Nantwich the local industries are agriculture, tanning and the manufacture of textiles. Crewe, although not covered by the survey, provides industry for many people living in Nantwich rural district. Besides the railway industry, there is a Rolls Royce factory, also clothing industries, the manufacture of steel and cast iron rollers and a horse and cattle market.

Purely rural

The county of *Cambridgeshire*, excluding Cambridge itself, was the one entirely rural area in the sample. Like the partly rural areas it is a safe Conservative seat and has a low proportion of jurors. This is a mainly flat and unremarkable inland countryside – the guide books quickly pass it over to describe the fens of the Isle of Ely to the north, or the racing at Newmarket which is just outside the eastern boundary. The main part of the county is a plain of reclaimed fenland, fertile and well-farmed. It is ringed on the south by the low chalk slopes of the 'Hills' of Gog Magog, a greener, gently rolling countryside reaching into Essex and Hertfordshire. The people of Cambridgeshire live in villages; farming and market gardening are virtually the only industry, producing hard and soft fruit, as well as wheat, potatoes and sugar beet.

Designated, open and restricted areas

Another way in which districts can be classified is by whether they are 'designated' – that is more doctors are encouraged to move into them because list sizes are large – intermediate or restricted where there are certain restrictions on new doctors moving in because list sizes are low, and open areas where doctors are not restricted but there is no particular financial incentive.

The great majority of patients, 76 per cent, lived in open areas, 16 per cent in designated and 8 per cent in restricted or intermediate ones. All Luton is a designated area and most – nine-tenths – of the Ashton-under-Lyne constituency. None of the other study areas contained any designated parts. Just over half of the Conway area was restricted or intermediate, a quarter of the Newcastle constituency and small parts of Nantwich and Cambridgeshire, 10 per cent and 3 per cent respectively. All the other study areas – Wandsworth, Kingston, Southampton, Worcester, Bristol and Sheffield – were entirely open. The variation in the number of patients the doctors looked after is shown in Table B.

TABLE B *Type of area and number of patients*

Estimated number of N.H.S. patients doctors looked after	Type of area		
	Designated	Open	Intermediate or restricted
	%	%	%
Under 1,500	–	3	19
1,500–1,999	4	9	20
2,000–2,499	8	30	23
2,500–2,999	20	25	33
3,000 or more	68	33	5
NUMBER OF PATIENTS (= 100%)	168	797	79

The study areas thus ranged from Newcastle in the north to Southampton in the south, and from North Wales to East Anglia. It covered parts of three conurbations, mountain valleys, market towns, and seaside resorts. And the proportion of people whose doctors looked after 3,000 or more patients ranged from 76 per cent in Luton to 20 per cent in Newcastle North.

INTERVIEW SCHEDULES FOR PATIENTS

(a) The main questionaire

1. First of all can you tell me about the people in this household?

	Relationship to subject	Sex M F	Age group Under 15 / 15 < 65 / 65 +	Are you on the list of a N.H.S. doctor in this area – who you would go to if you needed a doctor? Yes ... 1 No 2	Same as subject	Partner of subject's doctor	other doctor	
A	SUBJECT	1 2		IF NO (2) COMPLETE BUFF SHEET				
B		1 2	3 4 5	IF YES (1) Who is he? RECORD NAME INI-	6	7	8	B
C		1 2	3 4 5	TIALS AND ADDRESS OF SUBJECT'S DOC-	6	7	8	C
D		1 2	3 4 5	TOR	6	7	8	D
E		1 2	3 4 5		6	7	8	E
F		1 2	3 4 5		6	7	8	F
G		1 2	3 4 5	Sex Male...Y Female...X	6	7	8	G
H		1 2	3 4 5	TO ALL What about the other people here? Does	6	7	8	H
I		1 2	3 4 5	(B) have the same doctor? etc.	6	7	8	I
J		1 2	3 4 5		6	7	8	J

2. CHECK:
   (i) So there are......of you in the household.
   (ii) And......of you are related.

   (iii) And (of those related to you): You all have the same doctor 1
   Some have different

doctors in the same part-
nership 2
Some have doctor in
different partnership 3
D.N.A. lives alone or
with no relatives .... Y
IF 2 or 3 Why do you have
different doctors?
COMMENTS:

CODE:
Husband/wife kept old doctor
after marriage 4
Doctor's list too full 5
Other 6

3. Do any (other) relatives not living
here have the same doctor as you?
Yes 7
No 8

IF YES (7) Who? (relationship to
subject)
Parent(s) 9
Sibling(s) (& children) ..... o
Parent(s)-in-law 1
Spouse's siblings (& children) 2
Other (specify)............. 3

4. Subject's marital status
Single 1
Married (living with spouse) 2
Widowed 3
Divorced 4
Separated 5

IF MARRIED (2) Did both you
and your husband/wife live in this
area (near enough to go to present
doctor) before you were married?
Yes 6
No 7

IF YES (6) AND HAVE THE
SAME DOCTOR
Did either of you change doctors
so that you would both have the
same one?
Yes both 8
Yes wife 9

Yes husband .... o
No (i.e. had same before).... 1

5. How long have you had this
particular doctor?
Less than a year............ 1
1 year < 2 years 2
2 years < 5 years 3
5 years < 10 years 4
10 years < 15 years 5
15 years + ... 6

THIS INFORMATION WAS:
Checked with medical card .. 7
Not checked with medical card 8

IF LESS THAN FIVE YEARS (1,
2 or 3)
(a) How many times have you
changed your doctor in the last
five years?
Once 1
Twice 2
Three or more 3
(b) Why did you change your doc-
tor (this last, most recent time)?
Subject moved 4
Doctor retired, moved, died.. 5
Dissatisfied with old doctor 6
Other (specify)

IF DISSATISFIED (6). What
made you dissatisfied? Anything
else?

IF CHANGED MORE THAN
ONCE (2 or 3 at (a) During the
last five years have you changed
your doctor because you were dissatisfied (on any other occasion)?
Yes 7
No 8

IF YES (7) What made you dissatisfied?

6. How did you choose or get your
present doctor? RECORD COM-
MENTS

CODE ALL MENTIONED

Met or known him before .. 6
Nearness/accessibility 7
Was spouse's doctor 8
Recommended 9
He took over from another
doctor .... o
Had since childhood 1
Wanted woman doctor...... 2
Other 3

IF RECOMMENDED
(i) Who recommended him?
SPECIFY:

CODE

Subject's relatives 2
Spouse's relatives 3
People at work 4
Other friends/neighbours.... 5
Other doctors 6
(ii) Do you remember why they
recommended him – what they
said about him? IF GOOD
DOCTOR – In what way? (Q)

IF TOOK OVER FROM AN-
OTHER DOCTOR
(i) How long have you been
going to this practice then?
Less than a year 1
1 year < 2 years 2
2 years < 5 years 3
5 years < 10 years 4
10 years < 15 years 5
15 years + ... 6
(ii) How did you choose or get the
previous doctor?
Met or known him before 6
Nearness/Accessibility .. 7
Was spouse's doctor 8
Recommendation 9
He took over from an-
other doctor .... o
Had since childhood 1
Wanted woman doctor .. 2
Other (specify) 3

7. Does your doctor work on his own
or does he work with another
doctor or doctors?
On his own definite 3
With others definite 4
Believes on own 5
Believes with others 6
Don't know 7

IF WITH OTHERS (4)
(a) How many other doctors are
there besides him? ....
(b) Do you know your own
doctor:
Much better than the
others 6
PROMPT A little better 7
No better 8
Less well.......... 9

IF NO BETTER OR LESS
WELL Is there another doctor in
the partnership who you really feel
you know best and who you
regard as your doctor – even
though you're not actually registered with him?
Yes 1
No 2

IF YES (1)
(a) Who is that?
(b) Well now when I talk about
your doctor I want you to think of
him.

8. Is your doctor the nearest one to
you?
Yes definitely 1
Others about same 2
No definitely 3
Don't know 4

IF YES (1) Are there any others
reasonably near?
Yes 5
No 6

9. How long does it take you to get to your doctor's surgery normally?

IF HE ALWAYS CALLS – How long does it take him?

Less than 5 minutes 1
5 < 15 minutes 2
15 < 30 minutes 3
30 minutes + ... 4

10. How do you normally get there?

CODE ONE ONLY

Walk all the way 5
Public transport........... 6
Private transport 7
He always calls 8

11. Do you know how long it would take you to get to the nearest general hospital?

Less than 15 minutes 1
15 < 30 minutes 2
30 < 45 minutes 3
45 < 1 hour 4
1 hour < 1½ hours 5
1½ hours < 2 hours 6
2 hours + ... 7
Don't know 9

12. Can you give some estimate of how many times you have *ever* consulted *your* G.P. – either for yourself or for your children (when you were there too)?

None 0
Once 1
2 < 5 2
5 < 10 3
10 < 20 4
20 < 50 5
50 + ... 6

13. And again just an estimate of how many times he has visited your home – when you were present?

None 0
1........................ 1
2 < 5 2
5 < 10 3
10 < 20 4
20 + ... 5

14. If you met your doctor in the street do you think he would know you by your name?

Yes 1
No 2
Don't know 3

IF NO OR DON'T KNOW (2 or 3) Do you think he would realize that you were a patient of his?

Yes 4
No 5
Don't know 6

15. Now just during the last 12 months that is since this time last year, how many times have you consulted, that is seen professionally your doctor – or his partners, assistant or locum.

Not at all 0
Once 1
2 < 5 2
5 < 10 3
10 + ... 4

IF CONSULTED AT ALL (1, 2, 3 or 4)

(a) During that time have you seen:

Own doctor only 5
Own doctor mainly 6
Partners/locum as much as own 7
Partners/locum mainly 8
Partners/locum only 9

(b) During that time has your doctor – or his partner, etc. – visited you in your home (for yourself)? How many times?

Not at all 0
Once 1
2 < 5 2
5 < 10 3
10 + ... 4

16. **TO ALL.** During that time have you got any advice over the phone from your doctor or partners?

Yes 1
No 2

IF YES (1)
(i) How many times? ....
(ii) On what sort of occasion do you find that helpful?

IF NOT BEEN VISITED IN LAST TWELVE MONTHS GO ON TO QUESTION 18

17. On the last most recent occasion a G.P. visited you here:
(a) What was it for?
(b) The first time he came – for that episode – who decided he should come?

Patient or relative asked him 1
Doctor decided – after surgery consultation 2
Doctor decided – after phone call 3

(c) How many times did he come – for that episode – altogether?

Once 1
Twice 2
3 < 5 3
5 + ... 4

IF MORE THAN ONCE After the first time, did he call on his own accord or did you – or your family – ask him to come again?

Came of own accord........ 5
Patient or relative asked..... 6
Other (specify)............

(d) Just supposing doctors did not visit people in their own homes what do you think you would have done during that episode?
(e) Would you have:

Got his advice on phone 7
Got advice by others calling at surgery 8
Gone to surgery self 9
Managed on own 0
Or what?

How would you have felt about that?

TO ALL

18. Have you consulted another doctor *privately* at all – during the last twelve months (EXCLUDE EXAMS FOR INSURANCE OR PRE-EMPLOYMENT)

Yes 3
No 4

IF YES (3)
(a) Why did you go privately rather than under the N.H.S.?
(b) How did you choose that doctor?
(c) How many times did you see him in the last 12 months?

Once 1
2 < 5 times............. 2
5 < 10 times............. 3
10 + ... 4

19. Have you consulted or been seen by any other doctor at all? – at work or for insurance or anything like that – in the last twelve months?

Yes 5
No 0

IF YES (5)
(a) Who (Type of doctor) Anyone else?

Previous G.P. 5
Other G.P. 6
Works doctor 7
Other (specify)

(b) Why was that?

On holiday or away 8
Insurance 9
Routine check-up 0
D.N.A. (Previous G.P.) .... Y
Other (specify)

(c) How many times altogether?

Once 1
2 < 5 times............. 2
5 < 10 times............. 3
10 + ... 4

20. So altogether how many times have you been seen by any doctor professionally in the last twelve months – apart from at a hospital?

    None 0
    Once 1
    2 < 5 times 2
    5 < 10 times 3
    10 + ... 4

*21. *Occupational status.* During the last 12 months have you been working:

    Full-time, all time 5
    Part-time.................. 6
    Not at all 7

22. IF WORKING AND CONSULTED G.P. IN LAST 12 MONTHS Again during the last twelve months, have you suggested to a doctor that he should give you a certificate either to say you weren't fit for work or one to say you were fit again before he suggested it?

    Yes 9
    No 0

    IF YES (9)
    (a) Why was that?
    Fit for work 1
    Not fit for work 2
    Both 3
    (b) What happened?
    Gave it 4
    Did not give it 5
    COMMENTS:

23. IF WORKING In general would you say your G.P. was:

    PROMPT
    Too inclined to give certificates to stop off work 6
    Rather reluctant to give them 7
    Reasonable about this 8
    Don't know   9
    IF 6 or 7 Could you give me an example? (Q)

24. IF CONSULTED G.P. IN LAST TWELVE MONTHS During the last twelve months have you asked a doctor for a prescription or medicine that he hadn't given you before?

    Yes 5
    No 6

    IF YES (5)
    (a) What medicine was it?
    (b) What was it for? (Symptoms – how was it meant to help?)
    (c) Where did you hear about it?
    (d) What did he do?

    Gave it 7
    Did not give it 8

    IF DID NOT GIVE IT
    (i) Why was that?
    (ii) What do you feel about that?

25. TO ALL. In general would you say your doctor was:

    PROMPT
    Too inclined to give a prescription 1
    Rather reluctant to give a prescription 2
    Reasonable about this 3
    Don't know
    IF 1 or 2 Could you give me an example? (Q)

    IF NOT CONSULTED A G.P. IN LAST TWELVE MONTHS GO ON TO QUESTION 30

26. During the last twelve months when you've seen a G.P. have you had to undress at all, apart from outdoor clothing – so that he could examine you?

    Yes 1
    No 2

27. Was there any occasion when you think he might have examined you more fully?

Yes 3

No 4

IF YES (3) Why did you feel that?

28. During the last 12 months has your G.P. asked to see any other member of the family when you have consulted him yourself?

Yes 5

No 6

IF YES (5) When was that? RECORD DETAILS OPPOSITE

29. During the last 12 months have you discussed your diet with your doctor – or his partner, etc.?

Yes 1

No 2

IF YES (1)

(*a*) What did he say?

(*b*) Did you find it helpful or not?

Yes 5

No 6

(*c*) Were you able to carry out his advice?

Yes 7

No 8

IF NO (8) Why not? (Q)

30. What about smoking – have you discussed this with your G.P. – or his partners, etc. – in the last 12 months – or haven't you smoked during this time.

Hasn't smoked in last 12 months .... Y

Yes 1

No 2

IF YES (1)

(*a*) What did he say?

(*b*) Did he give you any advice?

Yes 3

No 4

IF YES (3)

(i) What?

(ii) Did you find it helpful or not?

Yes helpful 5

No 6

(iii) Were you able to carry it out?

Yes 7

No 8

IF NO (8) Why not (Q)

TO ALL

31. What are the qualities – the things about your G.P. that you appreciate? Anything else?

32. Are there any other qualities you feel a G.P. ought to have – that yours has not got?

33. I'm going to read a list of things people might consider important in a general practitioner. Will you tell me whether you think your doctor is good or not so good about these things?

(*a*) having a well equipped, up-to-date surgery?

Good..................... 1

Not so good 2

Don't know 3

In what way? (Q)

(*b*) having a pleasant comfortable waiting room?

Good..................... 4

Not so good 5

Don't know 6

In what way? (Q)

(*c*) always visits when asked?

Good..................... 7

Not so good 8

Don't know 9

Can you give me an example? (Q)

(d) sends people to hospital as soon as necessary?

```
Good..................... Y
Not so good .............. X
Don't know .............. o
```
Can you give me an example? (Q)

(e) doesn't keep people waiting long in his surgery?

```
Good..................... 1
Not so good .............. 2
Don't know .............. 3
```

(f) examines people carefully and thoroughly?

```
Good..................... 4
Not so good .............. 5
Don't know .............. 6
```
Can you give me an example? (Q)

(g) doesn't send people to hospital unless it is necessary?

```
Good..................... 7
Not so good .............. 8
Don't know .............. 9
```
Can you give me an example? (Q)

(h) takes time and doesn't hurry you?

```
Good..................... Y
Not so good .............. X
Don't know .............. o
```
Can you give me an example? (Q)

(i) listens to what you say?
```
Good..................... 1
Not so good .............. 2
Don't know .............. 3
```
Can you give me an example? (Q)

(j) explains things to you fully?
```
Good..................... 4
Not so good .............. 5
Don't know .............. 6
```
Can you give me an example? (Q)

*34. Which do you really prefer – a doctor working on his own or one in partnership?
```
One on own.............. 3
In partnership ............ 4
Does not matter .......... 5
```

*35. Do you think it is important from the patient's point of view – for a doctor to work on his own/in a group – or that it doesn't matter very much?
```
Important ................ 5
Doesn't matter much ....... 6
Other (specify)
```

*36. What do you think are the advantages, if any – from the patient's point of view – of a doctor working on his own?

*37. What do you think are the *dis*-advantages, if any – again from the patient's point of view of a doctor working on his own?

IF DOCTOR WORKS ON OWN
GO ON TO QUESTION 42

38. What do you feel about seeing other doctors in the partnership? (PROBE TO OBTAIN REASONS)

39. If you go to the surgery and find unexpectedly that your own doctor is not there, do you:
```
              Not mind in the least 1
              Feel quite prepared
              to see other doctor
              although would pre-
              fer to see own ..... 2
PROMPT  Feel quite put out
              because you can't see
              own doctor ....... 3
              Or prefer to see other
              doctor ...: ...... 4
```

40. Can you arrange to see your own doctor fairly easily if you want to?

   Yes 5

   No 6

   IF YES (5) How do you do that?

41. When you go to the surgery do you usually know beforehand whether your own doctor will be there?

   Yes 7

   No 8

   COMMENTS (Q)

42. If you could see another doctor in the group straight away or wait about half an hour and see your own doctor, which would you usually prefer to do?

   See other doctor 9

   Wait for own .... o

IF DOCTOR WORKS ON OWN

43. If you went to the doctor's surgery and found a strange doctor there because your doctor was away ill or on holiday would you:

   Not mind in the least 1

   Feel quite prepared to see other doctor although would prefer to see own 2

   Feel quite put out because you couldn't see your own doctor 3

   Prefer to see strange doctor.. 4

TO ALL WOMEN

44. Are there some occasions when you would prefer to see a woman G.P. rather than a man?

   Yes 5

   No 6

TO ALL

45. Are there some circumstances when you feel it might be helpful to see another doctor who was also a G.P. rather than your own doctor?

   Yes 7

   No 8

   IF YES (7) On what sort of occasion? Can you give me an example? (Q)

*46. Which do you prefer – A G.P. who does a number of tests and investigations himself 9

   Or one who sends you to hospital if you need any investigation... o

   COMMENTS (Q)

   Why is that?

47. Do you know the latest time in the evening when you can get in to see your doctor at the surgery?

   Before 5 p.m. 1

   5.0 but before 5.30 2

   5.30 but before 6.0 3

   6.0 but before 6.30 4

   6.30 but before 7.0 5

   7.0 but before 7.30 6

   7.30 but before 8.0 7

   8.0 p.m. or later 8

   Don't know 9

48. Do you ever go as late as that (IF DON'T KNOW TO 47). What is the latest you ever go?

   Yes 1

   No 2

*49. Just supposing general practitioners all finished their evening surgeries by 5.30. How would you feel about that?

*50. Would you find that:

   PROMPT ALL THREE

   Definitely inconvenient 3

   A little inconvenient 4

   Not at all inconvenient 5

51. Do you know what arrangements your doctor has for night calls?

    Don't know X
    Rota with partners 1
    Rota with neighbouring doc-
    tors 2
    Call service 3
    He's always on 4
    No one available 5

*52. Just supposing general practitioners never worked – or were available – at night, from 6 in the evening until 9 the next morning – and if you needed a doctor during that time you had to get in touch with an emergency service – How would you feel about that?

*53. Would you prefer that arrangement of getting in touch with the emergency service or would you rather go on as you do now?

    Prefer emergency service ... 1
    Go on as now 2
    Why is that?

54. Do you think you would be able to get hold of your G.P. – or someone acting for him – if you needed him on a Sunday afternoon or in the middle of the night?

    Yes 1
    No 2
    Don't know 3

55. During the last twelve months have you tried to get hold of him in a hurry or in the evening or at night at all – for yourself, your husband/wife, or your children?

    Yes 1
    No 2

IF YES (1)

(a) Who was that for?

    Self 3
    Spouse 4
    Child under 2.............. 5
    Child 2 < 5 6
    Child 5 < 15 7

(b) What was the matter with them?

(c) Was that in the evening, at night or in the day time?

    Evening 6 p.m. up to 11 p.m. 8
    Night 11 p.m. up to 9 a.m... 9
    Other 0

(d) What happened?

(e) Who did you get hold of (first) – to see patient?

    Own doctor 1
    Partner 2
    Other acting for him 3
    Other G.P. 4
    Hospital 5
    Other (specify)

(f) How long was it before the doctor came – or saw patient?

    Less than 15 minutes 1
    15 < 30 minutes 2
    30 < 45 minutes 3
    45 < 60 minutes 4
    1 hr. < 2 hrs. 5
    2 hrs. < 3 hrs. 6
    3 hrs. + ... 7

56. Was there any (other) occasion in the last 12 months when you wondered about getting in touch with the doctor at night and decided not to?

    Yes 1
    No 2

IF YES (1)

(a) What was the trouble?

(b) Who was it for?

    Self 3
    Spouse 4
    Child under 2.............. 5
    Child 2 < 5 6
    Child 5 < 15 7

(c) Why didn't you?

(d) Are you glad or sorry now that you didn't?

Glad 8

Sorry 9

Why?

57. Does your doctor have any sort of appointment system at the surgery or some other arrangements so people don't have to wait there all the time?

Yes appointments 8

Yes queue ticket 9

No 0

IF YES 8 or 9 What do you think of it?

Which do you prefer – to have the system or no arrangements – just waiting in turn?

System 1

Waiting in turn 2

IF NO (o) Would you like him to have an appointment system provided you could always see him the same day as you wanted to – or would you rather go on as you are now?

Like appointment system ... 3

Prefer to continue 4

Why do/would you prefer that?

58. The last time you went to the doctor's surgery do you remember how long you had to wait?

Less than 10 minutes 1

10 < 20 minutes 2

20 < 30 minutes 3

30 < 45 minutes 4

45 minutes < 1 hour 5

1 hour < 1½ hours 6

1½ hours < 2 hours 7

2 hours + ... 8

Don't know 9

59. Was that about:

Average 1

PROMPT Less than usual 2

More than usual ... 3

60. Do you think that was reasonable or unreasonable?

Reasonable 4

Unreasonable 5

Why do you feel that? (Q)

61. What time of year was that?

January–March 6

April–June 7

July–September 8

October–December 9

*62. Would you like a doctor to give you a regular check-up say every two years?

Yes 1

No 2

Can you tell me why you would like/not like that?

IF YES (1) Would you prefer your doctor to do this himself or would you rather some other doctor did it – at a clinic or hospital?

Own doctor 3

Other 4

Why is that?

*63. Is there any particular illness or symptom that you feel a regular check-up might set your mind at rest about?

Yes 3

No 4

IF YES (3) What is it?

*64. Have you had any sort of check-up such as a chest X-ray or general examination in the last two years?

Yes 1

No 2

IF YES (1)

(*a*) What did it involve?

	Yes	No
Chest X-ray	1	9
Physical exam	2	9

WOMEN ONLY

Internal (vaginal) exam	4	9
Other (specify)		

(*b*) Would you have liked a more general or extensive check-up?

Yes 5

No 6

(*c*) Who did it?

Own G.P.................. 1

Partner/Locum/Assistant 2

Other G.P. 3

Hospital 4

Chest clinic – mobile X-ray .. 5

Works doctor 6

Other (specify)

(*d*) Who suggested you should have it?

(*e*) Did you have any symptoms – or was there any other reason why you should have a check-up?

Symptoms 7

Earlier illness 8

Contact 9

Other (specify)............. 1

No particular reason 2

COMMENTS:

65. If you could have ten minutes uninterrupted discussion either with your doctor or with another doctor you found sympathetic is there anything particular you would like to ask him about? – for yourself or your family?

Yes 5

No 6

IF YES (5)

(*a*) What is it? (INDICATE WHICH CHILD ETC.)

(*b*) Would you prefer it to be your own doctor or another one?

Own doctor 7

Other doctor 8

IF OTHER (8) Why would you prefer that?

(*c*) Have you talked to your doctor about this kind of thing at all?

Yes 7

No 8

IF YES (7) What happened?

IF NO (8) Why haven't you?

66. Do or would you feel at all awkward or embarrassed at getting undressed at your doctor's surgery?

Yes 5

No 6

67. Do you feel more or less embarrassed at getting undressed at a hospital out-patient department – or is there no difference?

More embarrassed at hospital 1

More embarrassed at G.P.s .. 2

No difference 3

IF (1 or 2) Can you say why you feel that? (Q)

68. If you went to the doctor and told him you'd had stomach-ache off and on, indigestion, and feelings of sickness for the last six weeks, what do you think he would do? Anything else?

CODE

Examine you 1

Send for X-ray 2

Give medicine/prescription .. 3

Send you to hospital........ 8

69. If you cut your leg while you were at home so that it needed stitching, would you be more likely to go to your own doctor or straight to hospital?

Own doctor 7

Straight to hospital 8

Why would you do that?

70. If you *did* go to your own doctor do you think he would stitch it himself or send you to hospital?
    Stitch it himself 9
    Send to hospital .... o

71. Would you expect him to cope with these things himself or to send you to hospital?

	G.P. on own	Send to hospital	Don't know
A sprained ankle .	1	2	3
A small cyst which needed cutting out	4	5	6
An abscess which needed opening ..	7	8	9
A blood test	1	2	3

WOMEN ONLY
An internal – vaginal – examination	4	5	6

72. Which is more convenient for you – to go to the hospital out-patient department or to your own doctor?
    Hospital out-patient 6
    Own doctor 7

73. Which do you *prefer*?
    Hospital out-patient 8
    Own doctor 9
    Why?

74. Do you consider your doctor to be something of a personal friend or is your relationship pretty much a businesslike one?
    Friendly 1
    Businesslike 2
    Do you like it that way – or would you prefer it to be more friendly/businesslike?
    COMMENTS:

CODE
    Prefer it as it is 3
    Like it changed 4

*75. Do you think a general practitioner is a suitable person to talk to about problems such as children getting into trouble or difficulties between husband and wife?
    Yes 1
    No 2
    Uncertain 3
    Why is that? (Q)

76. If you were worried about a personal problem that wasn't a strictly medical one, do you think you might discuss it with your doctor?
    Yes 4
    No 5
    Uncertain 6
    Why is that? (Q)

77. Who (else) do you think you might discuss such problems with – (apart from your husband/wife)? Anyone else?
    Parents 1
    Children 2
    Siblings 3
    Other relatives 4
    Neighbours 5
    Friends at work 6
    Other friends 7
    Other (specify)............ 8
    Nobody 9

78. Is there anyone such as a minister, health visitor or social worker you think you might ask about such things? Who?
    No .... o
    Minister 1
    Health visitor.............. 2
    Social worker (specify)...... 3
    Other person (specify) 4

247

*79. Would you consult your G.P. if you had been feeling tired all the time for about four weeks – for no particular reason?

    Yes 1
    No 2
    Uncertain 3

IF YES OR UNCERTAIN (1 or 3)
How do you think he might be able to help you?

IF NO OR UNCERTAIN (2 or 3)
(a) Why (might you) not?
(b) What would you do?

*80. What about a constant feeling of depression for three weeks – would you consult your G.P. about that?

    Yes 1
    No 2
    Uncertain 3

IF YES OR UNCERTAIN (1 or 3)
How do you think he might be able to help you?

IF NO OR UNCERTAIN (2 or 3)
(a) Why (might you) not?
(b) What would you do?

*81. And difficulty in sleeping at nights for a week – would you consult him about that?

    Yes 1
    No 2
    Uncertain 3

IF YES OR UNCERTAIN (1 or 3)
How do you think he might be able to help you?

IF NO OR UNCERTAIN (2 or 3)
(a) Why (might you) not?
(b) What would you do?

*82. WOMEN ONLY Would you consult him about any unusual bleeding or discharge?

    Yes 1
    No 2
    Uncertain 3

IF YES OR UNCERTAIN (1 or 3)
How do you think he might be able to help you?

IF NO OR UNCERTAIN (2 or 3)
(a) Why (might you) not?
(b) What would you do?

*83. If you were going on a journey and thought you might be travel-sick, do you think you would:
    Go to the doctor to get some pills to prevent it 1
    Or would you buy them yourself from the chemist 2
    Or don't you believe in taking pills for that sort of thing?... 3

*84. If you had a heavy cold with a sore throat and temperature and running nose for two days would you:
    Ask your doctor to visit you.. 1
    Go to see him at the surgery.. 2
    or Not consult him at all.... 3
    IF (1 or 2) and WORKING
    Would you do that just because you need a certificate for work or would you want to see him about that in any case?
    Just because of certificate ... 4
    Consult in any case 5

*85. Would you consult your G.P. at all about:

	Yes	No	Uncertain
(a) dandruff	1	2	3
(b) loss of your voice for 3 or 4 days	4	5	6
(c) a boil on your neck..............	7	8	9

*86. Have you in fact had any of these things in the last 12 months – IF YES did you consult a G.P.

	Yes	No	Yes	No
Boil on neck ..	1	2	3	4
Loss of voice 3/4 days	3	4	5	6
Dandruff......	5	6	7	8
Heavy cold with sore throat, temperature and running nose ..	7	8	9	0
Difficulty in sleeping at nights	9	0	1	2
Constant feeling of depression for three weeks ...	2	3	4	5

WOMEN ONLY

	Yes	No	Yes	No
Unusual bleeding or discharge	4	5	6	7

*87. Now I'd like to ask you what you think about the prestige of general practitioners. Here is a list of six different occupations. I'd like you to tell me which you think has the greatest prestige, which has the next and so on.

	Rank
A general practitioner	......
A headmaster of a Grammar School	......
A hospital specialist (Consultant)	......
A manager of a branch of Marks & Spencer	......
A solicitor who is a senior partner in a small firm	......
A University Professor of History	......

*88. Do you think the prestige of general practitioners has been going up or down in the last ten years – or do you think it has stayed about the same?

Up 1
Down 2
Same 3

IF UP OR DOWN (1 or 2)
(a) Why has it changed do you think? (Q)
(b) What sort of difference has it made? (Q)

89. Have you ever thought of changing your present doctor?

Yes 3
No 4

IF YES (3)
(a) Why?
(b) Why didn't you?

*90. I want to read you a description of two doctors and then will you tell me if you had to choose between them which one you would prefer for your doctor.

The first doctor has his surgery attached to his house. He works mainly on his own, but he has an arrangement with a nearby doctor for some weekends and some night calls. His waiting room is comfortable, which is a good thing because patients often have to wait a long time. He knows his patients and their families well, and when you do see him he takes his time, doesn't hurry you, and listens to what you have to say. He prescribes well-established drugs and sends patients to hospital if they need anything more complicated.

The second doctor works in a partnership. There are four of them altogether and they share a well-equipped surgery where they have a nurse and a secretary. This doctor takes turns with his partners to be on duty for surgeries and for week-end and night calls. They all examine you very carefully, and are very up-to-date, and only send patients to hospital if they need very complicated investigation or treatment.

Which of the two doctors would you prefer?

First....................... 1
Second 2

Why is that?

91. Which is your doctor most like?

The first 3
The second............... 4
Neither 5

COMMENTS (Q)

*92. If you did not have a family doctor, but if there was anything the matter with you, you could go straight to the appropriate specialist – how would you feel about that?

*93. Which would you prefer – to have a G.P. – as at present or to go straight to specialists?

Prefer G.P. 8
Prefer to go to specialists 9

Why is that?

94. Do you know if your doctor takes private patients too?

Yes definitely 3
No definitely 4
Believes so 5
Believes not 6
Don't know 9

Do you have any views about this?

Does not approve of private patients 7
Does not mind, makes no difference 8
Other 9

CLASSIFICATION

As I explained before we don't use any names in our study, but we do like to know one or two things about the people we interview:

*95. Present occupation.

Self employed with employees 1
Self employed without employees 2
Manager 3
Foreman 4
Other employee 5

*96. IF AGED 65+ and A MAN or SINGLE WOMAN. Main occupation.

Self employed with employees 1
Self employed without employees 2
Manager 3
Foreman 4
Other employee 5

*97. IF MARRIED WOMAN or WIDOW. Husband's present or main occupation.

Self employed with employees 1
Self employed without employees 2
Manager 3
Foreman 4
Other employee 5

*98. How long have you lived in this district – that is near enough to go to present doctor's surgery?

Less than 1 year 1
1 year < 2 years 2
2 years < 5 years 3
5 years < 10 years 4
10 years < 15 years 5
15 years < 20 years 6
20 years + ... 7

*99. Have you got a telephone in this dwelling?

    Yes 8

    No 9

*100. At what age did you leave school?

    14 or less 1

    15........................ 2

    16........................ 3

    17 or more 4

*101. Have you had any further education or training?

    Yes 5

    No 6

    IF YES (5) What?

    University............... 1

    Training college 2

    Secretarial 3

    Technical college.......... 4

    Apprenticeship 5

    Other (specify)

*102. And your age?

    21–24.................... 1

    25–34.................... 2

    35–44.................... 3

    45–54.................... 4

    55–64.................... 5

    65–74.................... 6

    75 + ... 7

IF 65 or more (6 or 7) COMPLETE YELLOW SHEET

*103. During the last 12 months have you been to hospital as an out-patient at all – for an X-ray or to casualty or anything like that – or to a day hospital?

    Yes 8

    No 9

IF YES (8) COMPLETE GREEN SHEET

*104. And in the last *two weeks* have you consulted your G.P. or any other doctor at all?

    Yes 1

    No 2

IF YES (1) COMPLETE WHITE SHEET

*105. OTHER QUESTIONNAIRES

	Applicable	Completed
No regular N.H.S. doctor (Buff)	1	2
Hospital out-patient in last 12 months (Green)	3	4
Mother of children under 15 (Blue) ...	5	6
Aged 65 or more (Bright Yellow)...	7	8
Consulted G.P. in last two weeks (White)	9	0

*106. Number of calls   ......

*107. Date   / /64

*108. Interviewer (Number)   ......

(b) *Additional Questions for Mothers of Children under 15*

201. CHECK You have ...... children under 15 living here.

202. I would like to ask about any times during the last 12 months when your children have seen the doctor for any illness or symptom. (IF CHILD UNDER 5 YEARS. For the moment please don't think of any visits to immunization or special clinics). Could we take the children in turn?

Letter	Name	Sex M F	Age Under 1 year 1 < 2 years 2 < 5 years 5 < 10 years 10 < 15 years	How many times did they consult their G.P. or partners etc. in the last 12 months? Not at all Once 2 < 5 5 < 10 10 +	IF CONSULTED AT ALL During that time did the doctor visit them at home at all? How many times? Not at all Once 2 < 5 5 < 10 10 +	Been to hospital as an I.P. or O.P. in last 12 months O.P. I.P. Neither
		1 2	3 4 5 6 7	0 1 2 3 4	0 1 2 3 4	5 6 7
		1 2	3 4 5 6 7	0 1 2 3 4	0 1 2 3 4	5 6 7
		1 2	3 4 5 6 7	0 1 2 3 4	0 1 2 3 4	5 6 7
		1 2	3 4 5 6 7	0 1 2 3 4	0 1 2 3 4	5 6 7
		1 2	3 4 5 6 7	0 1 2 3 4	0 1 2 3 4	5 6 7

203. IF ANY CHILDREN VISITED BY G.P. IN LAST YEAR On the last most recent occasion a G.P. visited (one of) your child(ren) here:
(a) Which child or children was it for?
(b) What was the matter with them?

(c) The first time he came – for that episode – who decided he should come?
Patient or relative asked him. 1
Doctor decided – after surgery consultation 2
Doctor decided – after phone call 3

(*d*) How many times did he come – for that episode – altogether?

Once 1
Twice 2
3 < 5 3
5 + ... 4

IF MORE THAN ONCE After the first time, did he call of his own accord or did you – or your family – ask him to come again?

Came on own accord 5
Mother or relative asked 6
Other (specify)

(*e*) Just supposing doctors did not visit people in their own homes what do you think you would have done during that episode?

(*f*) Would you have:

Got his advice on phone 7
Got advice by others calling at surgery without child..... 8
Gone to surgery with child .. 9
Managed on own 0
Or what?

How would you have felt about that?

204. IF ANY CHILDREN CONSULTED G.P. IN LAST YEAR During this last 12 months have your children seen:

Own doctor only .. 5
Own doctor mainly. 6
PROMPT Partners/locum as much as own 7
Partners/locum mainly 8
Partners/locum only 9

TO ALL
205. During this last 12 months have you had any advice over the phone from your doctor or his partners about your children?

Yes 1
No 2

IF YES (1)
(*a*) About how many times?
(*b*) On what sort of occasion do you find that helpful?

206. Have any of the children consulted another doctor *privately* in the last 12 months?

Yes 3
No 4

IF YES (3)
(*a*) Which children?
(*b*) Why did they go privately rather than under the N.H.S.?
(*c*) How did you choose that doctor?
(*d*) How many times did they see him altogether? (EACH CHILD)

CHILD:

Once 1 1 1
2 < 5 times 2 2 2
5 < 10 times 3 3 3
10 or more times ... 4 4 4

IF NO CHILDREN UNDER FIVE GO ON TO QUESTION 211

IF ANY CHILDREN UNDER FIVE
207. Does your doctor or his partners have any special times for children – such as well-baby or immunization clinics?

Yes 1
No 2

IF NO (2) Would you like him to?
Yes 3
No 4
Doubtful................... 5
Why is that?

IF YES (1) Have you taken your children to these special clinics in the last 12 months?

Yes 6
No 7

IF YES (6) RECORD IN TABLE BELOW.

208. Have you taken your child(ren) to any other clinics in the last 12 months?

Yes 8
No 9

IF YES (8) RECORD IN TABLE BELOW.

209. RECORD FOR ALL CHILDREN UNDER FIVE:

Letter	Name	In last 12 months		Diphtheria Immunization		Smallpox Vaccination	
		Visits to G.P. clinic	Visits to other clinic	Ever	Who did it	Ever	Who did it
		0 1 2<5 5<10 10+	0 1 2<5 5<10 10+	Yes No	G.P. Clinic / Other (specify)	Yes No	G.P. Clinic / Other (specify)
		0 1 2 3 4	0 1 2 3 4	5 6	7 8	9 0	1 2
		0 1 2 3 4	0 1 2 3 4	5 6	7 8	9 0	1 2
		0 1 2 3 4	0 1 2 3 4	5 6	7 8	9 0	1 2

210. Which do you find most helpful when you want advice about feeding and problems like that – the general practitioner or the people at the clinic?

General practitioner 3
People at clinic 4

Why is that?

(a) Do you think it is helpful to be able to get advice about feeding and problems like that from either the general practitioner or the people at the clinic – or do you think it is confusing to have two possible people to consult?

Helpful to have two 1
Confusing to have two...... 2
Other (specify)

(b) Why do you feel that?

(c) Could you give me an illustration?

TO ALL

211. Would you like (any of) your child(ren) to have any more regular examinations or check-ups on their health – or do you think they have enough already?

Would like more 1
Enough already 2

IF WOULD LIKE MORE (1)
(a) Who would you like to do it:

The G.P. 3
The child-welfare
PROMPT clinic 4
The school doctor.. 5
The hospital 6
Or anyone else (specify)

(*b*) IF HAS MORE THAN ONE
CHILD Is that for all your children
or what?

CODE ALL THAT APPLY

Under 2	1
2 < 5	2
5 < 10	3
10 +	4

212. Is there any particular illness or
symptom that you feel a regular
check-up might set your mind at
rest about?

Yes	1
No	2

IF YES (1) What is it (INDICATE
CHILD IF APPROPRIATE)

213. It is often said that it is helpful for
mothers to have the same doctor as
their children. Can you give me an
example of any way in which you
have found it helpful – in the last
two years?

END OF QUESTIONNAIRE
FOR MOTHERS WITH
CHILDREN UNDER FIVE ONLY

IF HAS ANY CHILDREN AGED 5
OR MORE

214. Have any of your children been
examined by a school doctor
during the last 12 months?

Yes	1
No	2

IF YES (1)
(*a*) Which child(ren?)
(*b*) Did the doctor give you any
advice?

Yes	3
No	4

IF YES (3)
(*a*) What was it?
(*b*) Do you think it was helpful?
(*c*) Did you see your own doctor
about this, either before or after
the school examination?

Yes, before	6
Yes, after	7
No	8

COMMENTS:

215. Do you think that school medical
examinations are a good thing or
unnecessary?

Good thing	9
Unnecessary	0

Why is that?

216. Do you think it would be a good
idea for your general practitioner
to do a regular check-up instead of
having a school medical examination – or do you think it is helpful
for your child(ren) to see a different
doctor for that?

Prefer check-up from G.P.	1
Prefer different doctor	2
Other (specify)	

Why do you think that?

(c) Additional questions for those who had been to hospital as out-patients in the previous twelve months

301. Now you said you went to hospital as an out-patient in the last 12 months. What was that for? What was the matter with you? Was there anything else for which you went to hospital as an out-patient in the last 12 months?	How many times did you go – for that – in last 12 months?				How did you come to go to hospital O.P. for that in the first place?		IF G.P. SENT (5) Did you just go for a particular test or X-ray or did you have a consultation with a doctor? IF WENT DIRECTLY (6) Why didn't you to go your own doctor first?	What treatment and tests have you had for that in the last 12 months? Anything else?					How long ago was it that you first went to out-patients for this?						Have you been an in-patient for this during this time?		Are you still attending – have you got to go again?		
	1	2 < 5	5 > 10	10 +	G.P. sent	Went directly		Chest X-ray	Other X-ray	Physiotherapy	Surgical Appliances	Other (specify)	Less than 3 month	3 months < 6 months	6 months < 1 year	1 year < 2 years.	2 years. < 5 years.	5 years. +	Yes	No	Yes	No	Lapsed
	1	2	3	4	5	6	Just test or X-ray 7 / Consult. with dr. 8	9	0	1	2		2	3	4	5	6	7	8	9	1	2	3
	1	2	3	4	5	6	Just test or X-ray 7 / Consult. with dr. 8	9	0	1	2		2	3	4	5	6	7	8	9	1	2	3
	1	2	3	4	5	6	Just test or X-ray 7 / Consult. with dr. 8	9	0	1	2		2	3	4	5	6	7	8	9	1	2	3

Interview Schedules for Patients

IF MORE THAN ONE EPISODE

302. How many times then have you been to any out-patient department in the last 12 months?

    2 < 5 2
    5 < 10 3
    10 + ... 4

IF MORE THAN ONE VISIT DURING YEAR

303. (a) How long do you usually have to wait?

    Less than 10 minutes 1
    10 < 20 minutes 2
    20 < 30 minutes 3
    30 < 45 minutes 4
    45 < 60 minutes 5
    1 hour < 1½ hours 6
    1½ hours < 2 hours 7
    2 hours + ... 8
    Don't know 9

    (b) Do you think that is reasonable or unreasonable?

Reasonable 1
Unreasonable 2
Why do you feel that? (Q)

(c) Do you usually have an appointment?

    Yes 3
    No 4

TO ALL

304. Who do you find it easier to talk to – your own doctor or the doctors at the hospital?

    Own doctor easier 5
    Hospital Doctors easier......... 6
    No difference 7

305. As far as you can tell, is/was it really necessary for you to go to the hospital (each time) or do you think your own doctor could do what they do there?

    Hospital necessary.......... 8
    G.P. could do it 9
    Why do you think that?

(d) Additional questions for people aged 65 and over

401. Do you have any (chronic) trouble with:

	Yes	No	IF YES have you consulted anyone about this? Who? No	G.P.	Other (specify)	IF NOT CONSULTED ANYONE – Why not? IF HAS CONSULTED Have they been able to help you? How?
Your feet	1	2	3	4	Chiropodist 5	
Your eyesight	3	4	5	6	Optician/Oculist 7	
Your hearing	5	6	7	8		
Backache	7	8	9	0		

257

402. Do you – or have you had – any problems with shopping, cleaning the house, going up stairs, gardening, carrying coal – or anything like that?

Yes 1
No 2

IF YES (1)

(a) What is the difficulty?

CODE ALL THAT APPLY

Shopping 1
Cleaning 2
Stairs 3
Gardening 4
Coal 5
Other 6

(b) Have you ever discussed the problem with your doctor?

Yes 1
No 2

IF NO (2) Why not?

IF YES (1)

(a) What did he say?

(b) Did he give you any help or advice?

Yes 3
No 4

IF YES (3) What?

Did you find it helpful?

Yes 5
No 6

403. Do you find your house/flat convenient for you now you are getting older?

Yes 7
No 8

IF NO (8) What is the trouble?

404. Does your G.P. visit you regularly?

Yes 1
No 2

IF YES (1) How often?

Weekly or more often 3
Fortnightly < Weekly 4
Monthly < Fortnightly 5
Less than monthly 6

IF NO (2) Can you get down to the surgery to see him fairly easily if you want to?

Yes 3
No 4

IF NO (4) Would you like him to drop in say once a month?

Yes 5
No 6
COMMENTS:

405. During the last 12 months have you had any help from:

	Yes No	IF YES Who arranged it
A home help	1 2	
A district nurse	3 4	
A welfare visitor	5 6	
Meals on wheels	7 8	
or anyone else like that (specify)	9 0	

406. In the last 12 months would you have liked any (more) help?

Yes 7
No 8

IF YES (7)
(a) What sort?
Home help 1
District nurse 2
Health visitor.............. 3
Meals on wheels 4
Other (specify)
(b) Why did you need that? What was the matter with you? (CONDITION)
(c) How did it affect you? (DISABILITY)

IF LIVES WITH OTHERS UNDER 65 THIS IS END OF QUESTIONNAIRE

IF LIVES ALONE OR JUST WITH OTHERS 65 AND OVER

407. (a) Who is the relative (not living here) you see most of?
Daughter 1
Son 2
Daughter-in-law 3
Son-in-law 4
Sister 5
Brother 6
Other (specify)
(b) How often do you see them – on the average?

Every day 7
Weekly < daily 8
Monthly < Weekly 9
Less than once a month 0
(c) Is there anyone else – not a relative – you see more often?
Yes 1
No 2

IF YES (1)
(a) Who?
Next-door neighbour 3
Other neighbour 4
Other friend 5
(b) How often do you see them?
Every day 7
Weekly < daily 8
Monthly < weekly 9
Less than once a month 0

408. (a) When you are ill is it at all difficult for you to get in touch with your doctor?
(b) How do you do it?

CODE
Own phone 1
Through neighbours 2
Others in household 3
65 +
Card in window 4
Other 5

01. Have you ever registered with a doctor under the National Health Service – that is in the last 15 years?

    Yes 1
    No 2

    IF YES (1)
    (a) When was the last time you consulted him?

    Less than a year ago 3
    1 year < 2 years 4
    2 years < 5 years 5
    5 years < 10 years 6
    10 years + ... 7
    (b) Why did you stop going to him?
    (c) So he's no longer your doctor because:
    You moved 1
    He moved/died/retired 2
    You just stopped going to him 3
    (d) Why haven't you found another N.H.S. doctor?
    (e) Do you intend to register with an N.H.S. doctor again?
    Yes 4
    No 5

    COMMENTS:

    IF NO (2) Why not?

502. Do you have a regular private doctor – one you have consulted before and whom you would consult again if you were ill?

    Yes 6
    No 7

    IF YES (6)
    (a) Who is he?
    NAME
    INITIAL
    ADDRESS
    (b) Does he have any N.H.S. patients?
    Yes 8
    No 9
    Don't know 0

GO BACK TO BASIC SCHEDULE – THE TABLE AT QUESTION 1 – TREATING PRIVATE DOCTOR AS THEIR DOCTOR.

IF NO (7)
(a) If you needed a doctor would you go to a private one or one under the N.H.S.?
Private 8
N.H.S. 9
Other (specify)
(b) How would you choose him?
(c) What are the qualities you feel are most important in a G.P.?
(d) When was the last, most recent time you consulted a doctor, either at a hospital or anywhere else?

Less than a year ago 3
1 year < 2 years 4
2 years < 5 years 5
5 years < 10 years 6
10 years < 15 years 7
15 years + ... 8

IF LESS THAN A YEAR AGO (3) Who was that?

RECORD AT Q. 18/19/20/102 AS APPROPRIATE THEN ASK QUESTIONS WITH AN ASTERISK * FROM Q.21 ONWARDS

IF MORE THAN A YEAR AGO ASK QUESTIONS WITH AN ASTERISK * STARTING FROM Q.21 ONWARDS.

BE SURE TO COMPLETE CLASSIFICATION IN ALL CASES

f) Additional questions if consulted general practioner in previous two weeks

You said you consulted a G.P. in the last two weeks. How many times?

....

IF MORE THAN ONCE

Was that for the same illness or condition – or for different ones?

Same 1
Different 2

Can we talk about the last, most recent one first.

Whose idea was it that you should consult the G.P. that particular time?				Do you think the consultation was long enough for you to tell him all he needed to know and for him to do all that was necessary? IF NO In what way?		Did he give you or do any of these things: PROMPT								When you saw him on that particular occasion what did you think or hope he might do for you? Anything else? DO NOT PROMPT							Whom did you see?				Where was it?			Was that first time you had seen a G.P. for that?		What illness or condition was it for?
Own	G.P.	Relative (specify)	Other (specify)	Yes	No	Certificate First	Certificate Intermediate	Certificate Final	Medicine/Prescrip.	Exam./Check-up	Referral to Hospital	Advice/Reassurance	None of these	Certificate First	Certificate Intermediate	Certificate Final	Medicine/Prescrip.	Exam./Check-up	Referral to Hospital	Advice/Reassurance	Own G.P.	Partner/Assistant	Locum	Other (specify)	Home	Surgery	Other (specify)	Yes	No	
8	9	1	2	7	6	8	9	1	2	3	4	5	0	1	2	3	4	5	6	7	6	7	8	9	3	4	5	1	2	
8	9	1	2	7	6	8	9	1	2	3	4	5	0	1	2	3	4	5	6	7	6	7	8	9	3	4	5	1	2	
8	9	1	2	7	6	8	9	1	2	3	4	5	0	1	2	3	4	5	6	7	6	7	8	9	3	4	5	1	2	

LETTER AND POSTAL QUESTIONNAIRE TO DOCTORS

(9) Letter

Dear Dr.

I am writing to ask for your help. We are doing a survey about people's health and the help that they get from their general practitioners. In order to do this it is necessary to collect information from patients as well as doctors. It is a statistical inquiry, linking facts and opinions from both sources, but it will not of course identify any individuals. We are drawing our sample of patients by taking people at random from the electoral register.

We would like to know the views of general practitioners about the conditions in general practice to-day, and we are enclosing a short questionnaire and a stamped addressed envelope.

Most of the questions just need a tick beside the appropriate answer but we would also welcome your views in more detail if you would like to give them, so we have included an extra page for this. The questionnaire itself will not take more than about ten minutes to complete. We would be very grateful if you would answer all the questions and return the form to us as soon as possible.

We feel it is important to find out the views of a true cross-section of general practitioners, and we can only do that if the doctors we approach tell us what they think.

You may like to know that the Institute of Community Studies is a non-profit making research organization, which has carried out a number of studies in social and medical research. It has published several books, and one in which both patients and general practitioners described their views of the hospital service is to be published this summer. The identities of the patients, doctors and hospitals are not of course disclosed in this book, but the information is analysed statistically. In the same way any information we are given on this present study will of course be treated as confidential.

For this study the Institute has been helped by an Advisory Committee which consists mainly of general practitioners and other doctors. They have helped to draw up the questionnaires and will advise on the final report.

If you would like further information about the study or would like to discuss personally the problems and satisfactions of general practice, please let us know and we will get in touch with you.

Thank you for your help.

Yours sincerely,

ANN CARTWRIGHT

(b) Postal Questionnaire
CONDITIONS OF GENERAL PRACTICE TODAY

1. Do you, as a general practitioner, have direct access to any N.H.S. beds where you retain full responsibility for treatment of your patients whilst in hospital?
PLEASE TICK ALL THAT APPLY
Yes, obstetric ....
Yes, medical..................
Yes, surgical ....
Yes, convalescent ....
No ....

2. Would you like any such beds, or more beds or some of a different sort?
PLEASE TICK ALL THAT APPLY
Yes, obstetric ....
Yes, medical..................
Yes, surgical ....
Yes, other (specify) ....
No ....

3. Do you hold any paid or honorary appointment on the staff of any N.H.S. hospital (i.e. as a consultant, clinical assistant or other grade of medical officer), or would you like one?
Yes, have one now ....
No, would like one............
No, and no desire for one .....

4. Do you have direct access (i.e. not through casualty or a consultant) to these facilities:
PLEASE TICK ALL THAT APPLY
Full size chest X-rays ....
Bone and joint X-rays ....
Bacteriological examination of urine ....
Glucose tolerance tests ....
None of these ....

5. Do you feel you have access to enough diagnostic facilities?
Yes ....
No...........................

6. Are you satisfied with the arrangements and quality of those you do have access to?
Yes ....
No ....

7. How many nights in the week are you on call – on the average – for cases other than obstetrics?
Every night ....
5 or 6 ....
3 or 4 ....
2 or less ....

8. What proportion of weekends are you on call – for cases other than obstetrics?
More than half................
1 in 2.......................
Less than 1 in 2 ....

9. Do you ever use an emergency call service?
Yes ....
No ....
IF YES What do you think of it?

10. Do you do obstetrics? If so, how many cases have you had in the last twelve months?
None ....
1 – 9 ....
10 – 24 ....
25 – 49 ....
50 or more ....

11. (a) If general practitioners were not expected to be available at nights – from 6 p.m. to 9 a.m. and patients who needed a doctor during that time had to get in touch with an emergency service – how would you feel about that?

(*b*) which would you prefer?
Prefer to go on as now ....
Prefer emergency service ......

(*c*) Would you be prepared to be on duty at the emergency service to cover such calls for say two nights in a month – if that made such an arrangement feasible?
Yes ....
No ....

12. What do you enjoy about your work as a general practitioner?

13. What do you find frustrating about it?

14. On the whole do you enjoy general practice:
Very much ....
Moderately ....
Not very much ....
Not at all ....

15. Have you any special interests in medicine? What are they?

16. Please indicate the relative importance to you of the following ways of keeping up-to-date.
Put a '1' beside the most important, a '2' beside the next most important and so on.
Professional meetings..........
Informal discussions with doctors ....
Drughouse literature or representatives ....
Journals, books, other publications.....................
Courses.....................

17. Have you been on any courses for general practitioners in the last five years?
Number ....

18. Here are some statements about patients and general practice. Please indicate the extent of your agreement or disagreement with each by circling the appropriate number on the scale. 'O' indicates no opinion or no particular feeling either way.

A. One should try to give patients full explanations about the ætiology of their illnesses and the rationale of treatment.
Strongly 2 1 0 1 2 Strongly
agree .... disagree

B. A good practitioner can train his patients not to make unnecessary or unreasonable demands on him.

Strongly 2 1 0 1 2 Strongly
agree .... disagree

C. Patients nowadays tend to demand their rights rather than to ask for help and advice.

Strongly 2 1 0 1 2 Strongly
agree .... disagree

D. A doctor shouldn't expect patients to respect him just because he is a doctor. He has to earn their respect.

Strongly 2 1 0 1 2 Strongly
agree .... disagree

E. If general practitioners working in partnership are to establish satisfactory personal relationships with their patients, it is important:
(i) that patients should nearly always be able to see the doctor of their choice.

Strongly 2 1 0 1 2 Strongly
agree .... disagree

(ii) that patients should be encouraged to stick to the same doctor.

Strongly 2 1 0 1 2 Strongly
agree .... disagree

19. What proportion of surgery consultations would you estimate are for reasons *you feel* to be trivial, unnecessary or inappropriate?

90% or more ....
75% but less than 90% ....
50% but less than 75% ....
25% but less than 50% ....
10% but less than 25% ....
Less than 10% ....

20. How do you deal with people who consult you for reasons you feel are trivial, unnecessary or inappropriate?

21. When patients ask you about such things as children getting into trouble or family discord do you feel:

It is appropriate for you to be consulted about such things.....
or that such problems are more appropriately discussed with other people ....

22. Do you think middle-aged women should have regular cervical smear tests?

Yes ....
No ....

IF YES Do you think it would be appropriate for general practitioners to collect the smears if hospitals did the cytological examination?

Yes ....
No ....

23. Do you think that *ideally* general practitioners should carry out any (other regular check-ups on middle-aged people?

Yes ....
No ....

24. Do you undertake these procedures in your practice when they arise?

(*a*) Strap sprains.
More often than not ....
Occasionally ....
Never ....

(*b*) Excise simple cysts.
More often than not ....
Occasionally ....
Never ....

(*c*) Open abcesses.
More often than not ....
Occasionally ....
Never ....

(*d*) Stitch cuts.
More often than not ....
Occasionally ....
Never ....

(*e*) Vaginal examination with a speculum.
More often than not ....
Occasionally ....
Never ....

(*f*) Estimate hæmoglobin with a hæmoglobinometer.
More often than not ....
Occasionally ....
Never ....

(*g*) Use a laryngoscope.
More often than not ....
Occasionally ....
Never ....

25. What is the latest time in the evening that patients can come to the surgery in the ordinary way?

Before 5 p.m. ....
5.0 but before 5.30 ....
5.30 but before 6.0 ....
6.0 but before 6.30 ....
6.30 but before 7.0 ....
7.0 but before 7.30 ....
7.30 but before 8.0 ....
8.0 p.m. or later ....

Finally, a few details about your practice arrangements

26. Type of practice:
    Single-handed ....
    Self and assistant ....
    Self and partner ....
    Self and two others...........
    Self and three or more others....

27. What ancillary help do you have in the practice?
    PLEASE TICK ALL THAT APPLY
    Secretary (who can type) ....
    Receptionist ....
    Nurse ....
    Health Visitor ....
    No ancillary help.............

28. Would you say your patients are:
    Nearly all working class........
    Mainly working class but some middle class ....
    Half and half ....
    Mainly middle class ....

29. Appointment system:
    All surgeries.................
    Some sessions ....
    None ....

30. Approximate number of patients on your list. If in partnership please estimate the number of N.H.S. patients you yourself look after.
    None........................
    Under 1,500 ....
    1,500 – 1,999 ....
    2,000 – 2,499 ....
    2,500 – 2,999 ....
    3,000 or more ....

31. Under your present practice arrangements what do you feel would be the *ideal* number for you yourself to look after?
    Under 1,500 ....
    1,500 – 1,999 ....
    2,000 – 2,499 ....
    2,500 – 2,999 ....
    3,000 or more ....

32. Do you have any private patients?
    None........................
    1 – 19 ....
    20 – 49 ....
    50 – 99 ....
    100 or more ....
    Private only ....

PLEASE CHECK THAT YOU HAVE ANSWERED ALL THE QUESTIONS
THANK YOU FOR YOUR HELP

If you would like to discuss conditions in general practice today personally please put a tick here and we will make an appointment to visit you.

Please record any additional comments you feel are important – either about the questions we have asked, or more generally about the conditions of general practice under the N.H.S. – below and on the back of this sheet.

Question number to which comment refers | ADDITIONAL COMMENTS

APPENDIX 4

THE SAMPLE OF DOCTORS

All but 27 of the patients gave us the names of their doctors. These 1,370 people told us about 552 doctors.[1] The distribution is shown in Table C.

TABLE C   *Number of patients reporting the same doctor*

Survey patients with same doctor	Number of doctors	Number of patients
1	233	233
2	117	234
3	74	222
4	51	204
5	32	160
6	19	114
7	13	91
8	6	48
9	6	54
10	1	10
TOTAL	552	1,370

Four hundred and twenty-two of these doctors, 76 per cent, completed a postal questionnaire. A number of facts about both the doctors who replied and those who did not were obtained from the Medical Directory – their qualifications, the year in which they qualified and their medical school. In addition the Ministry of Health gave us information about the number of partners and the list sizes of the doctors. Table D shows how the

[1] For nine of these people it was their private doctor and for 76 it was a partner of the doctor whose National Health Service list they were on because they felt they knew the partner better and regarded him as their doctor.

proportion of doctors who responded varied with some of these characteristics. Four doctors, each reported by one patient only, could not be traced either in the Medical Directory or by the Ministry. The information from the patients must have been incorrect and these doctors may not have received the letters and questionnaires from us.

TABLE D   *Variations in the proportion of doctors who responded*

	Proportion of doctors who responded	Number of doctors approached (= *100%*)
Year of qualification:		
Before 1925	67%	46
1925–1934	67%	114
1935–1944	79%	155
1945–1954	82%	170
1955 or later	88%	60
Qualification:		
Licentiate only	69%	118
University degree – no further qualifications	78%	318
Some further qualifications	82%	109
Type of practice:		
Single-handed*	70%	126
With one partner	77%	147
With two others	80%	119
With three or more others	86%	145
Member of College of General Practitioners:		
Yes	84%	107
No	75%	445

* Includes 15 doctors who had an assistant.

The response was comparatively high among more recently and better qualified doctors and among those working in partnerships of four or more doctors. In addition members of the College of General Practitioners were rather more likely to fill in the questionnaire than others. (See Table D.) But there was no apparent bias in the response according to list size. This is shown in Table E.

TABLE E *Response and list size*

List size	Proportion of doctors who responded	Number of doctors approached (= 100%)
Under 1,500	79%	96
1,500–1,999	73%	52
2,000–2,499	77%	74
2,500–2,999	74%	90
3,000 or more	80%	214

The figures in Table E relate to the actual size of a doctor's list and were supplied by the Ministry of Health. In the report, the figures normally used have been the doctors' estimates of the number of patients they themselves look after. The two sets of figures are compared in Table F.

TABLE F *List sizes and number of patients doctors estimate they look after*

	Size of list	Number of patients they estimate they look after
	%	%
Under 1,500	19	6
1,500–1,999	9	9
2,000–2,499	14	27
2,500–2,999	16	26
3,000 and over	42	32
NUMBER OF PARTICIPATING* DOCTORS (= 100%)		407

* The 13 doctors who did not answer this question and the two for whom data were not available from the Ministry have been excluded from both series of figures.

As expected, list size shows more doctors with both small lists of under 1,500 and large lists of 3,000 or more. Because many of these doctors are in partnership, the work load is shared out and the number of patients they look after more evenly distributed. A crude estimate of the average numbers gives 2,500 for average list size, 2,600 estimated average number of patients looked after.

Patients' attitudes to doctors who replied were compared with their views on those who did not, but no significant differences were found.

Apart from the bias arising because some doctors did not reply there is the complication that the chance of a doctor being included in the sample is related to his number of patients. Table G compares the proportion of patients with doctors who look after different numbers with the proportions of participating doctors and the estimated proportions of all general practitioners with those numbers of patients. The estimates in the last column were made by a crude reweighting of the actual numbers of patients' doctors in the first column. Those on lists of under 1,500 were reweighted by $\frac{3,250}{1,250} = 2\cdot6$, 1,500–1,999 by $\frac{3,250}{1,750} = 1\cdot86$ etc.

TABLE G   *Numbers of patients doctors look after*

Number of patients	Patients' doctors*	Proportion of doctors with that number of patients	
		Participating doctors	Estimate of all general practitioners
	%	%	%
Under 1,500	4	6	8
1,500–1,999	9	9	12
2,000–2,499	26	27	29
2,500–2,999	25	26	23
3,000 and over	36	32	28
NUMBER (= 100%)	1,045	419	

* That is the proportion of patients with doctors who look after that number of patients.

Table H shows the effect of this bias on a number of characteristics related to list size. It is relatively small even on such things as the proportion of doctors with hospital appointments which varies quite widely with list size.

TABLE H   *Some characteristics of doctors which are related to their number of patients and the effect of the sampling bias on them*

Number of patients	Proportion of patient's doctors:				
	With a hospital appoint-ment	*With 50 or more obstetric cases in last 12 months*	*Feeling ideal num-ber of patients is under 2,000*	*Who are women*	*With a secretary or recep-tionist*
Under 1,500	41%	8%	83%	10%	63%
1,500–1,999	38%	3%	77%	12%	73%
2,000–2,499	32%	10%	46%	1%	65%
2,500–2,999	19%	25%	28%	4%	87%
3,000 and over	15%	35%	13%	4%	84%
Proportion in total sample of patients' doctors	23%	23%	34%	5%	78%
Estimated proportion of all general practitioners	26%	20%	39%	5%	76%
Proportion of partici-pating doctors	23%	23%	36%	5%	76%

In the report analyses have been done on the sample of patients' doctors when characteristics of patients are related to those of doctors. For simplicity, and because the effect of the bias is small, the unweighted sample of participating doctors is used for analyses which involve doctors only.

Doctors who were interviewed

At the end of the postal questionnaire doctors were asked if they would like to discuss conditions in general practice personally. Eighty-three of the 422 doctors, a fifth, said they would and all of them were offered appointments. Sixty-nine were eventually interviewed. They were asked what recommendations they would make if they were on the Fraser Committee[2], and what they felt the following bodies could do to help general practitioners: the Ministry of Health, the Local Authorities, the Regional Hospital Boards, the Executive Councils, the Local Medical Committees, the B.M.A., the College of General Practitioners, the medical schools and the press and television. Their comments have not been analysed statistically but used for illustration and discussion.

The younger doctors and the members of the College of General Practitioners were more eager to be interviewed than others who filled in the questionnaire, in the same way that they were more likely to fill in the questionnaire. But while single-handed doctors less often than others replied to the postal inquiry, if they did respond they were more anxious to be interviewed. A third of the doctors working entirely on their own wanted to be interviewed, compared with a sixth of the others.

Comparison with data from Ministry of Health

Our data can be compared with information from the Ministry of Health in two ways. First information collected from the doctors on the survey can be compared with data relating to these same doctors from Ministry records. Table I shows the comparison for type of practice. The Ministry data relates to 1st October 1963 and the survey data to the summer months of 1964. There was complete agreement in 88 per cent of the cases, and agreement 'within one doctor' in 95 per cent.

However data from the Ministry of Health relating to *all* doctors in practice on 1 October 1964 suggest that our sample contained a relatively high proportion working in groups of four or more doctors: 23 per cent (when the Ministry of Health data on our sample is reweighted) compared with 19 per cent. It would also seem that it contained a high proportion of doctors with

---

[2] A committee set up by the Minister of Health in the spring of 1964, under the chairmanship of the Permanent Secretary to the Ministry who was then Sir Bruce Fraser. It included twelve representatives of the medical profession, chosen by the profession itself and its terms of reference were, 'Having regard to securing the best possible standards of general medical practice, to consider the report and recommendations of the Annis Gillie Committee and any other matters relevant to the work of the general practitioner in the National Health Service, apart from the quantum of remuneration.'

The Sample of Doctors

TABLE I *Comparison of survey data and Ministry of Health data on type of practice*

Ministry of Health data	Single-handed	Self and assistant	Survey data Self and partner	Self and two others	Self and three or more others	All survey doctors
Single-handed	70	2	1	4	6	83
Self and assistant	3	5	–	–	–	8
Self and partner	4	1	102	8	1	116
Self and two others	–	–	7	77	6	90
Self and three or more others	1	1	1	3	104	110
ALL SURVEY DOCTORS	78	9	111	92	117	407

lists of 3,000 or more, 26 per cent against 19 per cent. As list size varies so much with area it seems probable that it is the small number of areas covered that has resulted in this bias.

ESTIMATING THE EXTENT OF PRIVATE PRACTICE

It is possible that people who go to general practitioners privately might be more unwilling than other people to participate in a study like this. If so, as the proportion of such people is small, the error caused by such a bias could be large. Because of this danger interviewers were asked whenever possible to find out for the non-participators whether they had a general practitioner under the National Health Service, a private doctor, or both, or neither. They were able to ascertain this for three-fifths of the non-participators, and 4 per cent of those who answered said they had a private doctor only. When compared with the 0·8 per cent of people who co-operated fully, this suggests a definite bias. If it is assumed that the people for whom this information was not obtained were similar in this respect to the other people who did not participate, the estimate of people with private doctors only is increased from 0·8 per cent to 1·2 per cent. On the other hand, if it is assumed that *all* the people who both refused to participate fully and did not answer this question had a private doctor only, this proportion would be 4·7 per cent. This last assumption seems rather unrealistic. Another problem is of course that all the people may not have answered this question correctly. Taking into account these various difficulties it seems reasonable to conclude that the proportion of people who use only private general practice is between 1 per cent and 3 per cent.

SCORE ON PROCEDURES

General practitioners were asked whether they undertook a number of procedures in their practice when the occasion arose – 'more often than not', 'occasionally' or 'never'. Their responses have been shown in Table 4.

For simplicity in analysis and presentation their responses have been combined in a single score on the following principles:

Score

−1   if do *not* do procedures carried out by three-quarters or more

+2   if do things carried out by a third or less

+1   if do things carried out by between a half and a third of doctors

In practice this meant the score was calculated in this way:

Score

−1   if strap sprains occasionally or never

+2   if excise simple cysts more often than not

+1   if excise simple cysts occasionally

+1   if open abscesses more often than not

+1   if stitch cuts more often than not

+1   if do vaginal examination with speculum more often than not

+2   if estimate haemoglobin with a haemoglobinometer *at all*

+2   if use a laryngoscope *at all*

The score was additive and could in theory run from −1 to +9 but in fact no-one had a negative score. The distribution was:

Score on Procedures

Score	%
0	12
1	12
2	12
3	13
4	13
5	11
6	10
7	11
8	2
9	4
NUMBER OF DOCTORS ($= 100\%$)	421

The average score was 3·7.

STATISTICAL SIGNIFICANCE AND SAMPLING ERRORS

There are a number of factors, particularly the nature of the data and the stage at which precise hypotheses are often formulated, which violate some of the conditions in which statistical tests of significance apply and make interpretation difficult. For this reason no mention of them has been made in the text, in an attempt to avoid the appearance of spurious precision which the presentation of such tests might seem to imply. But in the absence of more satisfactory techniques these tests have been used to give some indication of the probability of differences occurring by chance.

Chi-square tests have been applied constantly when looking at the data from this survey and have influenced decisions about what differences to present and how much verbal 'weight' to attach to them. In general, attention has not been drawn to any difference which statistical tests suggest might have occurred by chance five or more times in 100.

Another difficulty about presenting results from a study like this with over 200 items of basic information is that of selection. Not all cross-analyses are carried out, only about 2,000, and only a fraction of these are presented, which of course gives rise to difficulty in interpreting significance. Positive results are more often given than negative ones. Readers may sometimes wonder why certain further analyses are not reported. In many cases – but not all – the analysis will have been done but the result found to be negative or inconclusive.

Table J shows the sampling errors for a number of patient characteristics. They are all less than one and a half times the random sampling error if the sample had been a straight one over the whole country, and not just twelve areas.

TABLE J *Sampling errors*

Characteristic	Value in total sample	Range in twelve study errors	Sampling error	Sampling error if random sample of country	Range ± 2 sampling errors
Proportion of patients with no G.P. consultation in previous twelve months	33·6%	22·4%–41·3%	1·7%	1·3%	30·2%–37·0%
Proportion of patients with an O.P. consultation in previous twelve months	24·0%	17·5%–34·2%	1·5%	1·2%	21·0%–27·0%
Proportion of patients with a private doctor only	0·7%	0%–1·9%	0·2%	0·2%	0·3%–1·1%
Proportion of patients saying their doctor 'not so good' about explaining things to them fully	14·2%	7·3%–17·9%	0·8%	1·0%	12·6%–15·8%

CLASSIFICATION OF SOCIAL CLASS

The classification used is based on the Registrar-General's Classification of Occupations (1960).[1] This distinguishes five 'social
classes':

    I Professional, etc., occupations.
   II Intermediate occupations.
  III Skilled occupations.
  IV Partly skilled occupations.
   V Unskilled occupations.

These classes are intended to reflect 'the general standing within
the community of the occupations concerned.' Occupations in
classes II, III and IV are also classified as 'manual', 'non-manual'
or 'agricultural'. In the analyses here these five classes are used,
but Class III, skilled occupations, is divided into manual and non-
manual groups to give a six-point scale. In a number of instances
the main differences that emerge are between what can be described as the 'middle class' and 'working-class', the former being
most of the non-manual occupations – the Registrar-General's
social classes I, II and III non-manual – and the latter almost
entirely manual – III manual, IV and V. Table K shows the
proportion of patients in these groups. Men and single women
have been classified on the basis of their present occupation if they
were under 60, or on their main occupation if they were aged 60
or more. Married and widowed women have been classified
according to their husband's present, last or main occupation.

[1] General Register Office, *Classification of Occupations 1960*.

Classification of Social Class

TABLE K   *Patients' Social Class*

	%	
Middle class:		
Professional	4	⎫
Intermediate	19	⎬ 36
Skilled non-manual	13	⎭
Working class:		
Skilled manual	40	⎫
Partly skilled	18	⎬ 64
Unskilled	6	⎭
NUMBER OF PATIENTS*		
(= 100%)	1,341	

* The 56 patients for whom inadequate information was obtained or who were students have been excluded.

REFERENCES

ABEL-SMITH, B. and GALES, K., *British Doctors at Home and Abroad.* Occasional Papers on Social Administration No. 8. London, G. Bell and Sons Ltd. 1964.

ANDERSON, J. A. D., *A New Look at Social Medicine.* London, Pitman Medical. 1965.

BACKETT, E. M., 'Social Aspects of the New Patterns of Disease: the Role of the Family Doctor'. *Advancement of Science.* p. 541. 1961.

BALINT, M., *The Doctor, His Patient and the Illness.* London, Pitman. 1966.

British Medical Journal. 'G.P's Role in Hospital of Future'. *i*, p. 50. 1964.

BYNDER, H., 'Some Problems in the Doctor-Patient Relationship'. Paper presented at the Medical Sociology section of the Sixth World Congress of Sociology. 1966.

CARTWRIGHT, A., *Human Relations and Hospital Care.* London, Routledge and Kegan Paul. 1964.

CARTWRIGHT, A., 'Memory Errors in a Morbidity Survey'. *Milbank Memorial Fund Quarterly.* XLI, No. 1, p. 5. 1963.

CARTWRIGHT, A. and MARSHALL, ROSALIND, 'General Practice in 1963'. *Medical Care.* Vol. 3, p. 69. 1965.

CARTWRIGHT, A., MARTIN, F. M. and THOMSON, J. G., 'Community Aspects of a Mass Radiography Campaign'. *Medical Officer. 101*, p. 313. 1959.

CARTWRIGHT, A. and SCOTT, R., 'The Work of a Nurse Employed in a General Practice'. *Brit. Med. J. i*, p. 807. 1961.

Central Health Services Council, Standing Medical Advisory Committee. *The Field of Work of the Family Doctor.* London, H.M.S.O. 1963.

CLUTE, K. F., *The General Practitioner: A Study of Medical Education and Practice in Ontario and Nova Scotia.* University of Toronto. 1963.

COLE, D. and UTTING, D., *The Economic Circumstances of Old People.* Welwyn, Codicote Press. 1962.

College of General Practitioners. *Present State and Future Needs of General Practice*. London. College of General Practitioners. 1965.

College of General Practitioners. Report on *Special Vocational Training for General Practice*. London, The Council of the College of General Practitioners. 1965.

COLLINGS, J. S. 'General Practice in England Today. A Reconnaissance'. *Lancet, i*, p. 555. 1950.

COOPER, B., 'General Practitioners' Attitudes to Psychiatry'. *De Medicina Tuenda. 1*, p. 43, 1964.

CROMBIE, D. L., 'A Career Structure for General Practitioners'. *Lancet, i*, p. 368. 1965.

DAVIS, M. S. and EICHHORN, R. L., 'Compliance with Medical Regimens: A Panel Study'. *Journal of Health and Human Behaviour*. Vol. 4, p. 240. 1963.

EDGE, J. R. and NELSON, I. D. M., 'Survey of Arrangements for the Elderly in Barrow-in-Furness'. *Medical Care*. Vol. 1, No. 4 and Vol. 2, No. 1. 1963 and 1964.

FELDSTEIN, M. S., 'Effects of Differences in Hospital Bed Scarcity on Type of Use.' *Brit. Med. J., ii*. p. 561. 1964.

FLOYD, C. B., 'Car Service'. *Brit. Med. J., i*, p. 1,423. 1966.

FORSYTH, G., 'An Enquiry into the Drug Bill'. *Medical Care*. Vol. 1, p. 10. 1963.

FORSYTH, G. and LOGAN, R. F. L., *The Demand for Medical Care: A Study of the Case-Load in the Barrow-in-Furness Group of Hospitals*. London, Oxford University Press. 1960.

FOX, T. F., 'Personal Medicine'. *Bull. N.Y. Acad. Med. 38*, p. 527. 1962.

FOX, T. F., 'The Personal Doctor and his Relation to the Hospital'. *Lancet, i*, p. 743. 1960.

FREIDSON, E., *Patients' Views of Medical Practice*. New York, Russell Sage Foundation. 1961.

FRY, J., 'General Practice Tomorrow'. *Brit. Med. J., ii*, p. 1,064. 1964.

General Register Office. *Classification of Occupation 1960*. London, H.M.S.O. 1960.

GIBSON, C. D. and KRAMER, B. M., 'Site of Care in Medical Practice'. *Medical Care*. Vol. 3, p. 14. 1965.

GRAY, P. G. and CARTWRIGHT, A., 'Choosing and Changing Doctors'. *Lancet, ii*, p. 1,308. 1953.

GRAY, P. G., CORLETT, T. and JONES, P., *The Proportion of Jurors as an Index of the Economic Status of a District*. London, The Social Survey. 1951.

HADFIELD, S. J., 'A Field Survey of General Practice 1951–2'. *Brit. Med. J., ii*, p. 683. 1953.

HANDFIELD-JONES, R. P. C., 'General Practice'. *Lancet, ii*, p. 346. 1959.

HITCHENS, R. A. N. and LOWE, C. R., 'Laboratory Services in General Practice'. *Medical Care, Vol. 4*, p. 142. 1966.

JEFFERYS, M., *An Anatomy of Social Welfare Services*. London, Michael Joseph. 1965.

JEFFERYS, M., BROTHERSTON, J. H. F. and CARTWRIGHT, A., 'Consumption of Medicines on a Working-Class Housing Estate'. *British Journal of Preventive and Social Medicine*, Vol. 14, p. 64. 1960.

JEFFERYS, M. and ELLIOTT, P. M., *Women in Medicine*. London, Office of Health Economics. 1966.

LAMONT D., 'The Casualty Dilemma'. *Lancet, ii*, p. 1,190. 1961.

Lancet. 'House Calls and Home Visits'. *i*, p. 1,409. 1963.

LAST, J. M., *Objective Measurement of Quality in General Practice*. Cyclostyle. Edinburgh University. 1965.

LEE, J. A. H., DRAPER, P. A. and WEATHERALL, M., 'Primary Medical Care: Prescribing in Three English Towns'. *Milbank Memorial Fund Quarterly*. Vol. XLIII, No. 2. p. 285. 1965.

LEESON, J., 'Medical Care Tomorrow'. *Medical Care*, Vol. 4, p. 211. 1966.

LOGAN, R. F. L., 'Assessment of Sickness and Health in the Community: Needs and Methods'. *Medical Care*. Vol. 2, p. 173 and 218. 1964.

LOGAN, W. P. D., *Morbidity Statistics from General Practice*. Vol. II (Occupation). General Register Office Studies on Medical and Population Subjects No. 14. London, H.M.S.O. 1960.

LOGAN, W. P. D. and BROOKE, E. M., *Survey of Sickness 1943–1950*. General Register Office Studies on Medical and Population Subjects No. 12. London, H.M.S.O. 1957.

LOGAN, W. P. D. and CUSHION, A. A., *Morbidity Statistics from General Practice*. Vol. I (General). General Register Office Studies on Medical and Population Subjects No. 14. London, H.M.S.O. 1958.

MACGREGOR, J. E. and BAIRD, Sir DUGALD, 'Detection of Carcinoma in the General Population'. *Brit. Med. J., i*, p. 1,631. 1963.

MADDISON, J. (The Clinic for Preventive Medicine of Old People, Teddington, Middlesex). *How to Keep the Old Folks Young*. Duplicated. 1963.

MADDISON, J., 'Maintaining the Health of Older People' *Public Health,* Vol. LXXX No. 1, p. 5. 1965.

MCKEOWN, T., *Medicine in Modern Society*. London, George Allen and Unwin. 1965.

Medical Services Review Committee. *A Review of the Medical Services in Great Britain*. (Chairman Sir Arthur Porritt). The report of a Committee sponsored by the Royal College of Physicians of

London, Royal College of Surgeons of England, Royal College of Obstetricians and Gynaecologists, Royal College of Physicians of Edinburgh, Royal College of Surgeons of Edinburgh, Royal Faculty of Physicians and Surgeons of Glasgow, Society of Medical Officers of Health, College of General Practitioners and British Medical Association. London, Social Assay. 1962.

Ministry of Health. *Annual Report for the Year 1964.* Cmnd. 2688. London, H.M.S.O. 1965.

Ministry of Health. *On the State of the Public Health.* The annual report of the Chief Medical Officer of the Ministry of Health for the year 1964. London, H.M.S.O. 1965.

Ministry of Pensions and National Insurance. *Report of an Enquiry into the Incidence of Incapacity for Work.* Part II. Incidence of Incapacity for Work in Different Areas and Occupations. London, H.M.S.O. 1965.

MORRIS J. N., GARRON, H., LE GROS CLERK, F., HUWS JONES, R., LEVITT, H. and WARREN, M. D., *Our Old People. Next Steps in Social Policy.* London, Socialist Commentary. 1966.

MORRISON, S. L. and RILEY, M. M., 'The Use of Hospital Diagnostic Facilities by General Practitioners'. *Medical Care,* Vol. *i*, p. 137. 1963.

National Center for Health Statistics. 'Volume of Physician Visits by Place of Visit and Type of Service. United States July 1963–June 1964'. *Vital and Health Statistics.* P.H.S. Series 10. No. 18. Washington, 1965.

Nuffield Provincial Hospitals Trust. *Casualty Services and their Setting. A Study in Medical Care.* London, New York, Toronto. Oxford University Press. 1960.

PARSONS, T., *The Social System.* Glencoe Illinois, Free Press. 1951.

PARSONS, T. and BALES, R. F., *Family, Socialization and Interaction Process.* Glencoe, Illinois, The Free Press. 1955.

PETERSON, O. L., ANDREWS, L. P., SPAIN, R. S. and GREENBERG, B. G., 'An Analytic Study of North Carolina General Practice, 1953–54'. *J. Medical Education. 31.* No. 12, Part 2. p. 1. 1956.

REHIN, G. F., HOUGHTON, H. and MARTIN, F. M., 'Mental Health Social Work in Hospitals and Local Authorities: A Comparison of two Work Situations'. *Problems and Progress in Medical Care.* London, New York, Toronto. Oxford University Press. 1964.

Review Body on Doctors' and Dentists' Remuneration. *Seventh Report.* London, H.M.S.O. 1966.

SCOTT, R., Personal Communication.

SCOTT, R., ANDERSON, J. A. D. and CARTWRIGHT, A., 'Just What the Doctor Ordered: An Analysis of Treatment in a General Practice'. *Brit. Med. J., ii*, p. 293. 1960.

References

SCOTT, R. and GILMORE, M., 'The Edinburgh Hospitals'. *Problems and Progress in Medical Care*. Vol. 2. London, Nuffield Provincial Hospitals Trust. 1966.

SEDDON, T. M. and SMITH, F., 'Car Service in General Practice'. *Brit. Med. J.*, *ii*, p. 587. 1966.

SILVER, G. A., *Family Medical Care. A Report on the Family Health Maintenance Demonstration*. Cambridge Mass., Harvard University Press. 1963.

STEVENSON, C., and DAVISON, B.C.C., 'Families Referred for Genetic Advice' *Brit. Med. J.*, *ii*, p. 1,060 1966.

TAYLOR, S., *Good General Practice*. London, Oxford University Press. 1954.

TITMUSS, R. M., 'Role of the Family Doctor Today in the Context of Britain's Social Services'. *Lancet*, *i*, p. 1. 1965.

TOWNSEND, P. and WEDDERBURN, D., *The Aged in the Welfare State*. Occasional Papers on Social Administration. Bell, 1965.

TUNSTALL, J., *Old and Alone: A Sociological Study of Old People*. London, Routledge and Kegan Paul. 1966.

WARREN, M. D. and COOPER, J., 'Medical Officer of Health. The Job, the Man and the Career'. *Medical Officer*. Vol. CXVI. p. 41. 1966.

WARREN, M. D., COOPER, J. and WARREN, J. In preparation.

WEBER, A., 'Some Characteristics of Mortality and Morbidity in Europe'. World Health Organization, Regional Office for Europe. *European Conference on Morbidity Statistics*. 1963.

WILLIAMSON, J., STOKOE, I. H., GRAY, S., FISHER, M., SMITH, A., MCGHEE, A. and STEPHENSON, E., 'Old People at Home: Their Unreported Needs'. *Lancet*, *i*, p. 1,117. 1964.

WILLMOTT, P. and YOUNG, M., *Family and Class in a London Suburb*. London, Routledge and Kegan Paul. 1960.

WOLFENDALE, M. and HANDFIELD-JONES, R. P. C., 'The Prevention of Cervical Cancer: Who takes the Smears'. *Lancet*, *ii*, p. 901. 1964.

YOUNG, M. and WILLMOTT, P., *Family and Kinship in East London*. London, Routledge and Kegan Paul. 1957.

INDEX

Abel-Smith, B., 220 n.
Abscesses, opening of, *see* Procedures
Access to beds, *see* Hospital beds
Access to diagnostic facilities, *see* Diagnostic facilities
Accessibility of general practitioner, *102–7*, 120, 216
  and home visiting, 72–3
  as reason for choosing doctor, 18
  compared with hospital, 127, 189
  for older patients, 197–9
Administrators, 142
Age of doctors, *see* Year of qualification
Age of patients, *195–204*, 214–15
  and appointment systems, 155–6
  and consultation rates, 32, 186–7
  and doctors' year of qualification, 168
  and hospitals, 128, 130
  and partnerships, 147
  and personal relationship with doctor, 109
  and preventive care, 81–3, 86–7
  see also Older patients
Ancillary help, 22, 23, *160–1*, 220
  and doctors' list size, 161, 272
  and doctors' year of qualification, 159
  and for home visiting, 223
  and partnerships, 16, 146, 152
  and membership of College of General Practitioners, 181–2
  doctors' wish for, 199
  Review body proposals, 174 n.
  see also Health visitor, Nurse, Receptionist, Secretary
Anderson, J. A. D., 29 n., 186 n.
Andrews, L. P., 221 n.
Ante natal clinics, 26, 80
Appointment, hospital, *see* Hospital
Appointment, system, 92, 121, *155–60*, 166, 167
  and partnerships, 152
  and trivial consultations, 48
  as reason for choosing doctor, 21, 22
  proportion of doctors with one, 16, 23

Approachability of general practitioner *107–16*, 118, 191
Areas, *see* Study areas, Urban/rural, North/south
Ashton-under-Lyne, study area, 3
  choice of, 226
  description of, 227, 229
  designated area, 233
  doctors' size of list, 206
  in north, 212–14
  social class of, 206, 207
Australian practice, 122

Backett, E. M., 78
Bacteriological examination, *see* Diagnostic facilities
Baird, Sir Dugald, 86 n.
Bales, R. F., 195 n.
Balint, M., 49 n.
Bangor, 232
Barrow-in-Furness, 130–1, 203
Beds, *see* Hospital
Beeching type inquiry, 221
Bethesda, 232
Betws-y-coed, 232
Bone and joint X-rays, *see* Diagnostic facilities
Branch surgeries, 106–7
Bristol, medical school, 18
  study area, 3
  choice of, 226
  description of, 227, 229–30
  doctors' size of list, 206
  in south, 212–14
  open area, 233
British Medical Association, 273
Brooke, E., 24 n., 194 n.
Brotherston, J. H. F., 192 n.
Bureaucracy, 58–62 *passim*
Bynder, H., 113

Calls, 224
  a frustration of general practice, 40–2 *passim*, 75, 171–2, *see also* Night call
Cambridgeshire, study area, 3, 18
  choice of, 226
  description of, 227, 233